An Illustrated Encyclopaedia

WONDERS *of* ANIMAL LIFE

also available by the same editor

An Illustrated World Gazetteer

Peoples of all Nations

Their Life Today and Story of Their Past

In 14 Volumes

Volume One
Abyssinia **to** Azerbaijan
Volume Two
Belgium **to** British Empire in America
Volume Three
British Empire in Asia **to** Canada
Volume Four
Ceylon **to** Dahomey
Volume Five
Danzig **to** England
Volume Six
Esthonia **to** France
Volume Seven
Georgia **to** Iceland

Volume Eight
India **to** Italy
Volume Nine
Japan **to** Mexico
Volume Ten
Monaco **to** Oman
Volume Eleven
Palestine **to** Rumania
Volume Twelve
Russia **to** Sin-kiang
Volume Thirteen
South Africa **to** The Ukraine
Volume Fourteen
The United States **to** Wales
with General Index

About the Editor

Sir John Alexander Hammerton (1871-1949) was an English statesman and author, best-known for his editorship of popular encyclopaedias published in the first half of the 20th century, such as the 10-volume New Book of Knowledge.

From 1914 to 1919, Hammerton was joint editor with HW Wilson of the periodical "The Great War: The Standard History of the All-Europe Conflict", published by the Amalgamated Press. It was lavishly illustrated with photographs and with realistic drawings which were sometimes hardly distinguishable from photographs.

He was also a contemporary and friend of Arthur Mee, about whom he wrote a biography.

An Illustrated Encyclopaedia

WONDERS *of* ANIMAL LIFE

by Famous Writers on Natural History

Volume Eight

Edited by

J.A. Hammerton

Over Three Thousand Illustrations from Photographs and Thirty-three Colour Plates

LOGOS PRESS, NEW DELHI

ISBN -13: 978-81-7268-175-3 (Set)
ISBN -10: 81-7268-175-5 (Set)

ISBN -13: 978-81-7268-176-0 (Vol. I)
ISBN -13: 978-81-7268-177-7 (Vol. II)
ISBN -13: 978-81-7268-178-4 (Vol. III)
ISBN -13: 978-81-7268-179-1 (Vol. IV)
ISBN -13: 978-81-7268-180-7 (Vol. V)
ISBN -13: 978-81-7268-181-4 (Vol. VI)
ISBN -13: 978-81-7268-182-1 (Vol. VII)
ISBN -13: 978-81-7268-183-8 (Vol. VIII)

ISBN -10: 81-7268-176-3 (Vol. I)
ISBN -10: 81-7268-177-1 (Vol. II)
ISBN -10: 81-7268-178-X (Vol. III)
ISBN -10: 81-7268-179-8 (Vol. IV)
ISBN -10: 81-7268-180-1 (Vol. V)
ISBN -10: 81-7268-181-X (Vol. VI)
ISBN -10: 81-7268-182-8 (Vol. VII)
ISBN -10: 81-7268-183-6 (Vol. VIII)

Edition : 2008

Printed & Published by

LOGOS PRESS

Building No. 4788-90, Street No. 23, Ansari Road, Darya Ganj, New Delhi-110 002 (India)
Phone : 23272187

Foreword

Here is not a 'natural history' in the accepted meaning of that description. There exist many and excellent natural histories and more than fifteen years ago the present editor was associated with the publication of one which, in its authoritative letter-press and profuse illustration, had wide acceptance. But it is undeniable that the general reader finds large and exhaustive treatises on animal life, encumbered with Latin names, somewhat hard reading, however fine their illustrations, if they are arranged on the approved scientific divisions—order, family, genus, species—into which naturalists split up animated nature. A proper natural history, however, must follow this method of treatment if it is to form the basis of a scientific knowledge of the subject.

Does the ordinary reader desire such knowledge? Does he require it?

The answer to both questions is a negative: emphatic in the first and modified in the second case. No matter how slightly youth is drawn to the conventional study of zoology, not even the forbidding scientific approach to natural history can rob it of its inherent fascination.

A boundless curiosity about the infinite diversity of creatures that share the life of the globe with him is a deep and abiding and a most natural trait in man. The stories of a Adam naming the beasts, and of the animals, two by two, going into the ark are ancient evidence of man's interest in his fellow-creatures of the so-called lower orders. A study of the life-histories of many animals and birds, fishes and reptiles, or of the astounding social systems of certain insects, is calculated to limit man's pride in himself as the incarnation of the highest intelligence or the finest physical product of the animal world. Especially is it likely to extend his sympathy to all lowly things that are living out their little days with him upon this planet. It lies at the root of humanitarianism. Interest in animal life is never an idle curiosity, and it may prove more absorbing than any other interest that could be named.

Not, then, to add a new natural history to a list already adequate, but to meet this universal and most healthy interest in the astonishing realities and the mysterious ways of the animal kingdom is the purpose of WONDERS OF ANIMAL LIFE. Its title adequately suggests its scope: to enquire into and to illustrate all that is of uncommon interest in the life of the animal kingdom.

While the reader will find in our pages a constantly changing panorama of animal life, with no more apparent order than the naturalist finds in the Brazilian jungle, he can hardly fail to be interested and he is certain to be instructed, for though the only method that is observed throughout our chapters is a rough alternation of interest, now in mammals, next in reptiles, then in birds, fishes, insects, each chapter of this work is written either by one of the leading specialists on his subject or—where expert knowledge is less needed than vividness of descriptive style—by a popular author.

A glance at the list of contributors, their scientific and literary credentials, and the subjects allotted to them in our scheme, will indicate to the reader that though WONDERS OF ANIMAL LIFE is designedly popular in its appeal, it is not the less authoritative in being more entertaining than the conventional sort of natural history.

Never before has there been brought together so representative and so varied a collection of photographic documents covering the whole range of animated nature. In the last decade, and particularly within the latter part of it, naturalists have acquired an immense amount of new knowledge, and marked progress has been made in recording the wild life of the world by means of direct photography.

The exploits of the camera experts employed by the organizers of some of the great 'nature and adventure' films—'Simba' is a fine example—that have fascinated millions throughout the world in these years have produced so rich a body of material for illustrating such a work as this that editorially we are in a more favoured position than any of our predecessors in the same field and we hope the reader will agree with us in thinking that we have taken advantage of that fortunate circumstance for his entertainment and instruction.

J.A. HAMMERTON

Publisher's Note

We are happy to present the illustrated encyclopaedia—Wonders of Animal Life—to the learned readers. As its title suggests, it attempts to enquire into the astonishing realities and the mysterious ways of life of the animal kingdom—mammals, reptiles, birds, fishes and insects.

Presented in eight volumes, each chapter of this work is written either by one of the leading specialists on the subject or—where expert knowledge is less needed than vividness of descriptive style—by a popular author. The text is enriched with a representative and varied collection of photographic documents covering the whole range of animated nature. Our other notable illustrated encyclopaedias include *The Living Animals of the World* (4 volumes), *The Wonders of the World* (4 volumes), *Peoples of All Nations* (14 volumes), and *The Earth and Its Inhabitants* (8 volumes).

TABLE OF CONTENTS

Volume One

List of Colour Plates

Volume Two

List of Colour Plates

Volume Three

List of Colour Plates

Volume Four

List of Colour Plates

Volume Five

List of Colour Plates

Volume Six

List of Colour Plates

Volume Seven

List of Colour Plates

Volume Eight

List of Colour Plates

Chapter CXXXIII

Speed and Slow Motion Among the Animals

By W. Percival Westell

Author of "The Gates of the Forest"

By no means the least interesting factor connected with creatures of the wild is the means by which they move about, and the rate at which they travel. Bats, birds and insects, as we know, fly through the air, but the two last-named can also make their way over land. In this latter respect the bat—a flying mammal—is almost incapable as, at best, it can only shuffle along in a cumbersome, laborious way. There is, too, at least one species of British bird—the swift—to whom Mother Earth is not at all inviting, for this aerial voyager finds it difficult to move when on the ground, and is hard put to it to rise again.

Mammals progress by walking, running, trotting, and other movements. Snakes wriggle over ground at fast speed out of harm's way, or, if attacking, propel their sinuous bodies through the air. Lizards depend almost entirely upon their exceptionally rapid movements to enable them successfully to retreat from their enemies, whilst frogs and toads hop, shuffle, swim, and some at least can climb, such as the pretty little tree frog of tropical America. There is, too, the Javan flying frog which has large, webbed feet, having, on the toes, dilated disks for adhesion. Some snakes also have taken to an arboreal life, and they can swim. Newts, both on land and in water, are to be reckoned among the slow-motion animals, passing part of their time lethargically in muddy ponds, and the remainder in some cool retreat on land. They hibernate during winter.

Fishes propel themselves through the liquid element in which they dwell by swimming and darting, but there is at least one species, the so-called flying fish, which, on reaching the surface of the sea, takes flying leaps through the air, and the eel, as is now well known, is capable of travelling overland, being peculiarly adapted for this purpose.

Hosts of other dwellers in the shallow or deep seas, or other waters, such as shellfish, crabs and lobsters, are mostly slow-motion propellers. In their case, however, protection from enemies is manifest by the shelly covering with which their soft bodies are encased.

Other inhabitants of water, once they have become anchored, rarely, if ever, move from their anchorage, food being secured by means of hairlike attachments, called cilia, or fishing lines, which secure microscopic particles floating in the water.

Those who have taken part in the fascinating pursuit of watching mere atoms of life, specks of activity, through a high power microscope will need no reminder of the amazing speed at which some forms of life found in water move about, darting away, all unexpectedly, at a rapid rate, an apt illustration of the wonderful mechanism with which these mere but mighty atoms are endowed.

The whole subject of speed among the inhabitants of the animal world is, in reality, linked up with the importance to the creature concerned of being able to hie away from its enemies, or to pursue its own prey. In the case of deer and other vegetarian feeders speed is not necessary in order to secure prey, but it is a prime essential for putting a safe distance between them and their natural enemies. Speed may be useful, too, if food or drink become scarce, and a change of district has to be made.

Carnivorous animals, on the other hand, must, of necessity, be the possessors of quick methods of locomotion, for two prime purposes, namely, for procuring food by springing, leaping, or climbing, whilst fleetness of foot is also an absolute necessity when an enemy approaches.

Many wild creatures whose slow motions would, if put to the test, stand them in poor stead as a

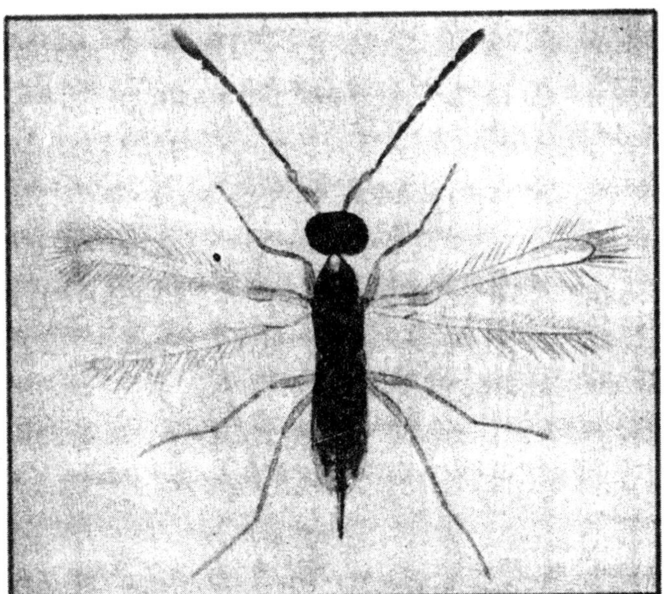

J. J Ward

WINGS FOR UNDER-WATER SWIMMING

Hatching out in the eggs of dragon-flies laid under water, the fairy fly uses its wings for swimming. In this illustration the fly is very much enlarged, for it is so minute that it is scarcely visible to the naked eye. The dragon-fly's worst enemy is thus in not out of the water.

nature of the environment is of prime importance, for whereas the inhabitants of jungle, wood, or forest can take cover without having to traverse a large stretch of country, and need not, therefore, be possessed of great speed, animals that frequent prairies and other open situations must be numbered among our fast-moving animals, or burrowers beneath the ground, or they would assuredly go under in the great struggle for existence.

There is, too, the question of how an animal is built, for whilst the largest land mammal—the elephant—can and does move at a good rate which it can keep up for a considerable time, and is, of course, possessed of great powers of strength, the hippopotamus will wade and sink into the water out of harm's

method of escape when attacked, rely almost exclusively upon the able protection with which Nature has furnished them. Thus, the beautiful sea anemone will, when its rosette of expanded tentacles is disturbed, retrieve these organs and transform itself into a blob of unattractive jelly-like substance. Crabs will, when their foreparts are exposed in water, withdraw within their hard coverings, or burrow in the sand, and shellfish—such as limpets, cockles, mussels, periwinkles, and others—will at once retire within the ample protection of their shelly homes when danger threatens. The closing of the lid, or front door, completes the process.

The further point has to be mentioned of vegetarian animals which are sought after by mankind for food or sport—deer, antelope, and their kindred—having, of necessity, to move quickly away from heir pursuers. They must be quick-footed, or few of them would survive. So, too, the

C.N.A.

BEARS RELYING MORE ON STEALTH THAN SPEED

Owing to their mode of life bears have no need to travel very quickly. Movements such as a blow of the paw or a snap of the jaws are rapid enough, but the bear neither runs down its food nor travels long distances for it. As a matter of fact, bears will eat almost anything from roots to honey. These animals are both American.

MONARCH BUTTERFLIES WHOSE QUICK WINGS TRAVERSE CONTINENTS

Owing to its enterprise in long distance flying and migration the monarch butterfly has circled the world and established itself in at least three new continents. Indigenous to North America the monarch is seen there in great swarms entirely covering some tree or shrub. When the cold weather comes the swarms fly south to more congenial temperatures. The monarch has crossed the Pacific by means of shipping, colonised Australia, established itself in Malaya and even reached as far as England.

U.F.A.

E.N.A

SPEED AND SLOW MOTION IN THE AFRICAN WILDS

While the elephant can charge with formidable speed for a short distance, yet its usual gait is an unhurried one, as befits the lord of the forest. Its long legs, however, cover the ground well, even if their owner is not moving them very fast. The gnu of the plains (top), on the other hand, lives in the open, and has to depend on a clean pair of heels for safety.

way, just leaving the top part of its head above the surface.

Crocodiles move laboriously—and small wonder when one realizes what they have to take about with them—but their armour well protects them, and their forbidding and capacious jaws are, when extended, capable of frightening the most venturesome explorer. Interesting examples of speed and slow motion, mapped out on this hypothesis of make-up, are supplied in the case of the hunter, or race horse, and the cart horse, and among wild animals in the one-humped, or Arabian camel, and the two-humped, or Bactrian camel. The former is the express train of the camel tribe, built for speed; the latter is the beast of burden, the carrier of goods, the goods-train of the desert.

Perhaps with the advent of motor transport the days of the Bactrian camel as a beast of burden are numbered, but from time immemorial it has served mankind, though, compared with its one-humped cousin, it is not a rapid mover. The giraffe is the trained athlete of wild tracts of country, and can, in spite of its somewhat ungainly appearance, move at a prodigious pace, travelling in companies.

The bison of North America has in the last fifty years decreased in numbers to an alarming extent, in spite of its strength, fierceness, powers of locomotion and endurance. Whales, on the other hand have, through persecution by man, also decreased in numbers, and this notwithstanding their watery habitat, tremendous strength, tenacity, and courage. Whales (which are mammals) and sharks (which are fish) travel great distances through the sea, and many kinds of fish beside the shark also undertake great migrations, as with our friends, the birds. Fishes must, of necessity, therefore, travel at a good, if not very fast rate, and if rest by the way is an essential factor in the life and movements of

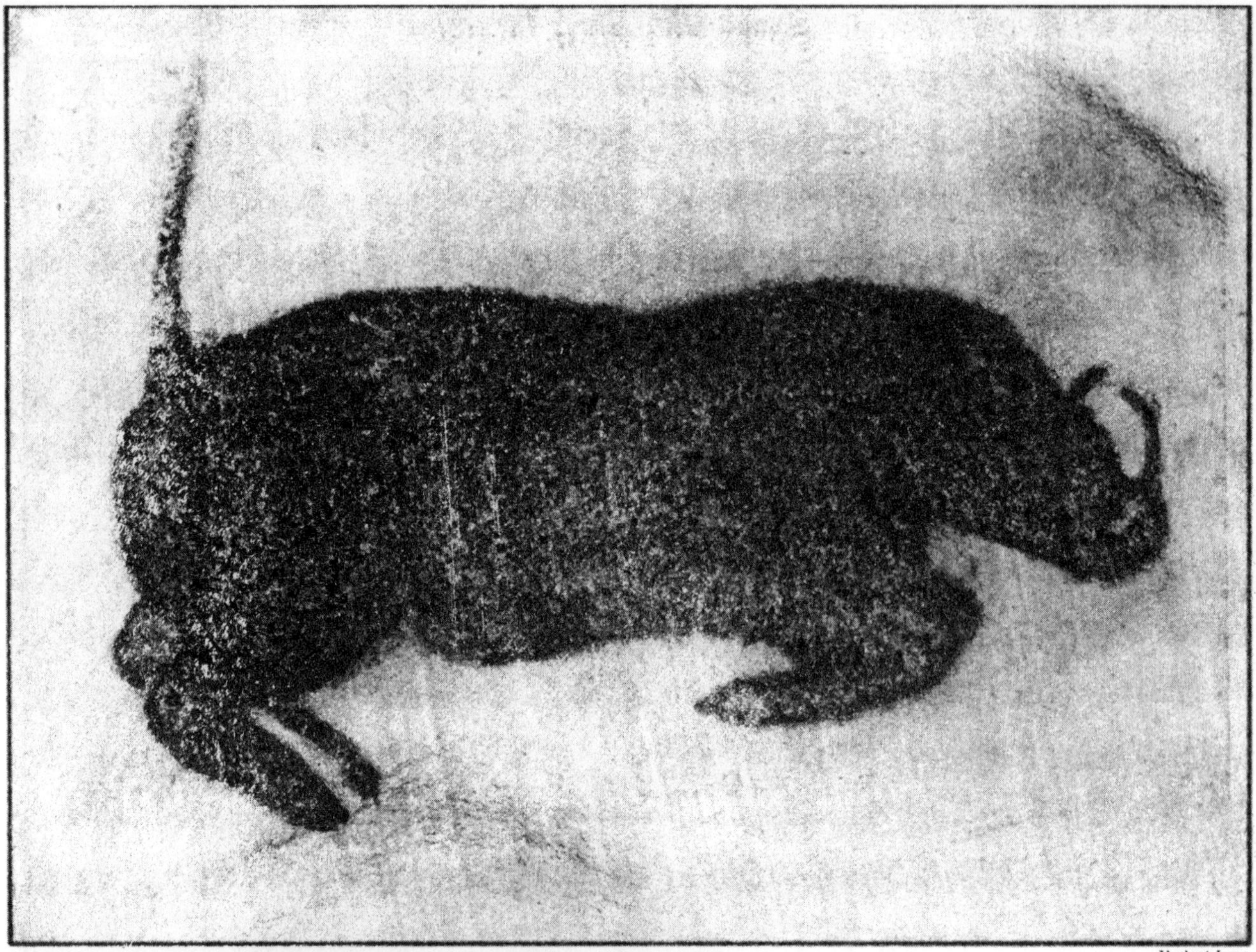

Herbert Lang

SPEED AS THE CAMERA AND PREHISTORIC MAN HAVE SEEN IT IN THE WART HOG

The lower photograph was taken from a motor car moving at thirty miles an hour. This is a very respectable speed for an animal and, indeed, the wart hog is one of the best runners in all Africa. The upper illustration shows a drawing of a wart hog made by prehistoric man on the wall of a cave in the Western Transvaal. Note how cleverly the primitive artist has caught the essential suggestion of speed in his drawing. This is a wonderful contrast in speed as seen at an interval, perhaps, of four thousand years.

SURPRISINGLY QUICK MOVER BOTH OUT OF AND IN THE WATER

Where the Nile runs through agricultural land the hippopotamus often does considerable damage to the crops, for it is an enormous feeder, needing a great bulk of food, as all vegetarians do. When alarmed the huge, unwieldy animal makes off at a surprising speed, running through the fields and finally plunging, with an awe-inspiring splash, into the water. In our photograph we see a hippopotamus swimming across the river. At all aquatic manœuvres this huge animal is a quick mover when it wishes to be.

HIGH SPEED RUNNERS PROTECTED IN THE GREAT AFRICAN GAME PRESERVES

Fastest of the antelopes when it comes to a burst of speed the impala (lower photograph) get over the ground in great bounds and, despite the rapidity with which they move, their progress seems utterly effortless. Impala always seem to keep near water and are fond of the banks of rivers, feeding among the scrub of the sandy plains. The upper photograph shows a scene from the Kruger National Park, South Africa. In it we see a wart hog and, in the distance, some wildebeeste. Both animals are very swift runners when alarmed.

Mondiale

MOOSE AND HERD OF WAPITI, STRONG SWIMMERS AND SWIFT RUNNERS

Both moose and wapiti are good swimmers and the former, especially, takes to the water very readily. One reason for this is the fact that the structure of the moose's body is more fitted for browsing on twigs and shoots than for grazing, and that, consequently, water plants are convenient food, for the animal simply wades to a spot where its floating food is at a convenient level for its short neck to reach. When alarmed, the moose makes off very quickly with great strides of its long legs. Above is a herd of wapiti swimming a Canadian river.

SPEED AT MAN'S BIDDING AND SPEED AT TERROR OF MAN: ENGLISH RACEHORSES IN ACTION AND NEVADA MUSTANGS

It is calculated that an English racehorse can travel, over a short distance, at a speed of approximately forty miles an hour. This is the result of several centuries of selective breeding which combined the qualities of quick movement and stamina. Below is a race with the animals at full gallop. As a contrast we offer the photograph above. Here is a herd of wild horses, in Nevada, stampeding. These animals are an admixture of the old American wild horse, a descendant of the animals imported and abandoned by the early European explorers and settlers in America, and those that have escaped and run wild since. The wildly galloping animals are an incarnation of speed itself.

E.N.A.

HIGH JUMPING AT SPEED AND QUICKNESS LENT BY FEAR

It is the especial power of the camera to be able to capture a moment from speed and record it for all time. Here we have the action, occupying a fraction of a second, of a golden retriever (bottom) as the dog clears a five-barred gate with a bird in its mouth. Above are some wild boars "snapped" while in flight through a forest, still a refuge for them in Germany

lung-breathing animals on land, this does not seem necessary among fishes which, whilst remaining stationary in one place, have to keep their fins and gills moving and be on the alert, ready to dash away at a moment's notice.

The giant tortoises of the Galapagos Islands, having such bulky bodies and enormous carapaces, or shields, to carry about with them, move with slow motion, but they can carry still heavier burdens—such as a man weighing fifteen stone.

The hare, on the other hand, which according to the old fable, once lost a race to a tortoise, though faster, would need to rest far more often on a long journey.

His whims and fancies have also to be considered, for, whilst all those who live in the country know the distance a Jack or Sally hare can traverse in an incredibly short space of time, they know also that this highly-strung animal will often squat and take stock of its surroundings and whilst thus engaged may, perchance, be stalked successfully by even a moderate paced hound. The rabbit is possessed of a good turn of speed, but it soon bolts to ground or cover. If the

Seton Gordon

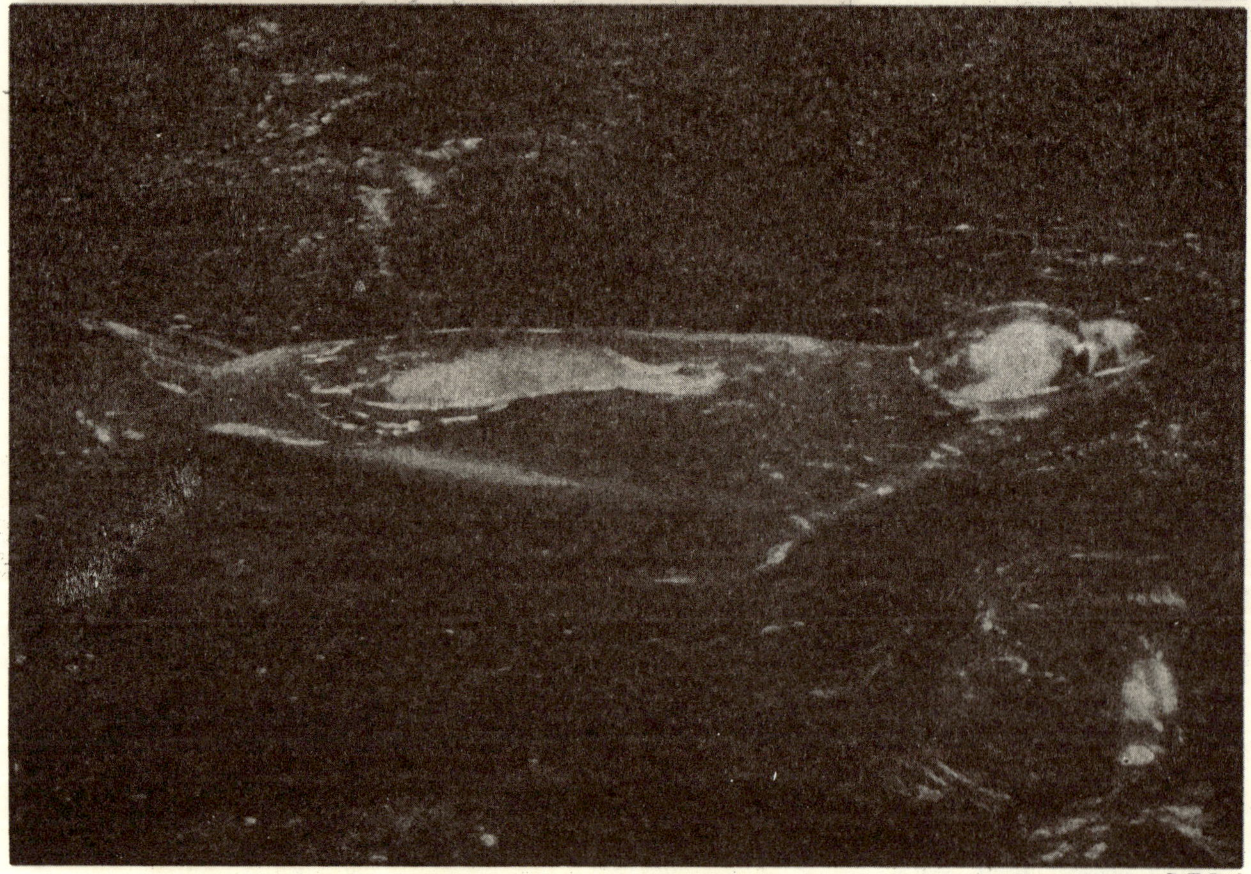

F. W. Bond

SWIFT SWIMMERS OF COASTAL WATERS AND THE DEEP SEA: BLADDER-NOSED AND ATLANTIC SEALS

Having, through the course of long ages, converted their limbs into flippers in changing from the shore life of their ancestors to their present pelagic life, the seals have contrived to equip themselves with a turn of speed that can cope even with the lightning movements of fish. In diving, and under-water and surface swimming their powers are extraordinary. The lower photograph shows a bladder-nosed seal, while above is a group of Atlantic seals showing off their swimming powers for the camera's benefit.

Fox Photos

SURFACE AND SUBMARINE SWIMMERS: QUICK-MOVING SWANS AND PENGUINS

With powerful drives of alternate legs the swan thrusts its big black web through the water and forges ahead with a swirl of foam about its breast. When enraged and drawing up to a rival the swan fairly lifts its breast out of the water with each lunge of its powerful swimming feet. Below we see two swans, one chasing the other off its own particular territory. Above is a trio of penguins which literally fly through the water. using their stunted wings as a seal uses its flippers.

O. Pike

E.N.A.

SPEED IN FLIGHT: KINGFISHER, GOLDEN EAGLE AND CRANE

People often wonder how fast this or that bird is flying as they watch it. The speed, of course, varies with the weather conditions, which affect birds as much as human fliers. The kingfisher (bottom left) is a comparatively small bird, and seems to go at a great pace as it flashes past us where we sit beside some stream. But the golden eagle (bottom right), which, if we see it at all, is probably so far away that its speed seems small, flies faster as it swoops upon some hare or partridge. The crane (top) goes in more for distance than speed.

E.N.A.

Fox Photos

OSTRICH, THE FASTEST THING ON TWO LEGS IN THE WORLD: MARABOU STORK

Undoubtedly the ostrich is nearly the fastest runner in the animal world, if not the fastest Experience seems to show that no horse could stay with it at full speed. Unfortunately for the bird, it always runs in a circle, and once it has been determined which way the ostrich is going, it is possible to ride along an arc of the bird's circle and so run into it again. The wings are used at the beginning of the run, but are kept close to the side when the bird is going " all out." Above is a marabou stork running across country.

on being disturbed, release what seems to be a living spring and literally flings itself through the air, trusting to chance as to where it falls and the resultant consequences.

Four-footed animals, as also insects incapable of flight, and arboreal and terrestrial creatures, cannot of course travel unaided other than over land. Thus, though they do move at a rare speed and cover great distances—as in the case of the lemmings, which undertake long, periodical wanderings—they are unable to traverse such distances as birds. Once an animal, unable to fly or swim, becomes a tenant of an island, it is there for life, unless, of course, as in the case of the Hanoverian rat, stray specimens of the smaller mammals (or snakes, insects, and other creatures accidentally imported with fruit and so on) are taken to foreign countries on board ship.

The fox is a classic example of a

latter, it remains quiet and unconcealed, its dress harmonising with its surroundings. The hare, however, is a dweller above ground, and speed is much more necessary for its survival. Its young, known as leverets, are born fully dressed, and with their bright little eyes wide open, whereas the young rabbit is at first both naked and blind.

Some kinds of caterpillars are quick walkers, and among those I have watched the well-known furry larva of the handsome tiger moth is worthy of mention. It is frequently called the woolly bear because of its hairy covering. When watched crawling along the ground it is amazing the distance this common object of our countryside can traverse in a short time, and I should feel inclined to back it for a place among the first three past the winning-post in any race it might engage in with its lepidopterous relatives.

Other caterpillars are slow in their movements, and can easily be overtaken. Some drop from trees and bushes by attaching their bodies to a silky filament, others loop or arch their bodies as they propel themselves along, and are called looper caterpillars, in consequence.

The cheery grasshopper progresses, as the latter part of its name implies, by hopping, and is quite difficult to catch unless, during its subsequent tumble, the nimble creature becomes mixed up among the herbage it frequents.

For amazing mechanism in a small creature, however, the little frog-hopper when in the adult state takes a good deal of beating. As a soft, yellowish-green larva embedded in froth it is inactive and unattractive, but having put on a hard coat of mail and faced the world bravely, the jumpy creature will,

GECKOS, QUICK RUNNERS UPSIDE DOWN

By means of specially adapted feet some geckos can scuttle along a ceiling at a remarkable pace, and also run up walls. The lower photograph, taken through glass, shows how the gecko's feet cling by the dilated surfaces of the toes. Above is a fringed gecko.

Otho Webb

TURTLES, SLOW ON LAND BUT QUICK IN THE SEA

Slow and full of effort as is the turtle's progress on land it is a fine and active swimmer and a strong one, too. In the breeding season the turtles come out of the sea to lay their eggs. Our photographs show the head of a turtle (bottom) as it swims towards us and (top) a hawksbill turtle making its laborious way up the beach.

speedy animal, and its powers need no elaboration. Irrespective of its being hunted, it must travel some distance to secure food for its cubs. Chicken runs will be visited by Reynard, or the nearest duckpond or pheasant preserve. The hand of the fowl-rearer and game-keeper is against this crafty, bloodthirsty haunter of the silences. The hunting packs of hungry, strong-limbed wolves also provide another example of speed and endurance. Bears, on the other hand, live in caves or other retreats. They are soft-footed, and splendid swimmers. Great speed is not necessary to them so much as cunning and stealth. They have means for taking cover, or otherwise escaping their pursuers. Quick in movement, adept in stalking, like the lion and his kin, most assuredly, but great speed and capacity to cover distance are alike unnecessary to them.

The ostrich is a splendid traveller over land, and the fastest horse would be no

Otho Webb

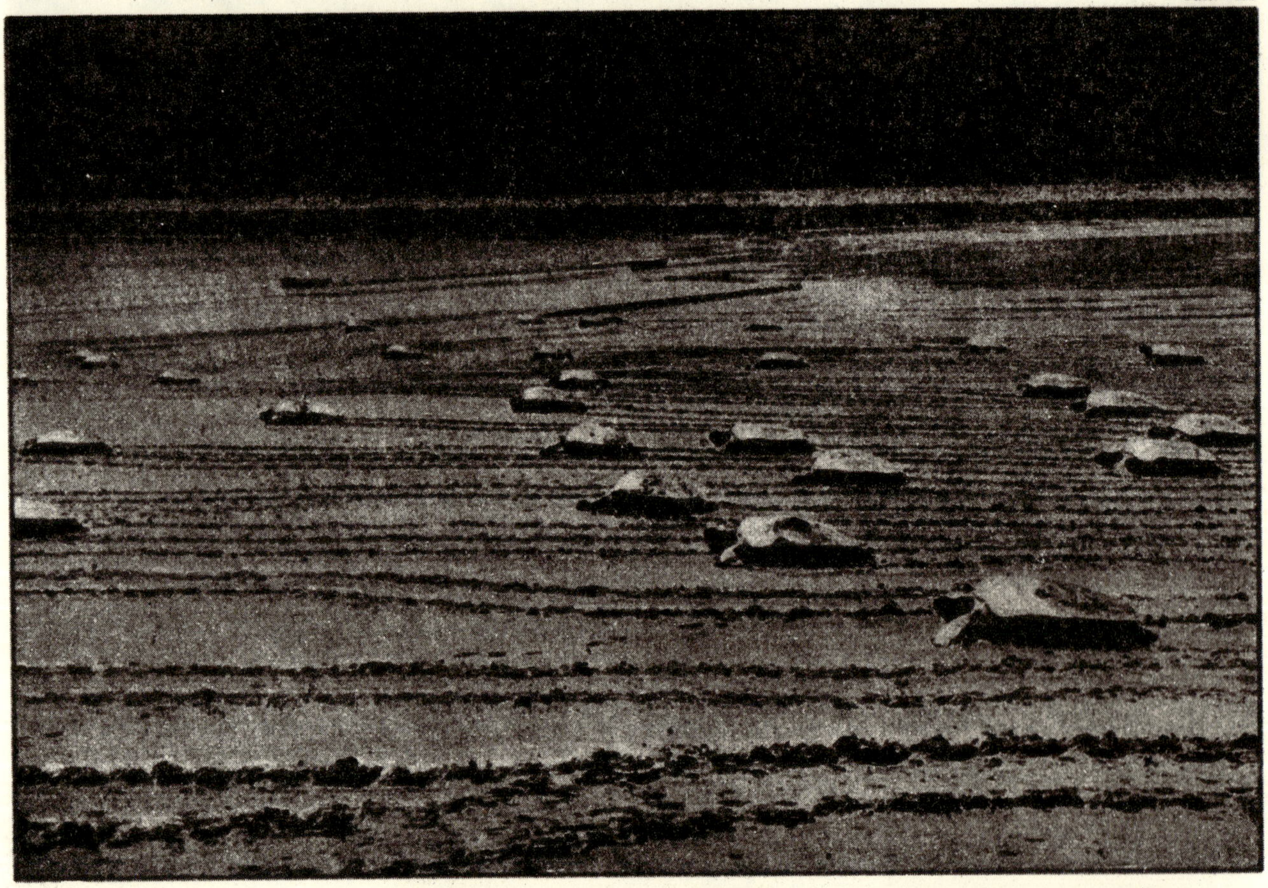

TURTLE TRACKS THAT SHOW THE EFFORTS NEEDED TO MAKE EVEN SLOW PROGRESS

Walking along one of the lonely beaches of the North-West Territory of Australia, one may come across tracks in the sand such as are illustrated above. These sights mean that, during the night, the turtles have been ashore to lay their eggs under cover of darkness. The turtles' limbs, which have been converted into flippers, are not at all suited for land travel, and the slow, laborious shuffle leaves traces in the sand speaking eloquently of the efforts made by the creature to get along.

ARCHETYPE OF SLOW MOTION: THE TORTOISE AS IT WALKS

Tortoises have sacrificed activity for security, and have preferred a long life to an exciting one. The very shell that is heavy enough to keep them safe from attack is the perpetual incubus they must carry about, and one that prohibits any movement faster than a slow crawl. The tortoise in the lower illustration is a hundred years of age, and there seems no reason why another century should not lie before it. Above is a full-length view of a tortoise as it walks its unhurried way.

TREE FROG AND A SOUTH AFRICAN FROG

The members of two quite distinct families of frogs have taken to a life among the trees. A frog is a poor crawler and relies on hopping when danger threatens. But some of the tree frogs make great glides through the air, using the webs of their teet as gliders. The upper photograph shows a South African frog in the water, the element where frogs are most active.

match for this practised dweller of vast tracts of untilled country. Compare, however, the wanderings of this fleet-footed feathered biped with the slug or snail in the nearest hedgerow or garden. Most of these soft-bodied animals are vegetarians, as we who tend our favourite flowers know to our cost, but they are slow-motion creatures because, not only are they fairly well protected by shell, slime, form, or colour, but once an abundant food-supply is at hand, there is no further need for another laborious trail to be undertaken, and whilst the stock holds out, the consumer can retire from any further prolonged wandering. He has temporarily made his fortune and can retire from business!

It is interesting to note the life periods of a few animals from the viewpoint of their activities. Thus the voracious pike, a lethargic enough creature except when hungry, has been known to become a centenarian. A like age is recorded for other slow-moving animals, such as the carp and crocodile. The elephant, however, a speed animal of the jungle, attains the ripe old age of 150 to 200 years. The skylark leads a

FRILLED LIZARD, A CREATURE OF BOTH SPEED AND SLOW MOTION

Found in Queensland and New South Wales the frilled lizard usually goes on all fours like other lizards. But when a burst of speed is necessary it forsakes the quadrupedal method and becomes a biped, running on its hind legs. Thus it is a creature of both speed and slow motion. The deep fringe round its neck is expanded if its owner is brought to bay, when the lizard looks like some fierce dragon.

Martin Duncan

Otho Webb

TWO EXTREMES OF SPEED IN THE SEA : TIGER SHARK AND SCALLOPS

With an immensely powerful tail as a propeller the tiger shark (bottom) cleaves the water like a torpedo when chasing its prey. We see one here photographed through the shallow, sunlit sea-water of a coral island. The other extreme of speed is reached when we consider the scallops (top). These we see moving about in the bottom of an aquarium. By opening their shells, taking in a quantity of water, then closing the shells smartly, thereby violently driving out the water, they move backwards in a series of jerks.

Martin Duncan

Martin Duncan

LETHARGY AND ACTIVITY : STARFISH AND FLYING GURNARD

Turn a starfish over so that its whitish underside is exposed and a close inspection will reveal hundreds of tiny little tubes, feebly stirring. These are the creature's feet and by their concerted action it moves along. The flying gurnard (top) of the Indian Ocean and Equatorial Atlantic has enormous pectoral fins which it can flap vigorously as it leaps out of the water.

very active life as everyone knows, yet, barring accidents, it lives sixteen to eighteen years, while Jenny Wren, who just dawdles about hedgerows and woods, lives only a few years. The slow and patient ass attains an honoured age of from 25 to 50 years. The busy bee (female) may attain an age of four years; the industrious and active beaver fifty years; the crow a hundred years; the goose fifty years; the wolf twenty years; the lion sixty years, and the tortoise a hundred years or more.

The distances travelled by birds, and the speed at which they fly, are among the most wonderful operations of Nature's children. A young song thrush, born in a nest in Aberdeen, was found three weeks afterwards in Portugal, a distance of 1,500 miles. The homing pigeon is, of course, a classic instance of speed upon the wing, for pigeons have not only been timed to cover 800 miles in 33½ hours, but, aided by a gale, well over a mile a minute.

Chapter CXXXIV

Unfamiliar Relatives of the Bees and Wasps

By John J. Ward, F.E.S.

Author of "Peeps Into Nature's Ways," "Insect Biographies," etc.

ONE day, when about to deliver a lecture on "Wasps," my chairman, a witty vicar, in his introduction, said that wasps were insects which should be envied by all public speakers, and for two reasons. Firstly, because they could always concentrate attention, and secondly, from the fact that they would invariably get in their point.

While it is true that wasps and bees are familiar to everybody largely because they carry a sting, yet there are numerous kindred species of these stinging insects which, although abundant in every garden, field and wood, are scarcely ever observed, chiefly because they do not make personal attacks upon us. Occasionally, a close acquaintance with one of the females of these lesser known species impresses us with its wasp-like, or bee-like, characters, and it is then carefully avoided; especially is this so when it is provided with a conspicuous egg-apparatus, or ovipositor. The insect may be quite harmless, but it looks as if it could sting, and instinctively it is left alone.

The main distinguishing features of these hymenopterous insects is their two pairs of membranous wings, united during flight by means of a row of minute hooks on the fore margins of the hind pair, these hooks engaging a bar on the hind margin of the fore-wings. It requires a magnifying lens to observe the hooks (see illustrations in page 250), but almost any insect with two pairs of semi-transparent wings, and a head and body of wasp-like, or bee-like, form, will generally be found to belong to the great insect order Hymenoptera; of which more than 30,000 species have been classified, while the world's undescribed species would probably total ten times that number.

Since, then, bees and wasps have many relatives, some of which are much larger than themselves, while others are so minute that they can scarcely be seen by the human eye, let us here consider a few types from the larger kinds downwards to some of the more minute species; for the life stories of some of the latter are more than remarkable.

The female wood-wasp, or giant sirex (*Sirex gigas*), is the largest of these insects that one is likely to meet with in England. Its popular name is misleading, for it is a member of the stem saw-flies (*Siricidae*). There is also its smaller relative, the steel-blue wood-wasp (*Sirex juvencus*), of metallic blue colour, which may be met with less frequently. In America these insects are called horntails.

ALTHOUGH harmless, the giant sirex appears to be a formidable insect when it approaches with a loud buzzing sound, and being coloured black and yellow, with a conspicuous ovipositor, it certainly gives a wasp scare to those that meet with it. Not infrequently during the summer I receive boxes labelled "Open with care. Live hornet," or with some similar inscription, but almost invariably the specimen proves to be a giant sirex. The hornet, it should be remembered, is simply a large species of wasp and, relatively with its larger size, its sting is no more conspicuous than that of the common wasp.

Strange to relate, but a few hours after writing the above paragraph a female giant sirex was brought to me for identification from the wood department of a large motor works. Most of the live specimens captured in England emerge from foreign wood, as the insect rarely breeds in the ordinary way in the British Isles.

The sirex grub's method of working has already been described in this work (page 442), and it is interesting to compare its powerful drill for penetrating strong pine wood, with the ovipositors of its relations, the true saw-flies (*Tenthredinidae*), each female of which is provided with a tiny pair of wonderfully constructed saws, the structural details of which identify her species. The saws are perfectly adapted for

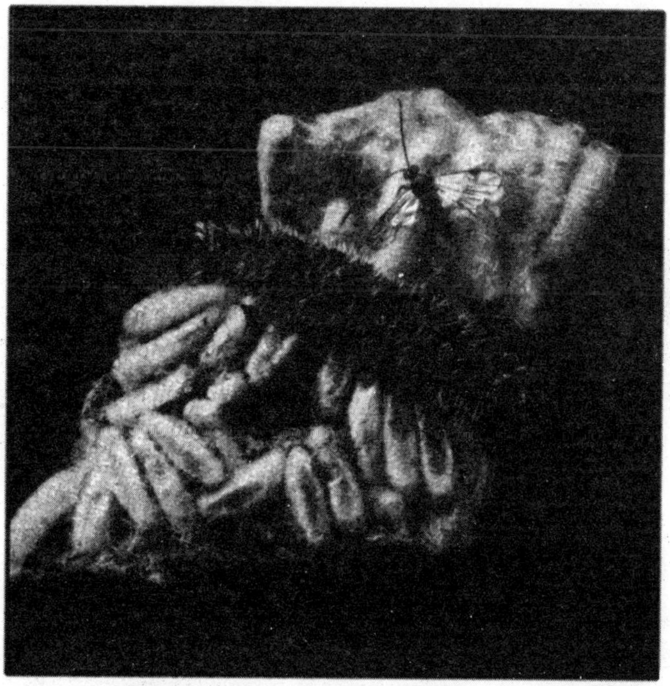

J. J. Ward

GRIM HATCHING OF AN ICHNEUMON WASP

Skins of the caterpillar of the large white butterfly and near them a heap of ichneumon wasp cocoons (bottom) show the end of the grisly story of the eggs that hatch inside a wretched caterpillar which is, literally, eaten alive. Above is a caterpillar skin and a newly-hatched wasp.

Grubs of gooseberry sawfly feeding

The gooseberry sawfly

Leaf-miner grub inside birch leaf

Grubs of rose sawfly at work

Rose sawfly cocoon

The female giant sirex

Alder sawfly grubs feeding tails erect against ichneumon

J. J. Ward

Tail end of a sawfly showing saws

SOME OF THE SAWFLIES, RELATIVES OF THE WASP, THAT DO GREAT HARM

There are many more insects coming under the heading of bees and wasps than most people ever imagine. Over thirty thousand species have been classified in various parts of the world, but as great a host probably remains to be accounted for. In Britain the sawflies are a case in point and some of them cause alarm by the long ovipositors being mistaken for stings. But it is not human skin that these egg-laying organs pierce. The sawfly and the giant sirex, illustrated here, do immense damage to trees and shrubs by laying their eggs in the wood.

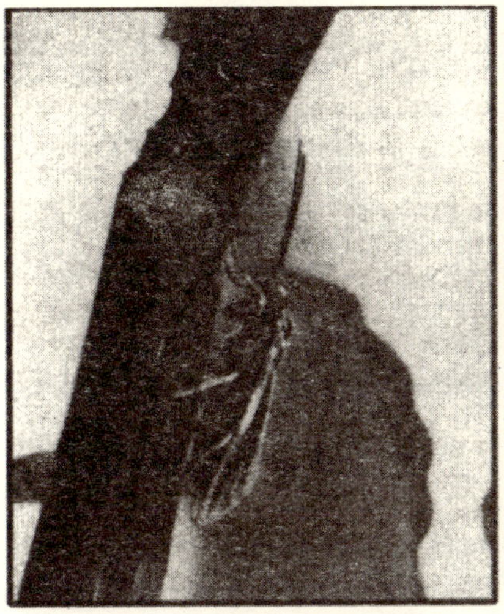

Palisade sawfly magnified five times

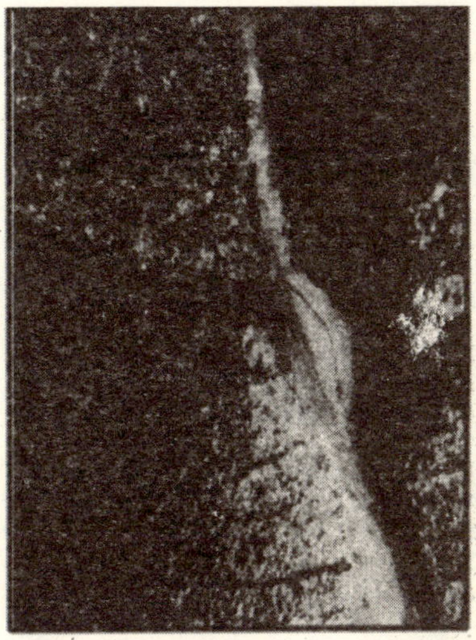

Egg in position on black poplar leaf

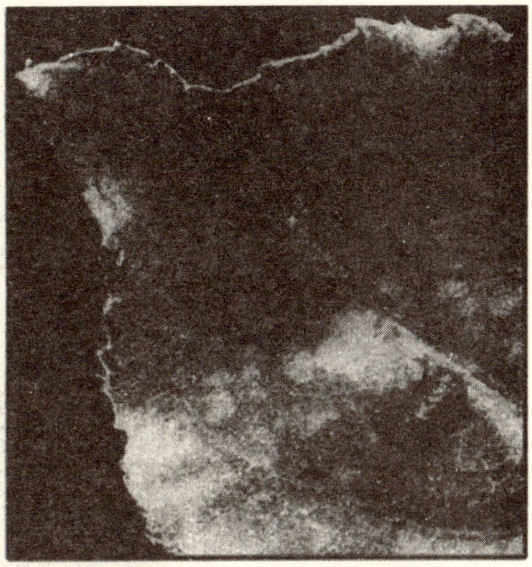

Cocoons of palisade sawfly on a fallen leaf

Two grubs feeding—note white palisades

J. J. Ward

The same poplar leaf three days later

PALISADE SAWFLY THAT SURROUNDS ITSELF WITH A 'CHARMED CIRCLE" AGAINST ANTS

A tiny black insect, about two-thirds the size of a house-fly, is shown in the above photographs and it is called, from an extraordinary habit it has, the palisade sawfly. It is found on the leaves of the black poplar and, when it has selected a leaf to feed on, actually builds a palisade all round to keep out the marauding ants which are always busy on the stems of plants and trees looking for food. The palisade is made of columns of saliva which have an effect as of some poison-gas on any ant that touches one. These photographs are magnified.

cutting the particular stems or leaves it selects for egg-depositing.

The drill of the sirex is a kind of elastic bar embracing two notched boring tools which work along it, while the saws of the saw-fly consist of two delicate serrated blades, which correspond with the notched boring tools of the sirex, covered with a pair of horny plates, or sheaths, into which the saws fit closely. The strong central bar is absent in the ovipositor of the saw-flý, and has probably become divided to form the strengthening bar at the back of each saw blade.

Not infrequently we find the foliage of our gooseberry bushes badly destroyed by the grubs of the gooseberry saw-fly (*Nematus ribesii*), and these larvae differ somewhat from the caterpillars of both butterflies and moths. A butterfly, or moth, caterpillar has only three pairs of true legs, and never more than four pairs of pro-legs, or claspers, on its abdominal segments, and one pair at its tail-end. The saw-fly grub, according to its species, can have from six to eight pairs of pro-legs in addition to its three pairs of true legs. So that the answer to the question: How many legs has a caterpillar got?—obviously depends on the caterpillar. Many of the saw-fly grubs, like those of the gooseberry saw-fly, when feeding, curl up their tail end; while others, like those of the alder saw-fly (*Croesus septentrionalis*), elevate the posterior part of their bodies, moving them up and down, in order to drive off their foes, the ichneumon-wasps. On account of these differences these saw-fly grubs are called "false," or "pseudo-caterpillars."

The life stories of saw-flies are often of an amazing character. In some species only three or four males appear to about each thousand females; and in certain others males are entirely unknown. The eggs of the latter all prove fertile, generation after generation of females being continually produced.

There is the tiny palisade saw-fly (*Lygaeonematus compressicornis*) which may serve to tell of some remarkable life story details. It is a tiny black insect about two-thirds the size of a common house-fly, and its grub feeds on the leaves of the black poplar tree. While feeding it displays a curious and unique defensive device of, apparently, most artful design.

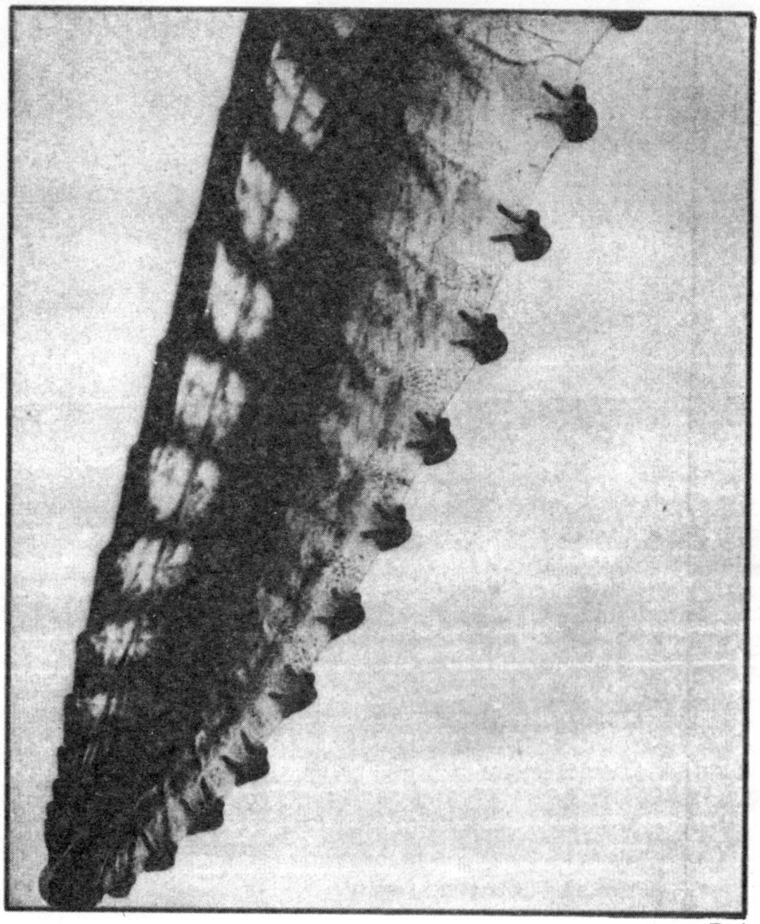

I. J. Ward

SAWS FOR EGG LAYING: ROSE GALL MADE BY A WASP

Each female saw-fly has a pair of wonderful little saws (bottom, magnified) to make holes for her eggs. Above is a bedeguar or pincushion gall from a wild rose which has been bored by a gall wasp female. The developing grub sets up an irritation in the plant which forms the gall and a home for the grub.

Stages in the emerging of an ichneumon wasp from the chrysalis of a butterfly

Caterpillar uses scent glands in defence

Ichneumon wasp resting on leaf

Searching for moth larvae victims

Puss-moth caterpillar resting

Caterpillar tries to frighten ichneumon

J J Ward

Puss-moth ichneumon wasp

ICHNEUMON FLIES AND THEIR DEADLY ACTIVITIES AMONG THE CATERPILLARS

While the caterpillar is eating hard and, incidentally, destroying some plant of service to man, a mortal enemy may be very near. This enemy is the ichneumon fly or wasp. Its method is to pierce the skin of the caterpillar with its sharp ovipositor and lay some eggs beneath the skin. The caterpillars are then eaten alive by the developing ichneumon grubs. The caterpillar of the swallowtail butterfly, as seen above, has invented a scent gland to stave off the ichneumon's attack. The puss-moth caterpillar tries to frighten its foe by inflating itself.

Before proceeding to feed, it builds around its feeding area an irregular barricade consisting of tiny, white palisades. The astonishing thing is the nature of these palisades. The grub secretes from its mouth a spot of frothy saliva, then, raising its head, stretches out the solution into a short pillar, suddenly snapping it off at the correct height. This column, built of tiny bubbles of saliva, then stands more or less erect, but remains viscid and flexible, and the remarkable feature is that, although of the finest hair-like structure, yet it can remain exposed to the open air for two or three weeks without becoming dry. There the grub has discovered a secret that baffles the expert chemist.

After having formed a series of these palisades on the under side of the leaf, it eats out a portion of the leaf in the midst of them, and goes through the hole it has made to the upper surface of the leaf, where a corresponding series of palisades are built. Being then barricaded on both sides of the leaf, it grips the eaten edge with its three pairs of true legs and a few pairs of its clasper-legs, and, standing on edge in this way, it elevates and slightly curls its tail-end. It is then in its characteristic attitude for feeding, and proceeds to enlarge the hole.

What kind of enemy does this seemingly skilfully designed defence protect the grub against ? One would at first suspect that it was a protection against parasitic ichneumon-wasps, but, in the course of three years persistent efforts to work out the mysterious life story of this insect (which was entirely unknown), I successfully reared ichneumon-wasps from its cocoons. The defence, therefore, failed somewhat in that direction.

Eventually, a clue to the mystery was forthcoming. While watching a grub feeding, I saw it change its feeding area to a new leaf, and I noted that it blocked the stalk of the leaf with its palisades. That action suggested to me that it was a creeping, and not a flying foe that it had to contend with.

Now, it is quite a common device amongst plants to produce rows of hairs on their stems and leaves to protect their flowers from the attacks of creeping insects, especially the troublesome ants, which are honey thieves. Ants, too, are always moving amongst the leaves and branches of plants in search of cast caterpillar skins and dead or injured insects which provide their meat diet. Also, they not infrequently attack with their strong mandibles newly-moulted caterpillars, which are then very tender, and, for a while, inclined to be inactive. Here, too, I may mention that I observed that the palisade saw-fly grub, after moulting, always immediately ate up its cast skin. The hint to the ant that a more juicy meal was resting nearby was in that way removed.

Ants, then, were under suspicion. Then came an experiment to prove the point. When the grub had well barricaded both the stalk of the leaf and the area it had selected for feeding, I introduced a common brown ant on to the surface of the leaf. If the palisades were effective as a protection, the grub was secure, for the ant could not reach its feeding area, nor could it escape down the leaf stalk, which was likewise defended.

The experiment provided a surprise, for the ant, alarmed with my handling of it, when released, rushed excitedly over the leaf surface, and, in doing so, cannoned into *one only* of the palisades. That was enough. The sticky pillar had broken away at its base, and the ant was carrying it about stuck to its head. The agitation of the ant with its encumbrance was, obviously, very great. It struggled violently to dislodge it, and finally it succeeded ; but that was only the beginning of its adventure.

It was easy to see that the ant was suffering from some form of shock, or paralysis ; its limbs vibrated considerably as it staggered about the leaf while furiously brushing its face with its fore-legs. Then, it suddenly halted, stiffened out its six legs into an upright position, and I quite expected it to roll over and die. Instead, it held itself erect on its rigid legs, and slowly brought down its head, at the same time lowering its tail-end until head and tail met beneath its legs. In that extraordinary position, with its body in the form of a ball, holding its tail-end by its mandibles, it remained for about two minutes, and then let go.

The vibration of its limbs had ceased, together with the violent contortions of its body. It was a little unsteady on its legs, and moved but slowly, but gradually revived. There was only one conclusion. The ant had been "gassed," and it had secreted something from its tail-end (probably formic acid) which had neutralised the effect of the poison. Further experiments with other ants produced the same result.

This orderly arrangement of the saw-fly grub's outworks around its feeding zone would seem to imply some mentality on the part of the grub, but, probably, in the course of its struggle for existence, it discovered that its saliva was objectionable to its enemy the ant, and, later, gradually evolved the art of depositing small quantities of it before commencing to feed. Although there is sometimes room for an ant to pass between the pillars, yet no ant ever does so ; the saliva columns apparently have a pungency which affects the ant's sense of smell much as a whiff of strong ammonia irritates our nostrils. It is astonishing to find that the tiny grub just hatched from the egg comes into the world with full instinctive knowledge how to protect itself ; that at once it proceeds to construct its miniature defence before taking its first meal.

There are many other equally remarkable saw-fly grubs, some of which even mine leaves. In Chapter XXXIX I have described in detail the methods of one of these which cuts a "jumping-disk" from the sycamore leaf ; and there are others, like the birch saw-fly (*Phyllotoma nemorata*), which derive protection when feeding by burrowing in the leaf tissues, but do not cut disks. In still other species the action

Unfamiliar Relatives of Bee and Wasp

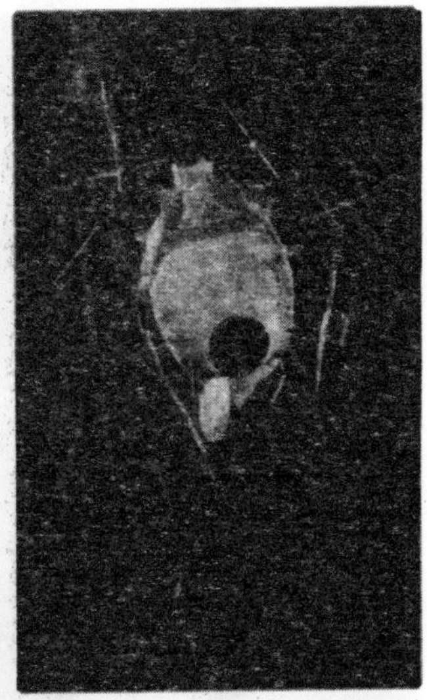

of egg-depositing causes the growth of an excrescence, or gall, a familiar example of which is the crimson bean-galls prominent on the leaves of the crack willow, the nursery of a species known as *Nematus gallicola*, and belonging to the same genus as that of the gooseberry saw-fly (*Nematus ribesii*) ; but the grubs of the latter, as previously mentioned, feed boldly in the open ; so variable are the methods of even nearly-related species.

J. J. Ward

APHIS-WASP THAT KEEPS DOWN GREEN FLY

So small is the aphic-wasp (top left) which preys on aphides or green-flies, that it can easily crawl through the eye of a fine needle. It lays its eggs in the body of an aphis (bottom and top centre) and the egg develops in the aphis which swells and changes to a brown colour. Eventually the wasp grub eats its way out of the empty skin of its victim (top right).

The marble and cherry galls found on the oak ; the bedeguar, or pin-cushion, gall of the wild rose, and similar formations on other trees, are not the work of saw-flies, but of their near relatives the gall-wasps (*Cynipidae*). Their life stories are complex—they have alternate sexual generations which often produce galls of an entirely different type. Some of them are parasites, and do not themselves produce galls, but deposit their eggs in the already formed galls of other species.

It need scarcely be stated that the saw-flies are very injurious to all kinds of trees. Fortunately, though, there are other beneficial relatives of the bees and wasps, known as ichneumon-wasps (*Ichneumonidae*), which render valuable service in destroying not only these destructive members of their order, but also caterpillars of butterflies and moths, the maggots of flies, and even aphides, or green-flies.

The ichneumon-wasps, like the saw-flies, vary very much in size, and there is one large species, coloured black and yellow, which may be met with in England, and immediately recognized by its conspicuous ovipositor, which is about twice the length of its body. It is the long-tailed ichneumon-wasp (*Rhyssa persuasoria*). When we learn that this particular species is a parasite upon wood-boring grubs, such as those of the giant sirex, we realize the meaning of its long tail, or ovipositor ; for it is by means of that instrument that it is able to penetrate the burrows of the wood-feeding grubs to deposit its eggs.

In every garden ichneumon-wasps may be seen running up and down the stems of plants. They are readily recognized by their narrow waists, and their active movements, their feelers bristling with excitement while they seek their caterpillar hosts. Their eggs may be laid on, or in, the bodies of the larvae they attack, many of their grubs being internal feeders. They render service of inestimable value to the gardener ; and the more destructive is the caterpillar, the larger is the number of species that prey upon it.

It is not always the larger and more conspicuous of the ichneumon-wasps that are most beneficial. Beyond the power of the human eye the same work

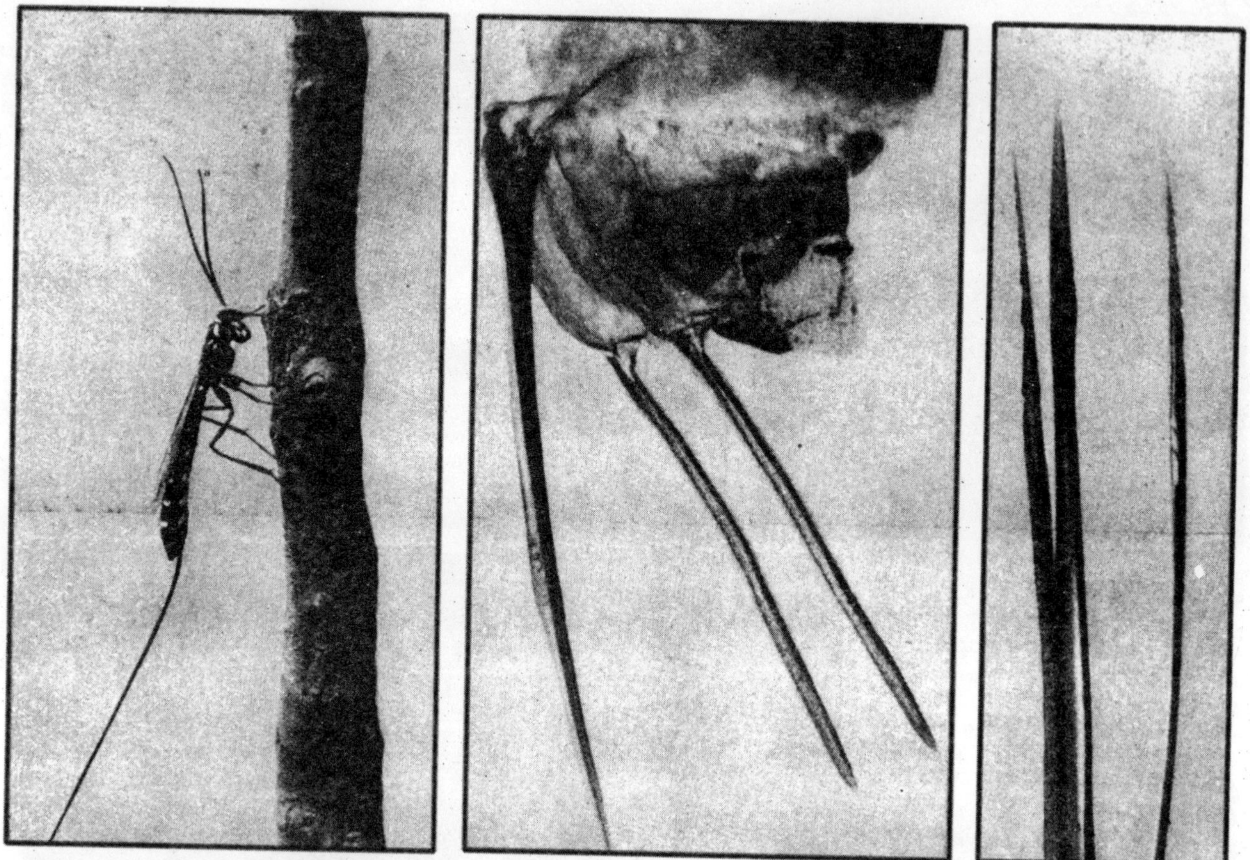

J. J. Ward

ICHNEUMON WASP AND ITS APPARATUS FOR LAYING EGGS IN ITS VICTIMS

As the caterpillars in any particular locality increase, so do their mortal enemies the ichneumon wasps—luckily for the gardener. The spectacle, or even the idea, of a caterpillar being devoured from within by grubs is not pleasant, but may be tempered by the thought of what would happen if there was suddenly a scarcity of ichneumon wasps. The left-hand photograph shows the wasp, while in the centre is the end of the insect with the lance-like ovipositor or egg layer; and on the right is the apparatus displayed to show the penetrating parts.

is going on in even a greater degree. There is the little aphid-wasp (*Aphidius*), so tiny that it can easily pass through the eye of a fine needle, and whose prey is green-flies. It is a fearless little insect, and is so intent on seeking its victims that it will allow you to approach it quite closely with a magnifying lens and observe its astonishing method of attack.

In seeking aphides, it approaches with its feelers raised and held close together, their tips curved forward in an enquiring attitude. Then, as it nears its quarry, the insect's delight immediately becomes apparent, its feelers actively vibrating with excitement, while the movement of its legs, wings, and body all express its pleasure. Pausing by the side of a plump aphis, its twitching movements momentarily cease while it brings down the tips of its feelers and touches its capture. All is well. The little wasp is satisfied; a moment later it is all activity again. Stepping to one side, and a little behind its victim, it grips its body with its first and second pairs of legs, and, holding firmly, raises itself on its hind pair and sets its wings rapidly vibrating. Then it turns its tail-end under its legs, and holds the aphis as if taking aim, when, like a flash, the dart-like ovipositor makes its deadly thrust. At that instant the fate of the aphis is sealed, for an egg has been placed in its body. I have seen one of these little wasps pierce the bodies of twelve aphides in three minutes, placing a single egg in the body of each one.

The green-fly after being attacked becomes inactive, and its body assumes a swollen appearance, its colour changing from green to brown in the course of a day or two. Meanwhile the egg hatches, and the wasp grub that emerges from it rapidly devours the internal parts of its host. In from twelve to fourteen days it has completed its development, and, near the tail-end of the now dry and hardened skin of its victim, it cuts from within a tiny circular door, which it pushes open and emerges from the hole a trim little wasp, just like its parent; its whole development having been completed in less than two weeks in the body of a single green-fly.

There is another of these aphid-wasps of the genus *Praon* which, when ready to pupate, hoists up the skin of its host, and forms a kind of woven tent beneath. Oftentimes, though, when this aphid-wasp should emerge, quite a different insect appears instead—a parasite that has attacked and destroyed it, just as the aphid-wasp did the aphis.

Chapter CXXXV

Winter and Summer Sleep

By Sir William Beach Thomas

Author of "From a Hertfordshire Cottage"

When frosts come and days shorten we become conscious of a slow disappearance of many animals. About the same time that the summer visitors among birds fly off to Africa, to the Caucasus, to the South of Europe, bats, dormice, hedgehogs, frogs, toads, newts, lizards, snakes, snails, flies, wasps, bees and a host of other insects "go into winter quarters," as soldiers used to in the old wars. In other countries such big creatures as bears and crocodiles adopt the same device. They all solve the question of winter catering by hibernating, as do the birds by migrating.

But the birds lead a vivid life in both their summer and winter homes. The hibernators keep hold of life by going very near to death. A bat seems dead in all respects. Its temperature sinks very low. Its heart beats so feebly as to be scarcely perceptible, and it takes long to wake. If you dig into the hole—often far underneath the earth—where a newt is spending the winter, you find a black, shrivelled object scarcely recognizable. Newts are hard to find. One of the greatest of our authorities on the amphibious creatures, of which the newt is the most interesting, confessed that he had never found the winter home of the biggest of the three newts. Frogs will bury themselves as far under watery mud as the newts underground; and their vitality falls very low. Lizards winter very much as the newts; and of the three British lizards the sand lizard, which is the first to disappear from sight in autumn, sleeps so soundly that it does not waken till April is well advanced. Among the rather small list of British creatures which sleep so deeply that they appear lifeless, the snail is in some respects the most remarkable. It appears to lose size like a dried mushroom and, instead of filling out the whole shell, shrinks into the deep recesses. It is one of the few animals (unless we reckon the chrysalis or pupa) which makes for itself a really tough defence. It retires to some hiding place, preferring a damp and rather warm atmosphere. When ensconced there it manufactures from its own juices a chalky covering across the mouth of the cell, and by puffing from the lungs separates this covering from contact with itself. But even sleeping snails must breathe, and this defensive covering is porous to the air. The frog buried in soft mud under water gets over the difficulty and escapes being smothered by aid of its skin, which has the capacity of inhaling oxygen, of which some is in solution in the water. How near the hibernating animal is to extinction may be told from the extreme difficulty of keeping alive some of the deepest sleepers, such as newts and lizards, if you accidentally disturb their hibernaculum, or place of winter's rest.

Though the animals that sleep so deep as to appear lifeless are few, the animals that hibernate in some degree are very many. Almost all living things adapt themselves to winter in some way or other. Even their bodies change, as you may see in the ptarmigan and ermine, which turn white in winter. Many plants hibernate after very much the same fashion as some animals. Indeed, we are just beginning to understand how very like one another in this are some flowers and some animals. Who would have thought, for example, of comparing a daffodil with a bear? But the two do actually prepare for cold weather on very much the same system.

The bulb of the daffodil after sucking in all the good food out of the green leaves and stalks, grows fat and lies covered in its earthy cavern until the days begin to grow longer and until there is more sunlight (which is its chief food). Then it becomes active, producing stalk and leaf, and grows thinner because of the new activities. What does a bear do? It eats largely and grows astonishingly fat at the first hint of cold weather, and may become completely encased in fat by the time it retires into some warm cave, where on some occasions it almost closes the approach with leaves. It can be as still almost as the daffodil bulb and live comfortably without eating at all.

G Hearn

FIELD MOUSE AT ENTRANCE TO WINTER NEST

Before retiring for the winter the short-tailed field mouse lays in a store of provisions. Every now and then it wakes up, has a little feed, and goes to sleep again. The meals are, of course, small, and long periods are spent without eating at all.

say that, by keeping warm, and moving very little, they can support life on half or less of the usual amount of food. We may decide, therefore, that even the highest animals, that men as well as insects, have some reserve power of hibernating, which they can exercise if they are compelled. The strongest force is undoubtedly the absence of food, rather than the absence of warmth. One reason for thinking this is that some few animals are able to 'aestivate' when compelled. In other words, they lie low without feeding, not in winter, but in summer. A certain number of fish are able, when the water dries up, to bury themselves in the mud, very

M. H. Crawford

SNAILS THAT SLEEP SOUND THROUGH THE WINTER

Among the not very large number of British animals that sleep very deeply in winter—so deeply that they seem dead—is the snail. It finds some moist warm spot and covers the entrance to its shell with a porous mass, called operculum, that lets in air. This is seen below while above is a group of snails (*Helix hortensis*) hibernating.

The bear and the bulb act in a like manner, but there is one great difference. The bulb may remain so far as one can see, quite unchanging (though this is rare), while the bear grows thinner and thinner. He does not sleep all the time, but uses up a good deal of energy, and so has to use up the fat which he stored in autumn. This means that the bear is not quite so good a hibernator or winterer as are some animals and very many plants.

Nevertheless, the bear gives one of the best examples of this quaint device for overcoming the cold of winter and, what is more important, the lack of food, because it comes midway in the list of winterers.

There are all sorts of degrees of hibernation or adaptation for winter, in which even some men may be included. It is scarcely too much to say that most animals make some sort of preparation for the hard times of winter, as if they were a little afraid that they would be forced to hibernate. Our domestic hens put on much fat towards winter, and they can go for a considerable time without food, though they would die in half the time if they were left without food in the spring. This is known by every expert poultry-keeper. It is proved that hens will lay few eggs unless fed and exercised in such a way that this supply of extra winter fat is taken down.

All sorts of things and animals can learn how to hibernate, if they are forced. The Eskimos, who live in the far north of Canada, have succeeded in some degree in putting on fat and wintering very much like the bear, only much less completely. That is to

much as a frog buries itself in winter, and lie there, probably scarcely conscious of any feeling whatever, until the rains restore the water. The mud-fish of Australia is one of these; but there are more examples in very dry, arid countries, where the summer rather than the winter is the hard time.

Much the best of all examples, illustrating how circumstances drive animals to such devices, is provided by the tribe commonly called crocodiles. Two divisions of this tribe are the crocodiles proper and the alligators. The alligators belong to America and hibernate very much like frogs. The African crocodiles, on the other hand, which only differ from alligators in rather unimportant details, such as the webbing of the feet and length of the jaw, do not hibernate but "aestivate," or sleep through the summer without feeding or emerging from the mud. They are said to be able to sleep in this almost lifeless state for a whole twelvemonth. The enemy to be avoided is dryness, not cold.

Many young collectors of moths and butterflies in Britain have proved how circumstances affect such habits. They have unintentionally forced animals to go into winter quarters—of a sort—before their proper time by cutting off the supplies of food. The caterpillars of most moths and butterflies moult a good many times before they turn into chrysalises, but if imprisoned and deprived of their proper leaves they will do without one or two of the usual moults or changes of skin and begin to make cocoons or anchor themselves by silk ropes at once. They do not fare so well as when Nature is left without interference, but they at least show this power of adapting themselves to the loss of their diet. Different sorts of insects, as well as of the larger animals, are very different in their power of fitting themselves to the weather or other unforeseen influences. Some winter well, others badly. The lady-birds are an example of an insect that

M. H. Crawford

J. J. Ward H. Bastin

QUEEN WASPS HIBERNATING AND A TOAD JUST AWAKENED

To preserve her race the queen wasp must survive the winter though her subjects all die. In September the queen (bottom photographs) finds a resting-place under a piece of soft wood and gradually settles down, only moving now and then. Above is a toad just emerging, very thin and hungry, after his winter's sleep.

does not deal with winter conditions very skilfully. They seem rather unwillingly to seek out a snug crevice and give up feeding. When the green-fly, on which they feed, are killed by frost or for any reason disappear, the lady-birds seek food, like the wasps, in the hollows of punctured fruits; and if these fall to the ground the lady-birds often perish. They have put off the day of retirement too long.

These insects, or beetles, are so very valuable to gardeners that some fruit or rose growers have had special winter quarters built for them; and a good many have been preserved in one experimental station by catching them and putting them forcibly into the artificial sanctuary. But they are slow to find these places for themselves. Most of the insect-winterers flourish if it is cold, but greatly dislike a wet winter. Frost is a friend rather than an enemy. It is perhaps a general rule that the wetter the winter the smaller the number of insects that successfully survive till the spring. The same is true of seeds. They, too, lie apparently lifeless throughout winter and revive suddenly in spring; but many more survive a frosty than a wet winter.

For the most part the insects that have several devices for helping their race to continue into the next year are the worst hands at wintering themselves in their proper persons. For example, most of the butterflies of the tribe called Vanessae have three

J. J. Ward

A. Brook

M. H. Crawford

HIBERNATING DORMOUSE: HEDGEHOG DURING ITS WINTER SLEEP AND WHEN THE SLEEPER WAKES

The dormouse is an artist in sleep: it makes a special study of the business. The nest in which it spends so many winter weeks is very cunningly contrived from dried grasses. When it is nearly complete the dormouse gets inside and weaves the entrance—as though it were mending a hole—so carefully that no sign of it remains to be seen from the outside. Below we see four of the little animals (left) when they have just retired to sleep and (right) after some weeks, the nest having been partly opened. Above is a hedgehog in the depths of its annual rest (left) and just after emerging once again with the warm coming of spring (right). This animal makes itself very fat by the time October comes and lives on the strength of that fat till the next year different methods—some few have four different methods—of defeating the attacks of winter. They lay eggs in autumn and these hatch themselves out (if they are not eaten or destroyed by weather) in the next spring or summer. That is one way. The second is for the caterpillar to turn into a pupa and lie through the winter very much like a seed, safely protected by its case. The third is for the butterfly itself to seek some warm and snug spot and itself go into winter quarters. The fourth, and very sure, way is to migrate like the swallows and seek a warmer place; but it is now thought that though some butterflies (especially the painted lady) fly over to Britain in the summer, none makes the return journey in the autumn. A few complete butterflies of these Vanessae survive as butterflies, but when they wake up in spring and fly out they are usually very much frayed and dull in colour. They have not found it easy work to hibernate.

PROBABLY the very best of all the hibernators are the bats, which are most completely deprived of food. They can only live on winged insects and must catch these in the air, so their feeding days are very strictly limited, and may be very short indeed, if frosts come early in the autumn. Winter to them is not a mere interval, a week or two of cold in December or January, but may be more than half the year.

Just as some birds do not arrive till May and leave again in August or September, so some animals come out into the open state in spring and go to their dark dormitories for as many as seven or eight months. But the bats differ among themselves. Much the commonest in England is among the smallest, known by the rather pretty name of pipistrelle. It is the only bat known to a good many people. This little creature is the liveliest of all, and will wake up and fly out even in winter, if the weather is very attractive. The noctule, on the other hand, which is much rarer and much bigger, is a profound sleeper that nothing less than a warm April day can arouse.

Most bats when fallen into their winter sleep look as nearly as may be dead. They grow cold, their hearts beat very feebly and, when they hang themselves head downward on some dusty beam or crouch in some mouldering wood, they might be taken for lumps of leather. Nothing about them suggests a living creature, and no one would imagine for a moment that they would presently be flying with a dash and a skill and a command of quick turns beyond the power of a bird.

THE longest sleepers within the British Isles are perhaps the bigger bats and the dormouse. The dormouse, of course, gets his name from his power to sleep, for "dor" means sleep, but in all probability it is not so deep a sleeper as the bat, and never looks so lifeless and, we must believe, is never quite so far from being conscious. Many places where the bats retire to pass the winter are tolerably cold. The animals are, as a rule, careful to find spots protected from the rain. They like a dark place and sometimes burrow into rotten wood, which must be fairly warm. But they have not the power or instinct to make themselves as comfortable as a dormouse, which weaves almost perfect bedclothes. The thick network of dry grasses is designed so neatly that it keeps in the heat, but allows a fair amount of air slowly to filter through.

How the dormouse gets inside is a problem much more difficult than how the apple gets into the dumpling. However carefully you examine this warm light wrapping, you will find no hole. The entrance is filled up after the animal has entered so skilfully that no hint of a join or a weakness appears.

It would be possible to arrange a list of animals in order according to the degree in which they hibernate, with the dormouse and big bat at the bottom, as being the longest and soundest sleepers, and at the top the birds which are supposed not to hibernate at all. But you can find the beginnings of the habit, the signs of at least an attempt to hibernate, even in some of the livelier birds. Many birds in the spring-time eat within twenty-four hours food equal to their own weight. Even such a big bird as the woodcock will devour more than its own weight of food within a day and a night. Some of the small birds eat even more voraciously.

LET us take one of the very smallest, the little cheerful Jenny wren, which faces winter so bravely that it will sing its energetic song even when the ground is covered with snow. Nevertheless, the Jenny wrens behave in some ways very like the bats. If the frost is severe and food very hard to collect, they will crowd together into old nests and snuggle up in the sleepy warmth for an unknown length of time. If they were to go so long without food in the summer-time they would certainly die; but starvation matters less in the winter.

On one occasion a naturalist saw an old nest tumble down one winter morning and out of the rubbish flew half-a-dozen wrens which had overburdened the nest. For half a moment he thought the little birds must be bats, which will crowd close together in caves, barns or old trees, helping no doubt to keep one another warm.

Perhaps we may regard this crowding of the wrens together in an old nest in the daytime as a sort of attempt to begin hibernation, for nearly all birds eat less in winter than summer, and very many, like the birds and the poultry, store up a certain amount of fat. Gilbert White and other naturalists used to believe that swallows hibernated in England; but no example has ever been proved. Most birds are too highly strung and active to endure any long sleep or quiet; and many, perhaps most, manage to live by changing their food as the days grow colder.

Partridges are perhaps the best example of all. They eat a good number of insects when the young are born and before; exist largely on grain (by far their favourite food is barley) during the summer;

MUD FISH AESTIVATING
Cut from a dried-up marsh which is almost a lake in winter, this lump of mud contains one of the curious fish that remain dormant through the summer when the water dries up. Mud fish breathe in both air and water, and leave an air hole in their retreat.

and in winter subsist almost wholly on the tips of weeds and grasses. They have made a habit of doing the only thing that enables them to live. through the winter, the same sort of life that they live in summer.

Next on the list to the birds and most of the mammals which do not hibernate at all in any real sense, would come several sorts of voles and, indeed, mice, which have a way of storing food, generally at the end of a tunnel, and in certain circumstances they will go half or wholly to sleep in their snug chamber for considerable periods without troubling to eat the food at all. The squirrels would come about the same place on the list. They, too, store food here, there and everywhere, and often forget, or so it seems, exactly where they have put it. They retire rather like the dormouse to a huge nest, known as a drey, but it is usually in an exposed place, and is not made with nearly so much skill as the mouse's. So the squirrel, which has a very lively character, does not spend longer hours than it can help in its winter quarters, but goes forth and scratches up the hidden hoards of food.

The hedgehog would come earlier on the list than the pipistrelle bat. He makes a sort of nest in a sheltered spot—a hole in the ground or some old root or stool of wood—he rolls himself round in a tight ball and seems singularly well equipped for a long winter sleep. Like the bear, he is fatter in October than at any other season. But he is wakeful, and though he has long bouts of lying still and probably sleeping, you are never quite sure when he will not poke his nose out and take note of his surroundings, and even move out to see if spring is on the way.

The hive bees, that give us our honey, are less sleepy than the bumble bees. Late in the autumn, the bee-keepers tuck them up for the winter, and no bees appear outside the hive for a long time; but they must have plenty of food and the hive is never quite asleep. If you put your ear to it you may usually hear a slight murmur made by the bees who have the duty of ventilating the hive, and there is almost always some movement to be detected. Nevertheless, they do hibernate in a real sense.

You might think that the colder the winter the more food they would need, but it is not so. The longer the period of frost, the less the amount of food consumed; and the reason is that they are less wakeful in the cold than the warmth, and so spend their time hibernating, as the bat hibernates, without troubling to eat or drink. Extra warmth wakes them up and makes them feel energetic and hungry and thirsty. As a rule, the first thing the first wakers do, often as early as January, is to leave the hive to fetch water.

Bumble bees and queen wasps would come close together on the list, just below the hive bees. The queen bumble bee of some varieties usually makes herself a hole in the ground and polishes the sides very thoroughly. It has been proved that she shifts her position and has moments of restlessness; but she does not attempt to leave her retreat, does not feed, and may be supposed to be to all intents and purposes asleep most of the time; and it is a long time. She usually disappears into her hole in October, and not late in October—and does not come out for another five months or so.

The queen wasps do much the same, but they have a much greater variety of hiding-place; and generally, at least in my experience, prefer a hole behind a piece of loose bark or in the wood of a decaying tree. They may retire there in September, but are very wide awake just at first if the weather is at all fine and warm. You may now and again see bees, the helpers and queen wasps, who all mean to hibernate, showing themselves as late as November; and they will make surprising appearances if the weather is very warm and sunny in February.

Perhaps no animal is fonder of the sun and more dependent on it than the snakes. When the days shorten they retire sometimes singly, occasionally in masses, to a convenient hollow and wait there till the weather is really warm. And of all the animals they suffer least from want of food. Their reawakening has especially interested some of the poets, notably Shelley, because they usually begin the new life by shuffling off the old skin, just as a dragon-fly leaves behind its old case.

Chapter CXXXVI

Little Dependents of the Great

By F. Finn, B.A., F.Z.S.

Author of "Ornithological Oddities"

OUR earliest record of a small animal in the service of a larger one seems to be founded on a misconception—that is, the legend of the jackal being "the lion's provider." Homer, in a vivid simile, describes the pulling down of a wounded stag by a pack of jackals, which are scared from their anticipated feast by a lion.

Such episodes must often have occurred, and doubtless occur still; and as the works of Homer were to the Greeks much what the Bible is to us, and all through the subsequent centuries have been familiar to educated people, the impression has arisen that the lion habitually depended on the jackal for easily-won food. Homer, however, was evidently only describing an accidental incident; if Leo looked regularly to his inferiors for his royalties he would usually go hungry, and what more usually happens, no doubt, is that they themselves poach on his cold meat whenever he leaves it unprotected. There is no modern evidence that he has any such helpers, nor any that a small carnivorous animal ever helps any larger one in the wilds.

Another great Greek author, however, put on record the earliest certain instance of association of the small with the great; this was Herodotus, the father of zoology as well as of history, in whose day, distant as it was from ours, Homer was already a classic.

The crocodile, he says in his account of Egypt, is a foe to all birds and beasts but the courser, which does it a service. For, living in the river, it gets its mouth full of leeches, and when it comes out and opens its mouth to the westerly breeze, the courser goes in and gobbles up the leeches, which good office so pleases the crocodile that it does the courser no harm.

This story has naturally enough been doubted, but has turned out to be strictly true. A special leech infests the mouth of the African crocodile, and a special bird, the black-backed courser or plover, does enter it and devour them. It is doubtful, though, if the crocodile's gratitude can be trusted; at any rate, the only "crocodile bird" the Zoo ever exhibited had the habit of starting into flight backwards, which looks as if it did not, when at home with the crocodile, even stop to turn round after gobbling the last leech! Another bird associated with the crocodile, the African spur-winged lapwing, has been seen to come out of the reptile's mouth after this had closed on it, the spurs no doubt serving as a reminder to reptilian absent-mindedness.

W. S. Berridge

COURAGEOUS CROCODILE BIRD

The crocodile's mouth is infested with leeches, and these the crocodile bird, the black-backed courser, removes. But it has a very cautious trick of taking off backwards when it flies away. It does not risk even turning round while perched in those dreadful and perhaps ungrateful jaws.

HERODOTUS never got far enough south in Africa to come across or hear a still more wonderful instance of association—that of the honey-guide with man and the ratel and African badger. Here the bird undertakes to guide honey-seekers on a commission basis, for his human friends reward him with a piece of the comb, and presumably the ratel, in looking out for himself, incidentally, if not purposely, leaves some pickings for his ally, for the pair must often come across a store which is too large for the quadruped to devour completely.

This story has also been doubted and confirmed, but no specimen of any sort of honey-guide (there are several species) has ever been brought to England. An observer in Africa, Mr. Sydney Porter, has kept one for some time, and found it a very intelligent little creature, so inquisitive that it would poke into any dark corner and even creep under a newspaper if it found one lying on the floor, a most unusual action for a bird. As it was also very tame and "confidential," and had a big appetite, it evidently had much of the dog character, so that it is not surprising that its kind should play a dog's part in hunting along with man.

E. N. A.

PATRON AND CLIENT: SAND SHARK AND ITS ATTENDANT SUCKING-FISH
Between the remora, or sucking-fish, and the shark there is no working arrangement. The remora just attaches itself by its very powerful suction disk to the shark and gets carried about. The area of the sea that it can sweep for food is thus far greater than it would possibly be if the remora were on its own. Titbits from the shark's meals are useful perquisites.

breeding-places of gulls on these islands the little wall-lizard, a very common reptile in Southern Europe and remarkably active and enterprising, is found haunting the nests of the birds, and feeding on the parasites which infest the young and on any chance scraps of food which may be overlooked. Here the association is quite local and casual, the wall-lizard being perfectly independent elsewhere, though in at least one Continental zoo it is found playing the part of the sparrow in ours, and looking for pickings among the animals and the refreshment tables.

Among fish there are several examples of curious associations, notably that of the pilot-fish, one of the mackerel family, with the shark. Here the small fish no doubt secures protection from other large fish by the presence of its grim patron, and no doubt gets scraps from any prey he may obtain ; at any rate, it has been seen to lead the shark to a bait put out for him, though in this case the service was a very kind one. The shark's gratitude is evidently not to be relied upon, for in an aquarium tank, where it had not a fair chance of getting out of the way, the pilot fish has been seen to fall a victim to its associate.

Another fish that is associated with the shark is the remora or sucking-fish, which can stick very firmly to any object by the curious oval pleated sucking-disk on the top of its head. The sucking-fish is out for a free passage, and gets it ; the shark gets nothing out of the association—not even a chance of snapping up his passenger, who sticks too fast in a safe place for that.

Fishes are also found in partnership with water-animals of a much lower grade. Such is the case with the bitterling, a relative of our common fresh-water fish like roach and carp, which is a sort of parasite on the fresh-water mussel when breeding. It is a small fish, not much longer than a minnow but deeper in the body ; and in the breeding season the female develops a long external egg-tube or ovipositor, with which she plants her eggs in the mussels' shells, where they remain in safety till the fry hatch out. This does not sound very comfortable for the mussel, but that passive bivalve has a chance of getting its own back when its turn comes to spawn ; for its young are hatched bearing a long sticky filament as feeler and anchor, and a hook on each valve of the infant shell for attachment. In this way the baby mussel manages to clamp itself on to any passing fish, finding it and adhering by its thread, and then holding on by its pincers. Thus it is carried by its fishy bearer to fresh ground, and can drop off to develop further, and

Another African association of bird with mammal is that of the tick birds with big game, and with rhinoceroses in particular. These birds are about the size of starlings, with strong condor-like bills and very sharp claws ; they live upon the parasites of large animals, and run all over their patrons as a woodpecker does over a tree. They also warn them against danger, and this is particularly important to the rhinoceros, which has very poor sight, and soon gets nervous and upset if his birds leave him. One of the older African sportsmen even says that he has known the birds remain with a rhinoceros after it had been shot when taking its evening drink, and do their best to awaken it—as they thought—in the morning before leaving.

In this case there appears to be a definite adaptation of client to patron ; but no doubt the courser could get on quite well without the crocodile, as most of the courser family frequent dry places, while the few and rare kinds of honey-guides found in Asia are not known to have any relation with man or other mammals.

THE attachment of the robin to us may be a similar case to those we have been noticing ; it was most likely far closer in the days before window-glass was in use and cats commonly kept, and for long after that period the habits of our ancestors were such that —to put it as delicately as possible—they entertained company more acceptable to an insectivorous bird than to themselves ; so that the association was stronger than it is to-day, when the various small creatures exposed by gardening operations are the robin's chief reward besides our protection.

A very curious association of reptile with bird is found in the islands of the Adriatic ; in this the reptile is the servitor and the bird the patron. At if the fish pressed into service happens to be a bitterling, justice of a rough sort is meted out.

The bitterling, though common enough on the Continent, is not found in Britain, but is often to be had from dealers in aquarium live-stock, and, as mussels will also live in amateurs' aquaria, the details of this curious parasite partnership can be studied at leisure, by anyone interested.

A fairer partnership appears to be that of the little fishes of the amphiprion group with the great Discosoma anemones of the Great Barrier Reef of Australia. These anemones are truly gigantic; Saville-Kent's discosoma is sometimes no less than two feet across, and Haddon's discosoma eighteen inches. Inside both of these a species of amphiprion is found living, Kent's anemone giving shelter to the three-banded amphiprion, while Haddon's shelters the two-banded species, and a kind of prawn as well. The fish and the prawn however, are not to be found inside the same specimen of the anemone. Both of the fishes and the prawn are coloured red and white, and this colour does not match that of their tentacled hosts, which also are very different from each other.

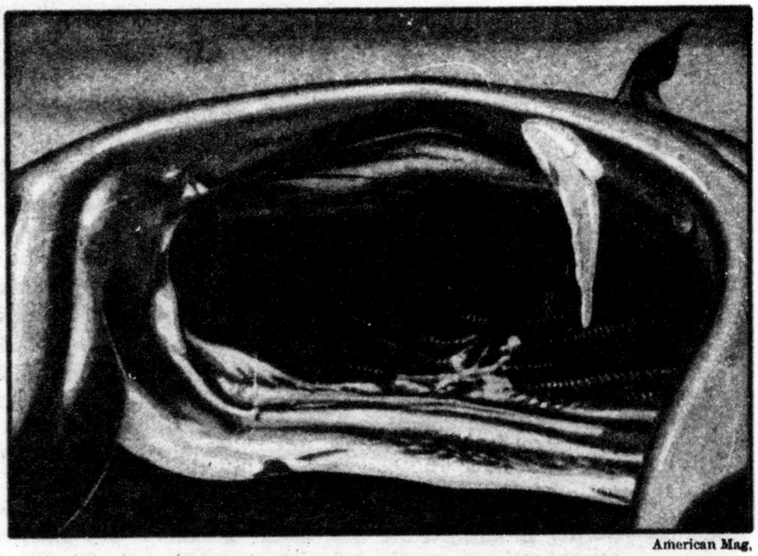

American Mag.

THE LITTLE DEPENDENT ON THE GREAT: SUCKER AND RAY

This is the awesome mouth of a giant ray with its rows of gill arches. Attached firmly to the upper part of this deathtrap of teeth is a little shark-sucker. Any food being torn by those teeth stands a good chance of being scattered so that some piece will float within the sucker's reach.

The anemones are as a rule living death-traps for any small free-moving creatures, owing to their formidable stinging-threads, but these particular animals must be immune to the poison, and no doubt benefit greatly by having a safe base to which to retreat after a foraging expedition, while they probably share any food that the anemones can obtain. The anemones for their part probably get an occasional windfall when one of their gaily-painted little guests rushes home with an enemy in hot pursuit which blunders into their deadly grasp. The three-banded amphiprion can be seen in the Zoo aquarium, where it gets on quite well without its living home. So can the little pea-crab, which lives inside bivalves, and was known to the ancients from this habit.

It is found off the British coasts, and a specimen was once exhibited in the Horniman Museum aquarium together with a mussel in which it was expected to shelter. The pea-crab, however, soon found there was no trouble to be looked for outside, and refused to enter its retreat; indeed, during the latter part of its career none was offered it.

Crabs can also themselves be the hosts, as in the case of the little shore-crab Melia of the Indian Ocean, which carries about an anemone in each claw, thus ranging the sea-floor like a hungry pigmy Dick Turpin armed with a couple of " barkers."

A better-known case is that of the hermit crab—really much more like a lobster—and its lodger the parasite anemone. Bernard the Hermit, as the French call him, is soft-skinned astern, and having by fair means or foul acquired a portable hermitage in the shape of a shell to prevent his soft tail being a handle to ill-wishers, is faced by the fact that there are desperate characters in the sea prepared to bolt him borrowed shell and all, and risk indigestion. He therefore finds it to his interest to have an anemone riding on his shell, as the stinging powers of his partner are calculated to discourage almost any assailant. An anemone, although able to crawl, is so slow that the snail is a lively sprinter in comparison, and therefore scores by what may be called rapid transport, to say nothing of chances of bits as the hermit tears up his prey, in addition to improved opportunities of capture on its own account. The hermit, as he grows, has to look out for new lodgings, and when he moves in, is able to persuade the anemone to let him detach it and put it on the new house. This sounds incredible, as the anemone is not to be persuaded to shift by soft human fingers; but anemones, though they have hardly any other sense but touch, are able to learn. The common independent species will, in an aquarium, learn to know the forceps by means of which they are fed and not shrink up at the touch of these, and presumably they also recognize the feel of the claws of their crustacean friend.

As the different kinds of giant anemones have different fish lodgers, so the hermit crabs are usually ridden by different parasitic anemones; the common Bernard the Hermit carries Rondelet's anemone, and Prideaux's hermit the cloaked anemone. In the latter case the hermit finds an additional advantage in that the anemone gradually absorbs the shell and relieves him of some of the weight, and, being soft, of the necessity for moving into a new house—a great advantage, for moving is as great a trouble to hermit crabs as to humans. It is very funny to watch a hermit feeling in a number of shells with his claws, and, when he does decide to shift, whipping his tail out of the old house into the new one with a haste which is eloquent of his deadly fear of back-biting and, after all, perhaps deciding that the new shell pinches him somewhere, and going back to the old one.

About the last partnership one would expect is one between the butterfly, the type of brainless frivolity, and the ant, the model of industry and intelligence. But Great Britain can show them in relations which make the ant appear the fool. The large blue butterfly, which is about the size of a small garden white, begins its career as a little caterpillar by feeding on the flower-buds of wild thyme. Soon, however, the syrup-secreting organ it bears at the end of its body attracts an ant, which strokes and milks it; other ants may come along and do the same, but the first-comer retains possession of the milch-caterpillar. This presently signals to the ant, by humping up its forequarters, that it wants a lift, and its attendant then takes it up and carries it down into the ant-hill. Here it behaves like a wolf in sheep's clothing, devouring the infant grubs of the ants, apparently with their full consent: presumably they continue to milk it, and their love for sweets blinds them to everything else. At any rate, the caterpillar feeds full by ant infenticide, turns into a chrysalis, and ultimately leaves the decimated anthill as a blue fairy-like creature with no hint of its hypocritical past.

More wonderful still is the relationship between the Sitaris beetle and the burrowing solitary bees, though here there is no hint of any benefit to the bee, which is robbed from start to finish by the beetle—another case of the proverbially brainless beating the canny.

From the egg of the sitaris hatches a minute and very lively little larva, not grub-like like most infant beetles, of which the indoor mealworm and outdoor wireworm are fair types, but with well-developed legs, each ending in three claws, whence it is technically known as a triungulin—*ungula* being the Latin for claw. The triungulin is in its habits a sort of bee flea, although it does not suck blood; it has a desperate desire to hook its little trident toes on to any hairy insect, and by a lucky fluke sometimes gets on to a bee, and a bee of the right sort, an Anthophora. Such bees construct a cell, fill it with honey, and lay an egg on the top of this.

The triungulin rides home on the bee, and when she is ready to lay her egg, slips on to this, and is left by her sealed up in the cell. These proceedings are naturally only guessed at, as no one can see what goes on in Anthophora's little home; what is known is that the beetlet opens the egg and proceeds to eat it, the supply lasting it just over a week. It then proceeds to change into an exaggeratedly grub-like form—a mere maggot, with the side breathing-holes so noticeable in large grubs placed high up towards the back. This is a provision against being smothered by the honey, in which the grub literally wallows for more than a month, steadily consuming it.

After this it goes through another change, becoming more like an average beetle grub, but its days of adventure are over, and it next proceeds to turn into an ordinary beetle chrysalis, and then into a beetle which also has nothing remarkable about its appearance. This beetle is now uncommon but it has a well-known relative whose history is much the same—the oil beetle, that fat, soft, flightless, blue-black, unwholesome-looking beetle that is sometimes seen feeding on plants in spring.

How the lives of these last little animals came to be linked together in this extraordinarily detailed manner is quite beyond our powers of guessing; the procedure, especially in the last case, is so complicated and blindly instinctive, and leaves so much to chance, as we see it. On the other hand, the relations of birds to larger animals with which we began do not seem to require much beyond intelligence.

Insects are far older than birds on the earth, and may have been in their early days less blindly instinctive and more intelligent than they are now; cockroaches are some of the most ancient types, and a modern cockroach has been known to bother even a distinguished professor considerably by trying to establish a one-sided association with him, sucking the moisture from his face and lips while he was asleep. This was one of the large winged cockroaches so common both on land and ship-board in the tropics, which, like the rat, are great travellers, and apparently can be nearly as cunning. Thus, at one time, insects may have had the aptitude for acquiring new and intelligent habits that birds and beasts now display.

We know, too, that what was originally a habit may be transformed into an instinct under man's selection. The first tumbler pigeons were, no doubt, unusually intelligent birds, which "looped the loop," as other birds than pigeons will sometimes do, for the fun of the thing. But the habit has been so developed by selection of the most persistent performers, that tumblers have been bred which simply have to tumble whether they like it or not; and though this habit is not only useless but would be prejudicial to a wild bird, it shows very plainly how the transition from purposeful to mechanical or involuntary action can take place. Another exaggeration of the tumbling habit is found in the roller pigeon, which descends in a series of somersaults, and sometimes comes to grief thereby; and if we imagined a breed of rollers which habitually tumbled down people's chimney-pots and nested in the grates we should get some approximation to the extravagant eccentricities of our insects.

Further than this we cannot see at present; but if naturalists ever make a practice of rearing animals of curious complicated habits and observing how these develop in the lifetime of the individual we may in time come nearer to understanding the wonderful associations dealt with in this article.

Chapter CXXXVII

More Animal Wonders Revealed by the Microscope

By W. H. S. Cheavin

Corresponding Member of the Manchester Microscopical Society

In a preceding chapter, pages 1399 to 1418, we have already dealt with a part of that wonderland which is revealed to the man who looks through a microscope. We now resume our exploration of that marvellous territory at the point where we left it—in considering the leg parts of insects.

The forelegs of the earwig, for instance, are small in comparison with the hind legs, whilst the middle legs form a medium between the two extremes. The earwig relies on its legs for escape from its enemies, and its legs are particularly adapted for rapid locomotion.

The dragon-fly in its larval and adult forms shows two types of legs; one type changing completely when the larva becomes a fully-grown insect. In the larval leg we have a very simple type, devoid of hairs or projections, because they are not actively employed and are only used as a support for steadiness, holding prey or grasping pond weeds. In the fully developed insect we find a great change both in shape and general features. A double series of long bristles is present on each leg, these bristles or stout hairs being used for holding prey when the insect is flying. The legs are held forward so that they meet at the same level in front of the mouth. Further, these bristles help to hold the prey more securely and form a complete trap in the legs.

The marvellous gymnastic feats of many two-winged flies which we see walking upside down on ceilings are often a source of wonder, but this is easily explained when each foot is examined. At the base between the claws are seen two or more pads which secrete a sticky fluid from a series of minute tubes found distributed over the surface of each pad. When the fly is desirous of moving, the powerful hinged claws are applied to the surface of the ceiling, and they act as levers lifting the pads away from the surface. Thus is explained how the common house-fly can apparently overcome the laws of gravitation.

In normal walking in an upright position, the fly uses the claws only, the pads being carried in a raised position well above the claws. The adhesive substance secreted by the pads also explains why in the winter we find dead flies on the walls of our rooms. The flies, on the approach of colder weather, become weaker and cannot find enough strength to raise the pads, and consequently they die, being unable to obtain food.

It is interesting to examine the legs of another two-winged fly, the gnat. These are very long and are seen to be covered with clusters of delicate hairs resembling fins when examined edgewise. The hairs no doubt act as a protection against water when the insect is in the act of constructing its egg-raft on the surface of a pool. At the tip of each leg is a pair of claws, of equal size, which are moved by powerful joints. There are no pads on these claws, which explains why the gnat is hardly ever found on window panes or other smooth surfaces.

In the flea, a degenerate form of the two-winged fly, we have a leg particularly adapted for making enormous leaps. The hind pair are the most developed and strongest for this purpose, and the same proportion of power in mankind would enable any of us to leap over the highest of buildings with the greatest of ease. The enormous development of the coxa is responsible for this feature, and in most other leaping insects the muscles of the lower joints are used in this way. In walking, the flea uses all the lower joints and the claws function as a grip to enable the insect to drag itself along rapidly through the hairs of its host. Also the two claws act as modified bristles or setae.

H. S. Cheavin

HOW THE CRICKET HEARS

It would be of no use to the cricket to chirrup if its mate could not hear the sound. The cricket's "ear," seen above, is situated on its leg, and appears here as an oval spot—magnified greatly in this photograph, of course.

In the large family of beetles we find the greatest variety of legs, each one adapted for the different functions which the insects perform. The tarsi or last segments show peculiar structures and in almost every species of this family we find a new feature. It is noticeable throughout the whole family that there are no pulvilli or

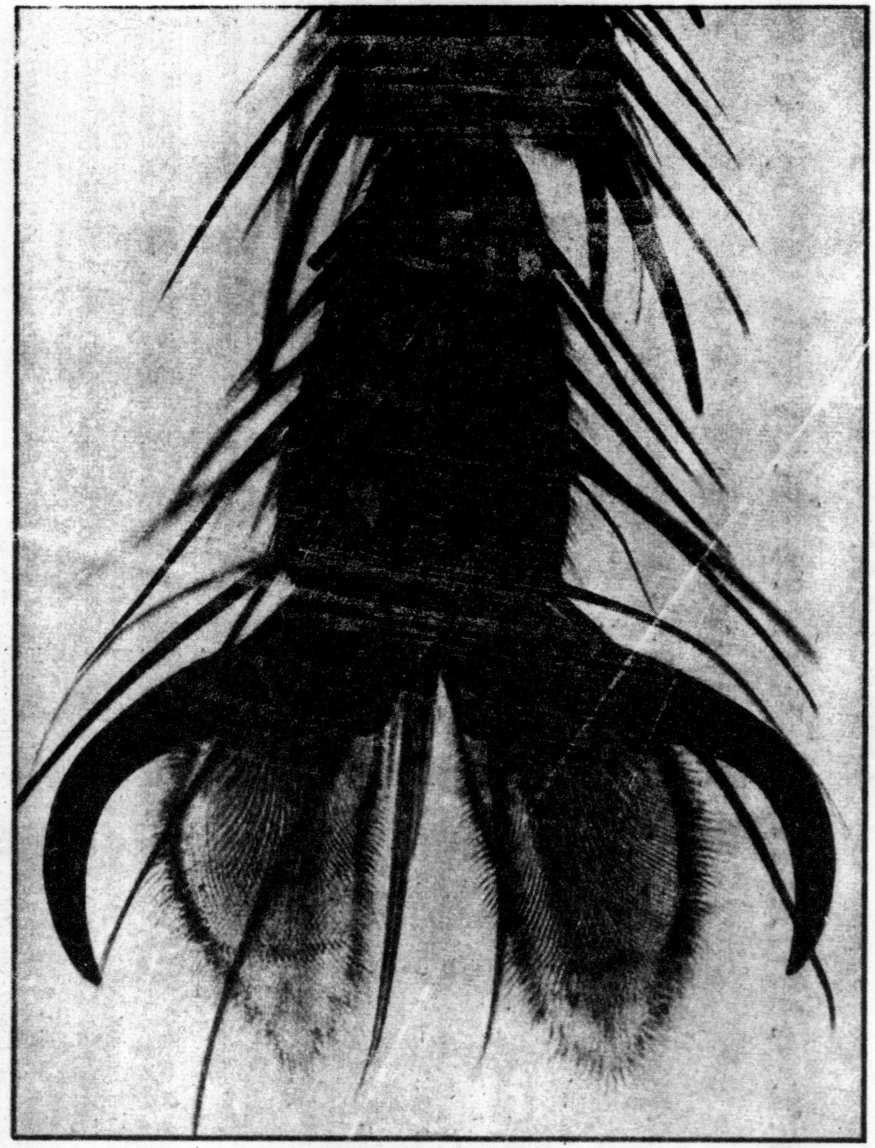

H. S. Oneavin

LEGS AND FEET OF FLY AND BEETLE SEEN AS WONDERFUL PIECES OF MECHANISM UNDER THE LENS

On the left we have one of the legs of the dung fly (*Sarcophagida*, x 101) with the foot. The last joint of the leg is provided, as we see, with strong hairy projections, and the powerful claws are strongly curved. These claws are hinged, and used for levering up the foot each time the leg is moved. The sole of the foot clings very tightly, enabling the fly to walk upside down and, to overcome the clinging action, these hinged claws are provided. On the right is a magnified view of the foreleg of a water beetle (*Dytiscus*, x 29). The first three joints are fused and modified to form a powerful sucking organ, and are used for clutching the tadpoles on which the beetle preys, and for holding the female in mating.

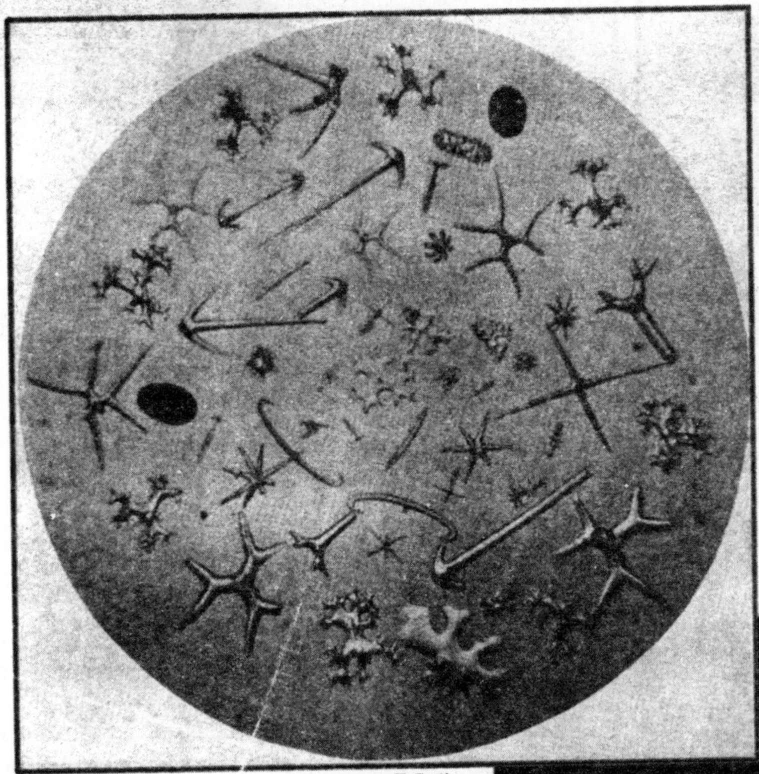

H. Bastin

In the female glow-worm we see a further modification of this joint which can be used as the flat sole of a foot, and this helps the insect to move about amongst thick vegetation, the claws at the tip acting as levers.

It is in the leg of the water beetle that we find the greatest modification. The foreleg of the male has the first three joints of the tarsus specially adapted to form a very powerful suction arrangement produced by a large number of adhesive hairs or cupules. Each cupule produces a viscid secretion and is carried on projecting elastic stalks which enable the radiating ribs of each cupule to close when not in use. The suction of the leg is very powerful and is used for holding prey such as young tadpoles or fish; also it is used for holding the female when mating.

pads, but as if to make up for this apparent deficiency the last joint is modified to act as a stabilising organ to be used in the act of walking. This joint is generally well developed and covered with fine hairs which are very sensitive and can also act as a grip when the insect is walking on smooth surfaces.

In the lady-bird we find this joint is wider at one end than the other, and covered with fine hairs, the base of the segment, bearing the claw, being mounted in such a way as to give the joint freedom of action and no doubt acting as a lever in walking.

In the Colorado beetle this joint is circular and covered with fine hairs. A powerful hinged pair of claws is present which no doubt act as an anchor when the insect is feeding.

In the soldier beetle we have another new feature; the whole of the last joints in the tarsus are the same shape, but the last segment is slightly more developed. This joint holds a pair of smaller claws than usual, but these claws are straighter and more curved at the tip, a modification which agrees with the quarrelsome nature of this insect. It seems to be always fighting its own species.

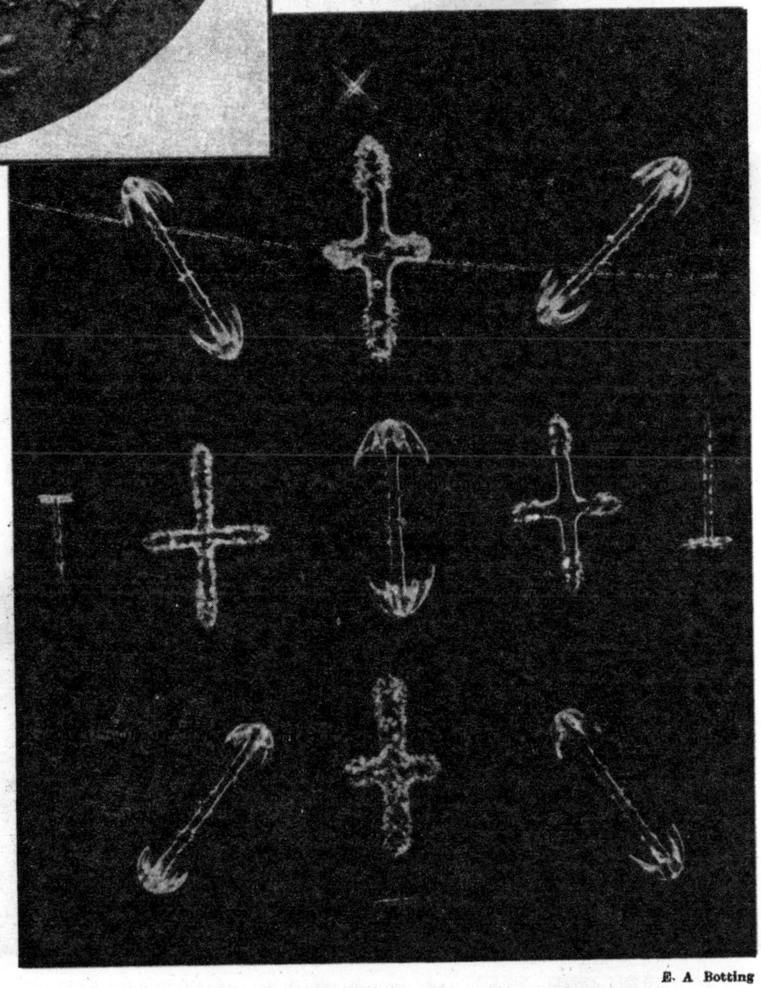

E. A Botting

HIDDEN BEAUTIES IN A SPONGE REVEALED

These photographs show what beauties there are hidden from the unaided human eye in some kinds of sponge. Under magnification the spicules of the sponge look like charms carved in ivory. Below we have what seem like little anchors and crosses, while above are semblances of antlers and picks.

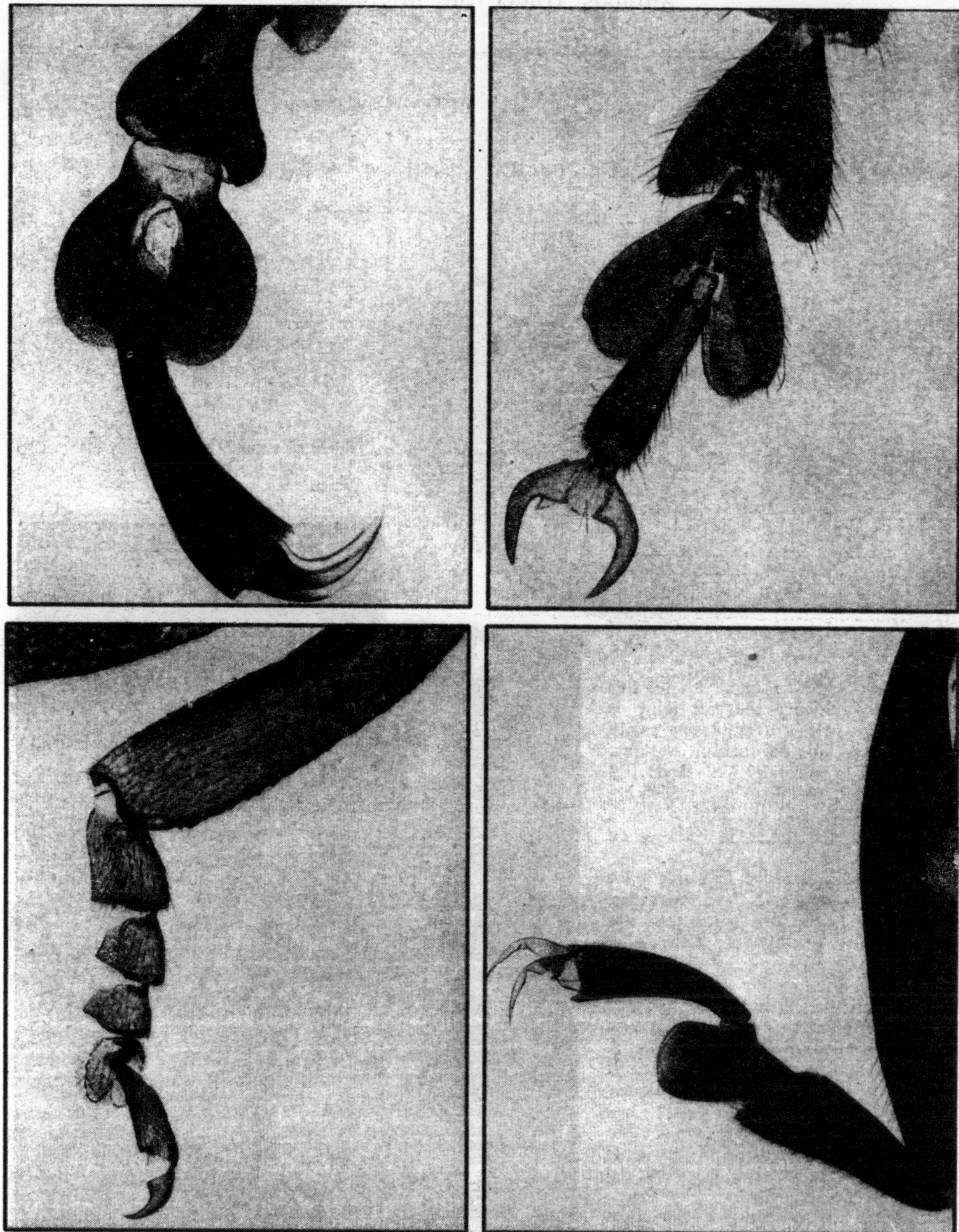

H. S. Cheavin

LEGS AND FEET OF GLOW-WORM, LADY-BIRD AND COLORADO AND SOLDIER BEETLES

A glow-worm's foot sounds rather a trifle but, seen at sufficient magnification, we find that it is a wonderful thing. The " foot " is really the last segment of the leg which acts as a " sole " with a claw to lever it up (bottom left). The same arrangement is used by the seven-spot lady-bird (bottom right). The Colorado beetle has also a specially adapted walking arrangement (top left), the last joint of the leg being rounded and having a claw-like limb which is used as an anchor. The leg of a female soldier beetle (top right) has a pair of clasps for fighting

H. S. Cheavin

CLINGING LIMBS OF SAWFLY, HORNET, FOREST HOPPER AND FLEA UNDER THE MICROSCOPE

Peculiar oval-shaped pads are attached to each of the lower segments of the leg of the sawfly (bottom left) and these are covered with fine hairs. These features are perhaps used for purposes of defence. The leg and foot of a hornet (bottom right), show specially adapted tarsi (joints to which the feet are joined) armed with strong spines used for releasing the feet from soft surfaces, powerful claws used for walking on the rough surfaces and pads for negotiating the smooth ones. Above are the legs of a scarlet forest hopper (left) and of a flea (right).

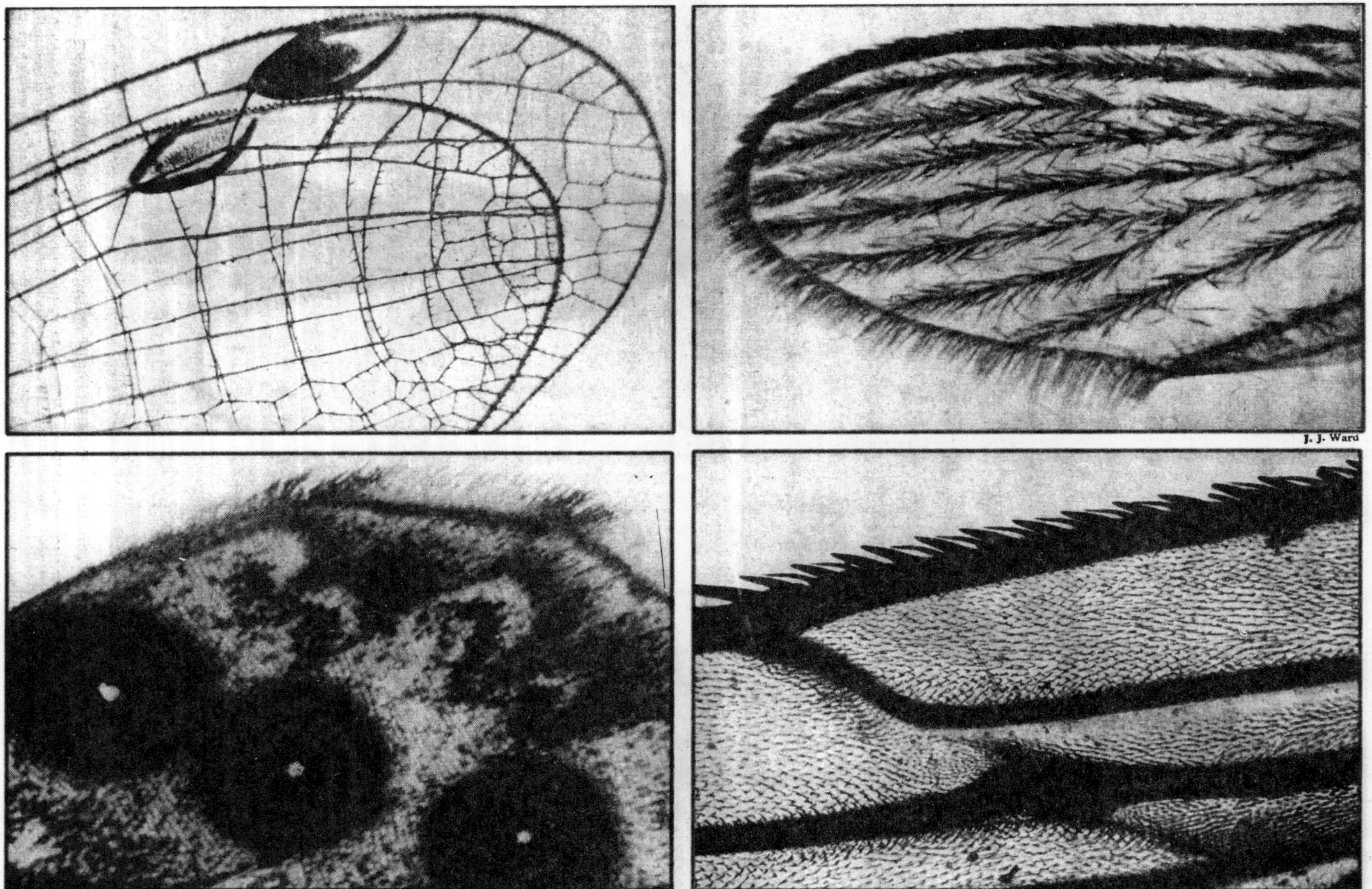

J. J. Ward

DETAILS OF DELICATE WINGS AS SEEN ON THE MICROSCOPIC SLIDE: BUTTERFLY, DRAGON-FLY AND GNAT

H. S. Chea[illegible]n

Fairly common in the southern counties of England is the wall butterfly (*Purarge megaera*) which may be seen sunning itself on walls and tree stumps, or anywhere where direct sunlight falls. It is beautifully marked in yellow, brown and black, but what the naked eye misses is the wonderful minute scales which make up the wing (bottom left). The edge of the blow-fly's wings (bottom right), when magnified, is seen to be provided with nervures or channels through which the blood flows. These nervures also form a network which supports the wing like a frame. The top left-hand photograph is of a dragon-fly's wing with its framework and gauzy membrane. The gnat's wing-tip (top right) has most delicate scales when seen on the slide of a microscope.

On each foreleg of the male are about 170 sucking hairs and on each middle leg about 1,590 sucking hairs, which explains why a water beetle is difficult to move when attached to a stone or the stem of a water plant. The adhesive power of these suckers is very great and an experiment, tried by Plateau, with a freshly-killed insect when applied to a cylinder of smooth glass showed that the suckers could support more than thirteen times the actual weight of the insect.

Caterpillars have two kinds of legs, specially modified in the front set for walking. These are furnished with two claws to give a firm grip on the leaf. In the hind legs another modification appears, namely, a fringe of hook-like projections around the base, which serve as clasping organs and anchor the larva in the fine hairs of the leaf.

H. Bastin

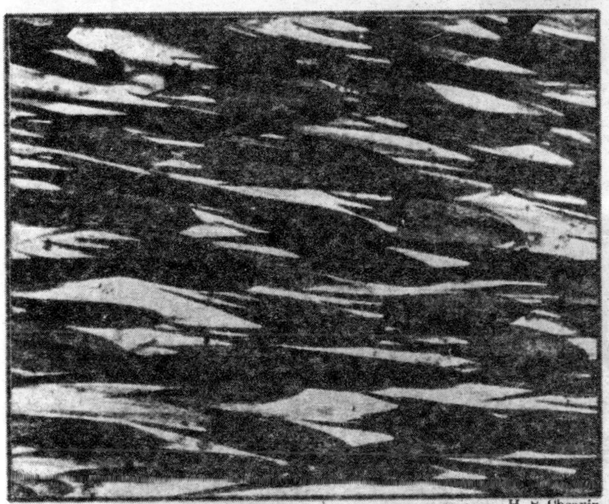

H S Cheavin

MAGNIFIED WINGS OF MOTH AND BUTTERFLY

Wings of both butterflies and moths are covered with scales or feathery particles so put together as to overlap and form a perfect flying surface. Here are magnified parts of the wings of an emperor moth (bottom) and a South American butterfly (top).

This fact explains why the larva has such a firm hold on whatever part of the plant it is feeding on.

The second leg of the hive bee has a long spur projection which is said to be used as a weapon for the purpose of killing the drones when they are driven out of the hive in autumn. The whole leg of the bee and other members of this family have the last joints furnished with pointed projections, and the tip of the leg carries a pair of stout double-pronged claws between which is a small adhesive pad used for the same purpose as in the house-fly, for walking in upside-down positions.

In the froghopper there is a modification of the tarsal joints, but they have in addition powerful projecting spines which endow the insect with enormous leaping powers.

The green-fly has an elongated femur with the tarsal joints fused together, and so insignificant as to be overlooked. At the tip will be found equally insignificant claws; and these factors all conform to the habit of an insect of this kind which leads a sedentary life in the same place.

The ant lion is furnished with powerfully developed muscular legs armed with sharp, sensitive projections used for anchoring the insect in the sand, and also for heaving stones out of its sandpit or lifting the remains of devoured victims. The equally powerful claws no doubt assist a good deal in this work.

The saw-fly shows a peculiar development of each tarsal joint, which is provided with a small, oval-shaped pad covered with fine hairs, suggesting that it is used as a sucker attachment to give the insect a better foothold when walking on smooth surfaces.

The grasshopper has each leg armed with powerful spines, and the last segment is developed into large claws, used for the purpose of making powerful leaps. The cricket's leg is also adapted in the same way for leaping, but in addition there are two oval spots on the fore tibia, one on the outer part and another smaller one on the inner part. These spots are believed to be used as ears.

THE spider has the claws of each leg specially modified for climbing or clinging, and they can also be used as combs for the web when it is in the course of construction. The legs are useless on a polished surface, but a special development consisting of a pad of hairs allows the spider to negotiate a smooth surface. A viscid fluid is secreted which is adhesive, and this allows the animal to perform what seem like gymnastic feats. The well-developed combs are used for guiding the threads of silk as they are produced from the spinnerets, or used for walking on the threads, giving the animal unique balancing powers.

E. A. Botting

J. J. Ward

E. A. Botting

MOTH, MOSQUITO AND BUTTERFLY WINGS SHOW MARVELLOUS DETAILS WHEN MAGNIFIED

Under a powerful lens the scales of the wing of a yellow-tail moth appear as we see them here in the lower left-hand photograph. These scales are typical of the moth, being long and narrow and quite distinct from those of a butterfly, such as we see in the top right-hand illustration, which shows the lower surface of the underwing of a red admiral butterfly. The wing of an insect is actually an outgrowth of skin—just as it is in the case of the flying mammals, such as the phalangers—and this skin is supported by hardened blood vessels called nervures. Below, on the right, we have the wing scales of a malaria-carrying mosquito and (top left) scales from the wing tip of another mosquito.

E. A. Botting

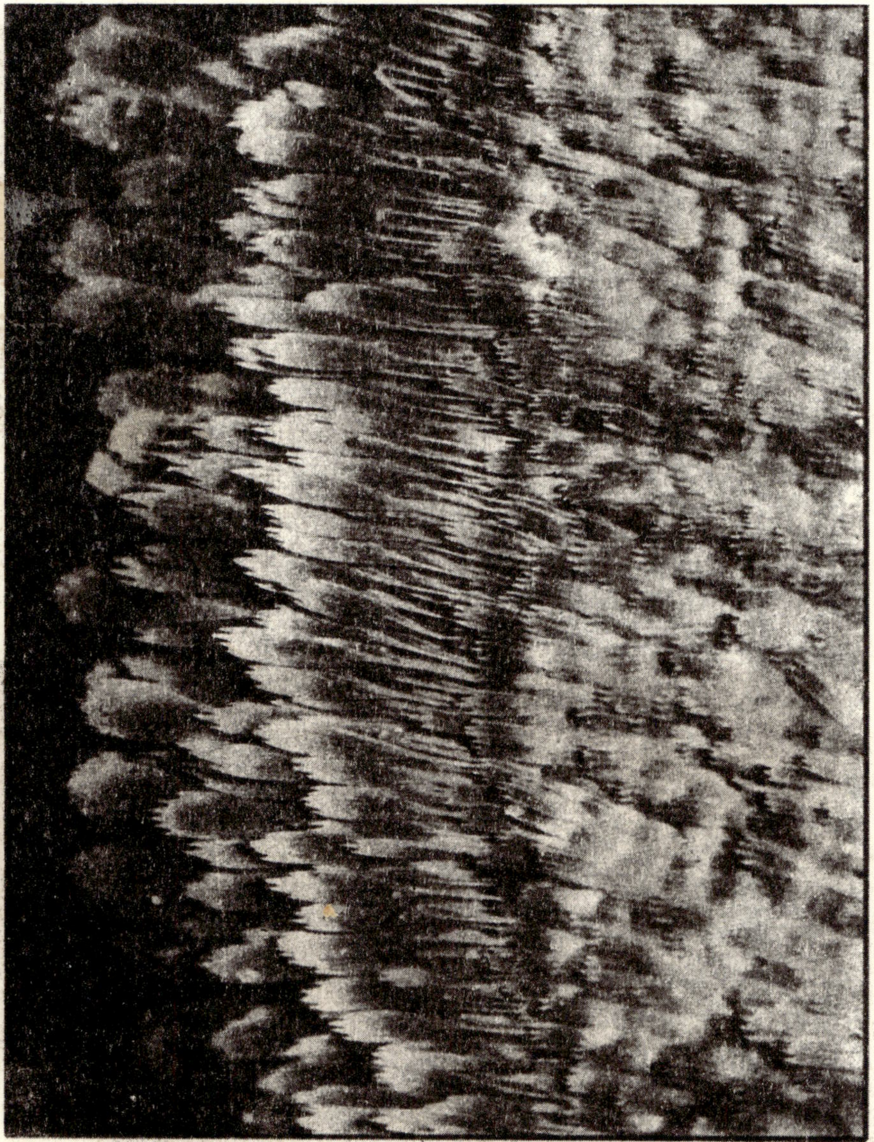

E. A. Smith

HIGHLY MAGNIFIED PORTIONS OF WINGS OF TORTOISESHELL BUTTERFLY AND A MOTH

The wings of insects show a very great variety of both structure and form as well as, in many cases, marvellous colours. The principal function of these wings is the distribution of the species at mating time, for it is only when ready to propagate its kind that insects such as butterflies and moths change from a crawling to a winged state of life. By means of flight, the adult butterflies and moths are able to disseminate their eggs over a wide area, and so ensure the continuance of the race. The iridescent marking on their wings is due to the breaking up of light into the colours of the spectrum by the scales composing the wing surfaces. Left, a black spot on the wing of a tortoiseshell butterfly, and, right, part of a moth's wing showing the structure.

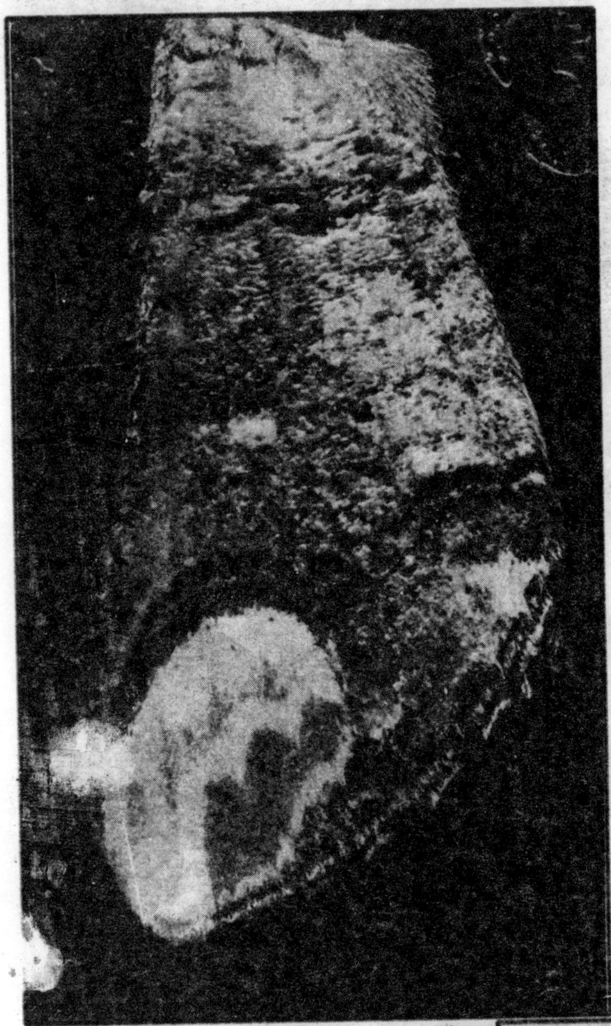

E. A. Smith

The wing proper is an outgrowth of the skin and the membranous expanse is supported by nervures or veins, whose arrangement serves as a means of classification of the great insect family. The nervure is really a channel through which the insect blood circulates, and it is sometimes crossed by a trachea or breathing tube. Wings and their power of flight play a great part in the distribution of the species, especially at breeding times, and help in the wide distribution of eggs and the subsequent larvae which later produce adult forms.

The buzzing sounds produced in two-wing flies such as the blowfly and bee are generally due to vibrations of the wing, which in the former reach 335 beats per second and in the latter 440 beats per second. The actual buzz is produced by the rapid vibration of muscles situated at the base of each wing, which causes a chitinous percussor to strike the body. The resonant part of this apparatus consists of a compound rib and its attached membranes, which are thrown into a state of combined vibration.

The wing of the dragon-fly has at the outer edge a dark coloured compartment. This is wrongly called the stigma. It is really a depression or pocket, the two membranous divisions at this point being kept apart by thick cellular tissue. This "stigma" is obviously an apparatus for producing sound in much the same way as the bull roarer familiar in our childhood days.

The wings of the hornet, bee, and wasp possess a series of hooklets bent obliquely outwards, varying in number from 29 to 50. The membrane opposite to these hooks is specially strengthened and bent under to form a kind of trough. When the wings are

The wings of insects exhibit a great variety of form and structure; they also show great beauty of colour as seen in the iridescent wing cases of many beetles. The wings of many butterflies are also highly coloured, especially those of the tropical varieties. In most insects there are two pairs of wings present; but in other types, such as the diptera, only one pair exists, the missing pair being replaced by halteres, or balancers, which have the general shape of a dumb-bell and a rounded end provided with sense organs. These halteres vary in size and outline. The type found in the crane-fly is covered with short, pointed hairs which act in a sensory manner; the haltere of the snout-fly is larger in size with a very wide tip; and in the gadfly the haltere is very large with a flattened oval area at the wide end, giving the whole structure the shape of an Indian club.

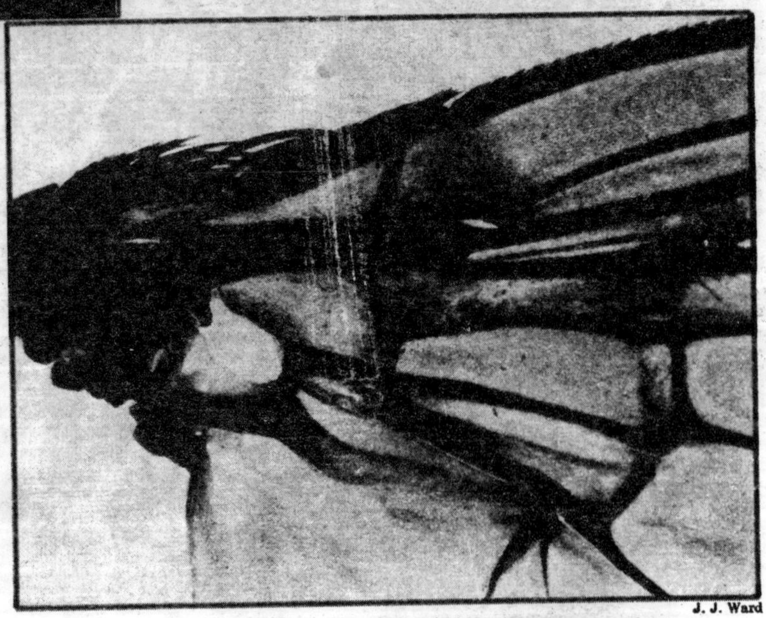

J. J. Ward

HOW THE BLOWFLY BUZZES: A MOTH'S WING

The buzzing of a blowfly is caused by the rapid vibration of structures at the base of each wing (bottom). The wings make about 335 beats a second, and a part of the structure mentioned above strikes the body each time like a rapidly vibrating hammer. Above is part of a moth's wing. Both photographs are magnified.

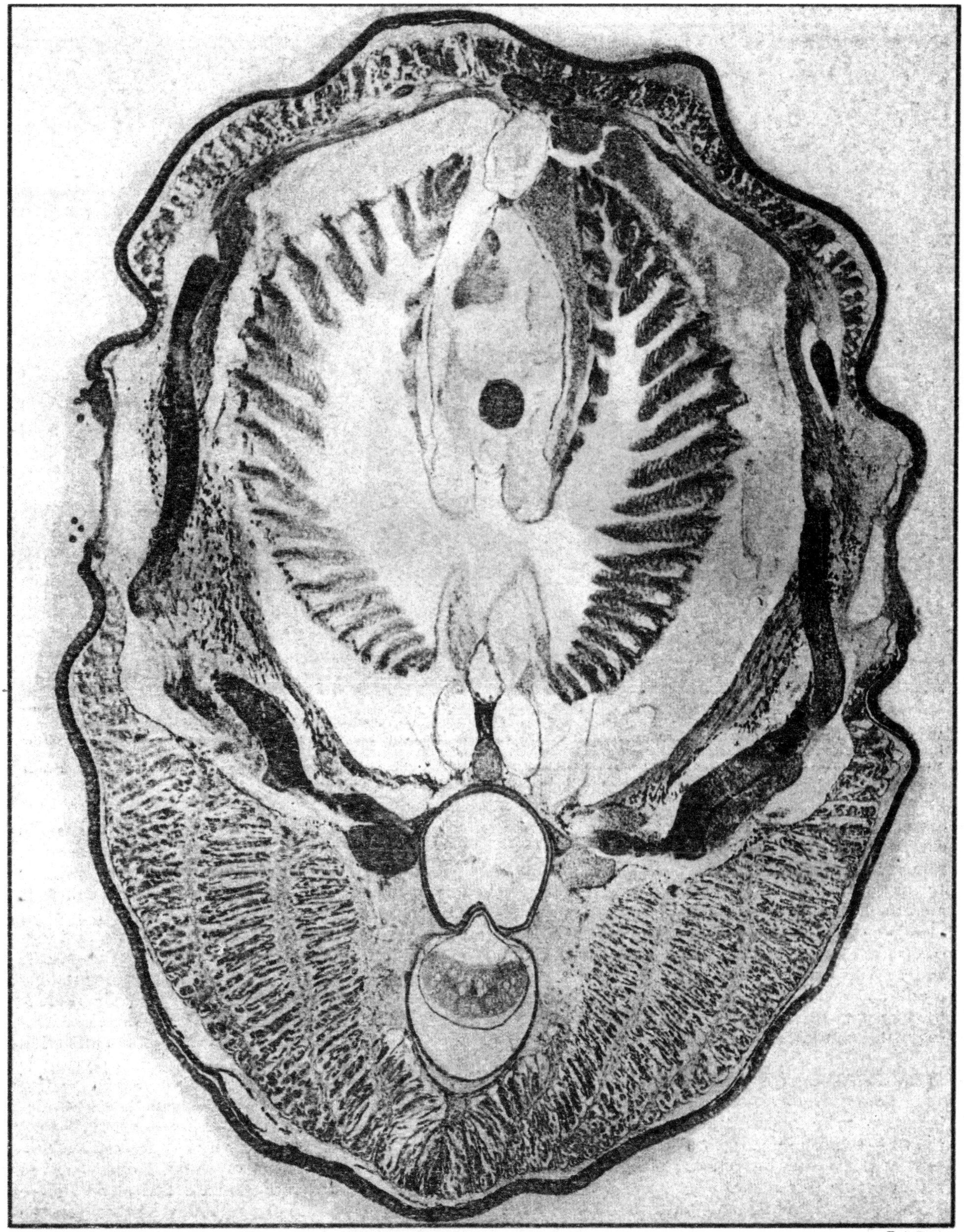

E. A. Botting

TRANSVERSE SECTION THROUGH THE BODY OF A LAMPREY

This extraordinary photo-micrograph shows a transverse section through the body of a lamprey. This strange creature, species of which exist both in fresh and salt water, was for long classed with fishes but has since been removed by scientists into a section of the animal kingdom of its own. Lampreys ascend the Severn, Thames and other British rivers, as they do many of those of the Continent, for the purpose of spawning and in historic times were esteemed a great delicacy. The lamprey attaches itself to any dead body but will sometimes attack living fish.

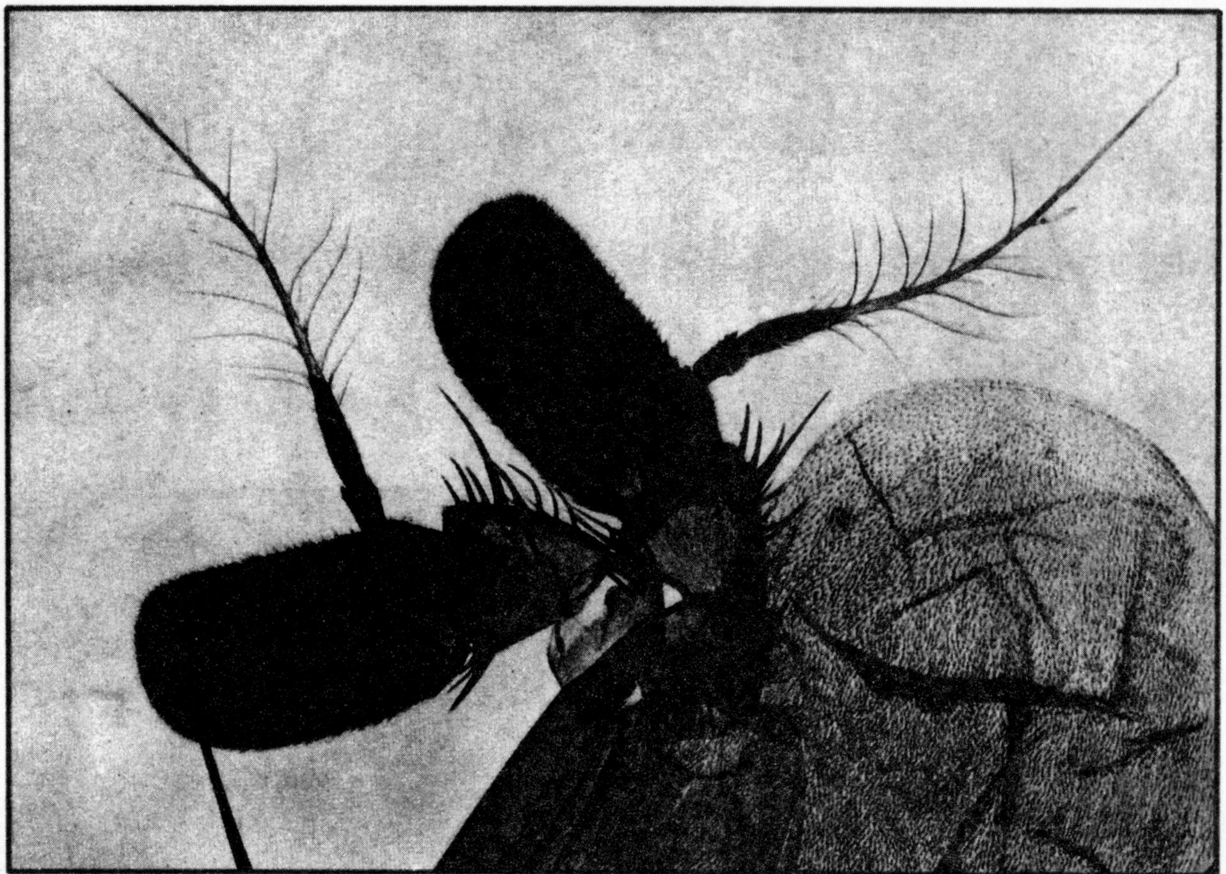

H. S. Cheavin

ORGANS OF MYSTERIOUS SENSITIVENESS: A MARSH FLY'S ANTENNAE

When examined microscopically the antennae of the marsh fly, seen above, are found to be borne on flattened processes growing out of the head. The antennae are filamentous and taper gradually to a point. At irregular intervals along their length there are a number of strange out-growths composed of very fine hairs. It is possible that the mystery of the "sixth sense" may be solved when we know more of the functioning of these wonderful organs of the insects.

expanded the hooks of the hind wings hang over the edge of this trough and they are firmly locked together, thus producing a combined wing in each case. In this family we find the principal muscles of flight are attached to the fore wings, which are larger and more powerful than the hind wings; thus the linkage compensates for lack of muscular strength in the hind wings. This method of attachment if reversed would result in a weaker grip; the hold of the hind wing on the fore wing therefore gives a close attachment, and so greater power for propulsion through the air.

THE hooks are really modified hairs, and in the hornet we have a gradual change of form, becoming more apparent as we pass from those showing completely hooked types to the scarcely bent, stout hair-like projections which have obviously little clasping power left.

The wings of moths and butterflies are covered with scales or feathery particles which overlap each other and produce iridescent effects due to refraction of light rays on their surfaces. On the outer portions of the gnat wing there are innumerable short hairs arranged in clusters forming a heavy fringe, commencing at the tip of the wing. The veins or nervures are also covered with these thick hairs or scales which are broad at one end and pointed at the other.

The wing of the earwig when not in use is neatly folded and tucked away under the very small wing cases or elytra. In the unfolding or folding of its wings, this insect uses its flexible abdomen by bending the latter forward over the back. The delicate membrane of the wing is crossed by radiating lines or veins which unite with a delicate vein running parallel with the outer edge, and it is by these radiating veins that the wing can be folded like a fan into small compass.

Wing covers, or elytra, are present in many beetles, particularly the water beetle, where the fore wings have become modified in this way by much thickening, and the upper and lower surfaces are clamped together by minute pillars of chitin, having between them fat bodies, nerves, tracheae and blood. These elytra are used also for retaining air between the felted hairs covering the back of the abdomen where the air is held as a large flattened bubble.

The function of respiration in insects is effected by means of a complicated system of minute tubes which ramify through the body and its parts and so come into contact with all the internal organs. They thus resemble the vascular system of higher animals. The air is taken in through a series of openings, spiracles, situated on segments of the body, and may vary from one to two in each segment. These spiracles can be opened or closed, their general outline is oval in shape, and numerous filamentous projections grow from the sides meeting in the centre. The filaments are covered with very fine hairs which act as a filter, preventing foreign matter, such as dust, from entering.

Many insects, in their larval stage, have special modifications present in their tracheal system. Some forms take in air through their body walls by means of diffusion ; in others, air is taken in by a special tube or gill arrangement. The tracheae in aquatic forms are modified in position during the period spent in the water and the spiracles are found at the end of an elongated process.

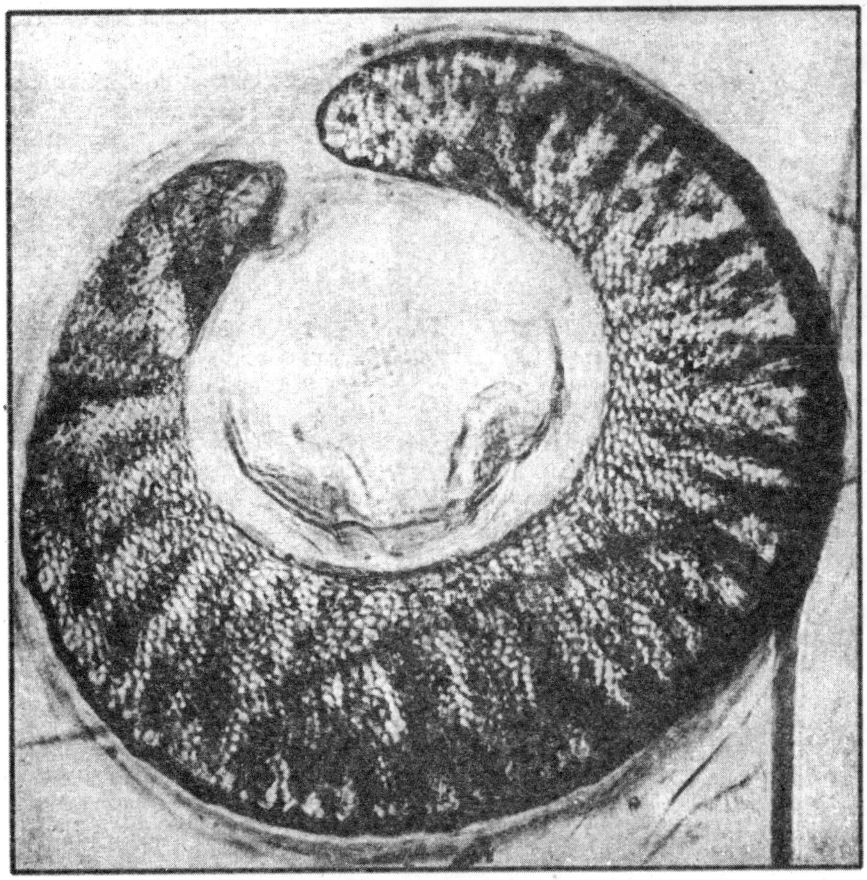

BREATHING HOLES IN THE LARVAE OF INSECTS

Spiracles are the breathing holes in the body by means of which larvae obtain the necessary oxygen. Below is a spiracle belonging to a cockchafer larva. The spiracle is bent upon itself so as to allow a larger breathing surface in the segment of so small a creature. Above is a caterpillar spiracle which is opened and shut by very fine hairs as breathing takes place.

The gnat in its larval form has a long, tube-like projection at the tail end of the body, which is thrust out of the water whenever the larva rises to the surface for breathing purposes. At the end of this tube is a small, five-rayed star of fine hairs which expands as the body of the larva reaches the surface, and in this way water is prevented from entering the tube. The star is closed over this breathing tube when the larva sinks from the surface of the water. When the larva passes into the pupal stage this tube disappears and is replaced by two horn-like projections, one on each side of the head. Each tube has on the inner surfaces a large number of fine hairs which serve as a protection against the entry ot water.

The act of emergence is one of wonder, and takes place in a few moments. The pupal skin splits along the back, the new insect makes a brief pause whilst the wings and head parts

E. A. Smith

DOGFISH SKIN: SCALES FROM SHELLS OF SCALLOP AND WHELK

The shells of the molluscs are composed of three layers made of carbonate of lime and an organic substance akin to chitin, the material forming the outer covering of insects. These photographs, much enlarged, show (top right) one of the minute scales on the outer layer of the shell of a scallop and (top left) a similar scale from a whelk shell. Below is a fragment of dogfish skin.

dry, and then it flies away to carry out its life history.

The larva of the water beetle has, at its tail end, two projections covered with very fine hairs, by means of which the body is suspended from the surface film of the water. Whilst it is suspended, air is taken in by two spiracles situated at the extreme ends of this tail, and they lead to large tracheal tubes found on each side of the body. Each body segment of the larva contains a spiracle, but these are only rudimentary and quite closed till a later stage, when the change over to the pupal form takes place.

A further modification is found in the larval form of the dragon-fly. At the extreme end of the body is a rectum tube, having on the inner walls a series of fleshy folds which multiply the surface area to a very large extent. These rectal gills, as they are termed, have the power of absorbing oxygen from the dissolved air in the water.

When the larval form changes

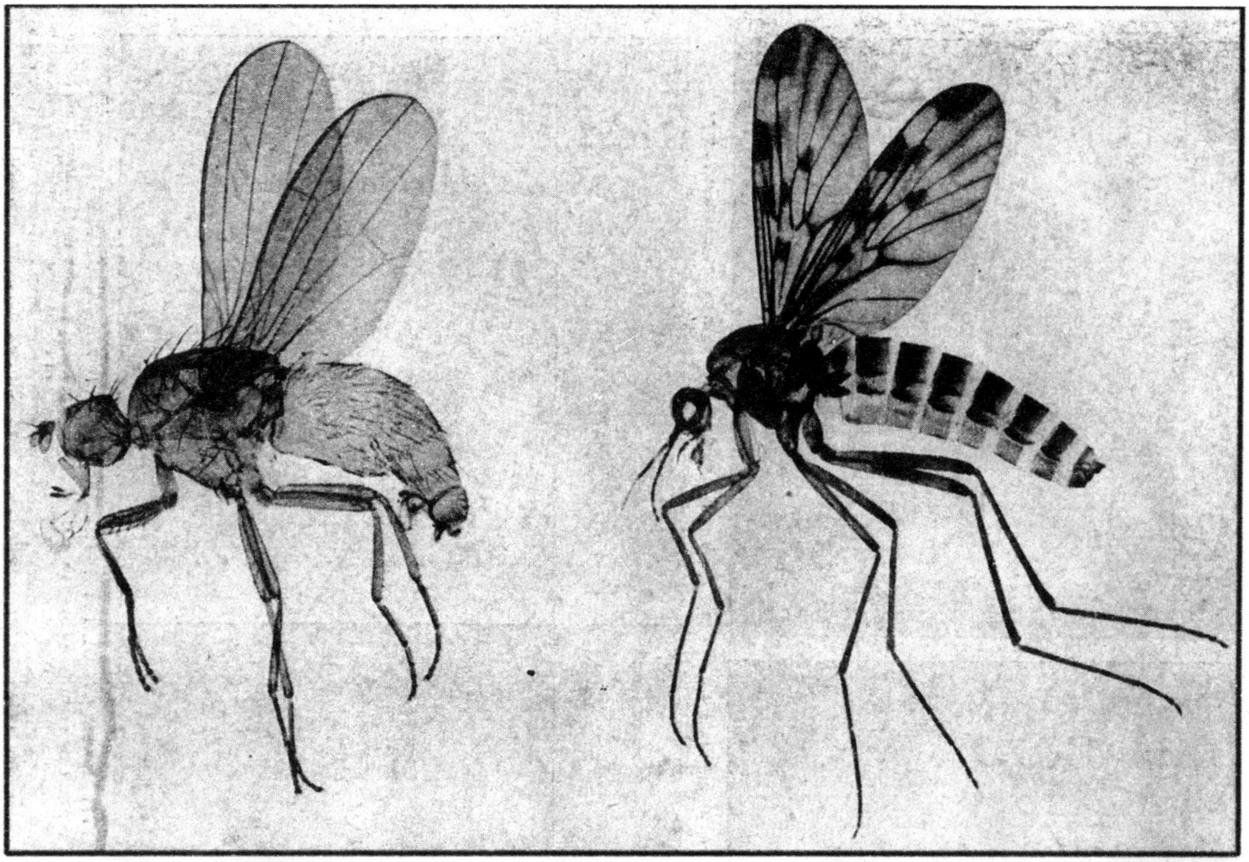

J. F. Carrigan

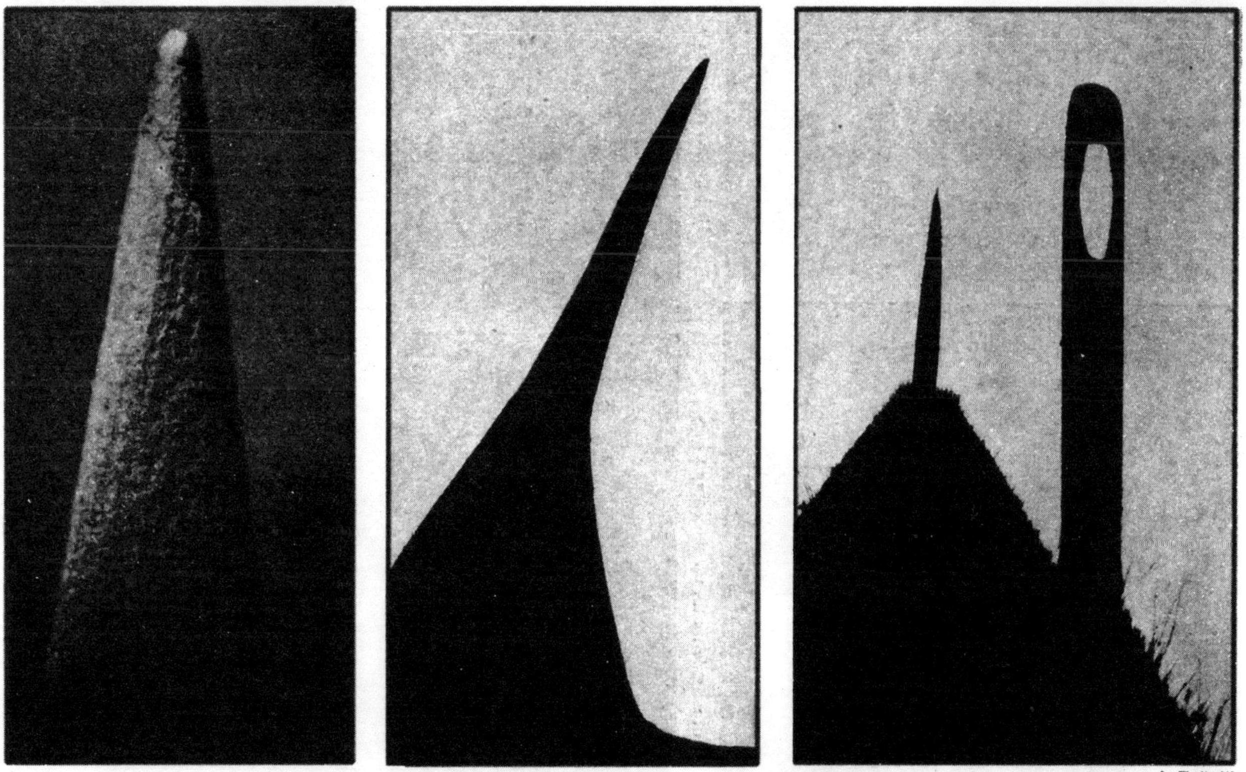

A. E. Smith

COMPARISONS UNDER THE MICROSCOPE AND TWO FLIES MAGNIFIED

If our eyes had the magnifying properties of a microscope's lens, everything in the world would have an utterly different appearance. The lower photographs show the point of a lead pencil (left, x5) the spike of a holly leaf (centre, x15), and a wasp's sting compared with the eye of the finest needle that a factory can make (right). Above are two of the smaller insects as they appear when magnified; (left) an onion fly and (right) a window fly.

Eggs of magpie moth, magnified 35 times

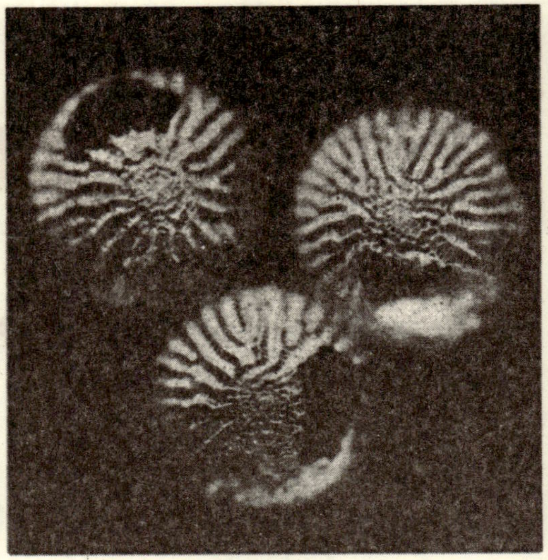

Red underwing moth eggs after hatching (x 40)

The brindled beauty moth's eggs magnified by 35

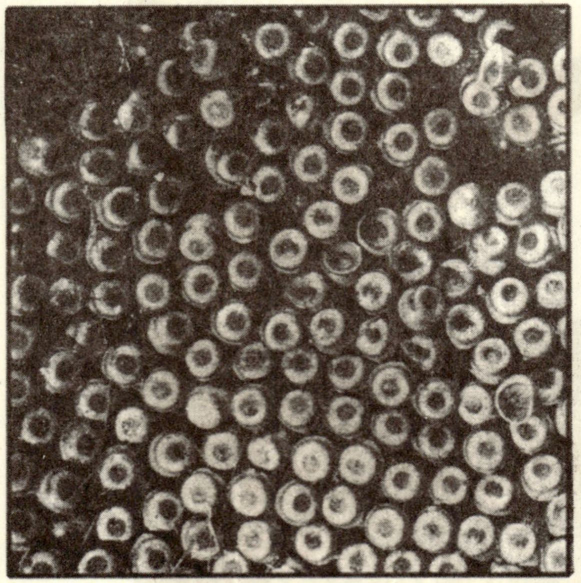

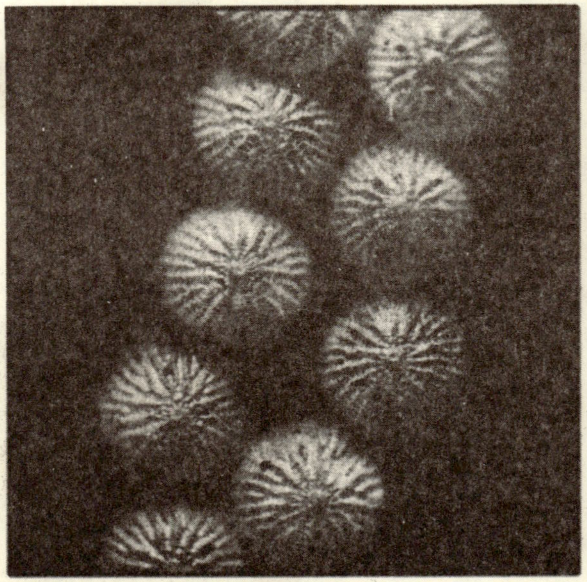

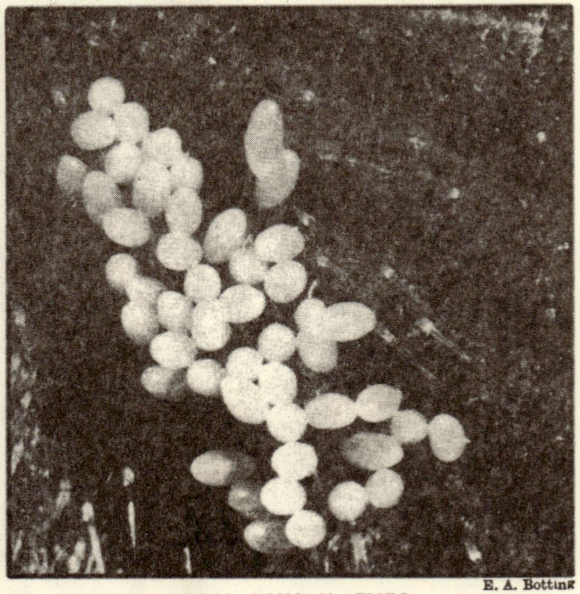

E. A. Botting

BUT FOR THE MICROSCOPE MARVELS OF BUTTERFLY AND MOTH EGGS WOULD BE HIDDEN FROM HUMAN EYES

If we could see moth and butterfly eggs, say twenty times the actual size, we might well be puzzled as to what those strange objects were. Certainly we might look at them a long time before it occurred to us that they were really eggs. For there is nothing egg-like either in their shape or their surfaces and the colours vary greatly. The eggs of the lackey moth seen here (bottom left) are photographed on an apple leaf, and those of the painted lady butterfly (bottom right) on a nettle leaf. But the magnification is so high that the portion of leaf surface in either case is hardly recognizable as such. To the naked eye it is a difficult matter to detect the difference between the eggs, but the microscope reveals Nature's infinitely wonderful work.

to the nymph stage the abdominal tip of the larva is replaced by a bunch of leaf-like plates which can be used for swimming or respiratory purposes. These plates are covered with a ramification of air tubes which absorb the dissolved oxygen in the water, and this is carried by fine tracheal tubes to the larger tracheae in the body.

The respiration of this nymph form can also be effected by means of a pair of spiracles found just behind the head. Entomologists for a long time were puzzled by this extra power of respiration until it was shown that the nymph, when in the water, used its tail leaflets, but when out of water it was the spiracles that were used for breathing. The last segments of the insect body are often modified for the purposes of reproduction.

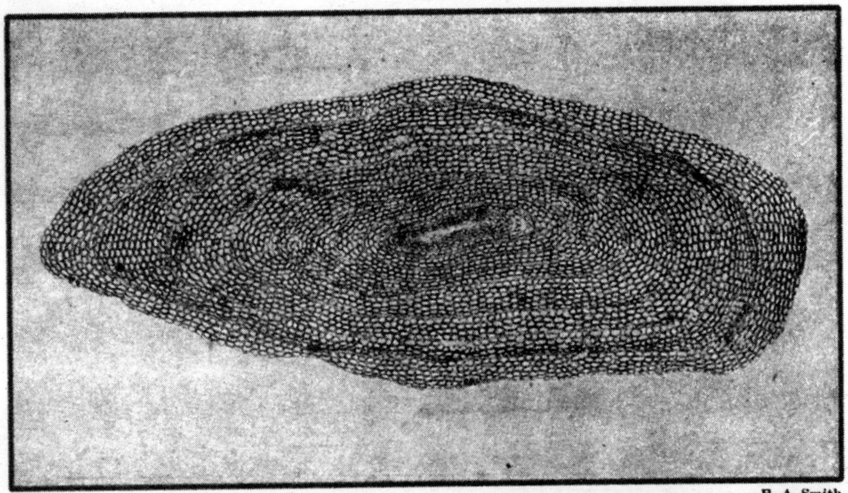

E. A. Smith

MINUTE SCALE OF AN EEL MUCH MAGNIFIED

Eels have scales, but these scales do not comprise the somewhat stiff armour of ordinary fish. The eel depends much on its slippery qualities for its safety, and the scales are embedded in the skin. Furthermore, they are very small. This photograph of a single scale is very highly magnified. As an additional protection the eel's skin is covered with a slimy substance which makes it very difficult to capture.

In the cockroach the eighth and ninth segments bear forcep-shaped appendages, with an upper and lower jaw; these forceps in the female are used to grasp the eggs as they issue from the oviduct, and to place them in a safe position.

The greatest modification of this kind is seen in the earwig. In some species the adult insect is furnished with a pair of ferocious-looking, calliper-shaped projections of enormous size, which in the female are nearly straight and curve symmetrically at the tips. On the inner edge of each is a row of irregular grooves resembling rough teeth, which are used by the insect to move her eggs about from place to place. The callipers are also used to fold and unfold the wings. The callipers of the male are very much larger than those of the female, are more formidable in appearance, having longer curves and large, blunt teeth on the inner edge, and they resemble more closely the claws found on the feet.

The anterior segments of the bee show a different modification. They are developed into the well-known sting which in the female is, strictly speaking, part of the reproductive system and corresponds with an ovipositor, for the eggs escape at the base instead of passing through as in the case of other insects.

The whole organ is very complicated, consisting of a protecting sheath, the director, which prepares the hole, and then guides the sting proper in a groove. The sting, consisting of very fine needles, slides freely forward in this groove. The director is serrated at the extreme end with the serrated tips turned inwards as in a fish-hook. An inner groove forms the poison channel; also between each barb is another channel which distributes the poison fluid in the wound. It is due to these barbs that frequently the sting is left in the wound and the internal organs are dragged out with fatal results to the insect when it attempts to fly away.

In the ichneumon-fly the ovipositor consists of a single director-shaped tube, which is very elongated and used for inserting eggs into the bodies of caterpillars. These eggs hatch out in a few days and completely destroy the host. The extreme end of the ovipositor is furnished with strong serrations, and acts as a borer by means of a side-to-side action or even a twisting motion resulting in a deep hole into which the egg is deposited.

The female sawfly is furnished with a pair of saws, and these are used for making small holes in branches of trees into which an egg is deposited, the hole being sealed with a drop of frothy liquid. The irritation caused by this puncture produces a morbid growth in the branch resulting in an excrescence of varying size. Within this excrescence the larvae, protected by the walls from weather and enemies, feed and undergo pupation awaiting the final metamorphosis.

Myriapoda is the name given to the lowest class of articulated animals, and these are included among the insect types because of their close affinity. They differ from insects in the absence of wings, and the body is composed of an extensive series of segments, each of which bears a pair of legs.

The myriapods belong to a very ancient order which appeared during the coal period. They are sluggish in habit and live on vegetable matter or animal excrement, but some forms are carnivorous. They avoid light, and lurk in damp places under stones. Myriapods are found all over the world; the largest species living in tropical regions. Their economy in Nature is to destroy decomposing organic matter. In their ranks are the centipede and millipede, which possess mandibles of a very similar type to those seen in true insects.

W. S. Berridge

FISH OF FRESH AND SALT WATER THAT USE ELECTRICITY TO LIVE

For long ages certain lowly members of the fish tribe have been using electricity either to obtain food or to prevent themselves being turned into food by some other creature. These photographs show (bottom) an elephant mormyrid which has an electric organ on either side of its tail: and above it is another member of the same family which emits shocks from centres at the sides of its head. Both these fish are confined to Tropical Africa. The next photograph (top but one) is of the electric cat fish. This is found in the Nile, and its entire body is covered with electrical apparatus. The top illustration is of an electric star-gazer, a sea fish of the Atlantic and Pacific.

Chapter CXXXVIII

Nature's Electricians

By E. G. Boulenger

Director of the Zoological Society's Aquarium

Fresh wonders of Nature are constantly being brought to light, but the fundamentals of life are of very long standing. Thousands of inventions which have become necessities of our complex civilization were anticipated many millions of years ago in a world in which mankind was merely in the making. Electricity, for example, which promises to rule the earth—so far as man is concerned—was actively employed by many animals before any human being had made any effort to harness this terrific force.

What is electricity ? To answer this question, even an expert loses himself in a whirl of words. Electricity, he tells us, is a collective term for various phenomena, such as the attraction and repulsion exhibited by certain bodies under friction, magnetic attraction, chemical decomposition and so on. Whilst few of us could better this concise, if unsatisfactory, definition, we are fully aware as to what electricity can be made to do. The force that possibly lies at the beginning of life, and still makes the savage bow down and worship when it manifests itself in the form of a thunderstorm, has now been coaxed into a thousand useful channels—lighting and heating our dwellings, cooking our food, bridging the gulfs of space, and healing the sick are but a few of its capabilities. Electricity is possibly the key to the riddle of the universe, and is doubtless behind what has been called the " life force "—the force that drives all animate nature forwards.

Man, with his relatively gigantic brain, has made use of electricity for all kinds of useful purposes, but the only animals at present known which have developed the force to any marked extent, are creatures of lowly origin, and electricity is employed by them as a form of protection, and a means of obtaining food. In none of the higher creatures is the force developed to any extent. The crackle and fly of sparks often accompanying the combing of a cat's hair are phenomena which may be produced by many other equally simple means, such as the friction of glass on silk. The hair of most mammals can produce such sparks, if the subject is of high vitality. These sparks are easily drawn from the hair of the human, especially when moistened previously, or the atmosphere is sufficiently humid. Dark hair, curiously enough, by reason of greater resiliency, is more disposed to emit sparks than fair hair, which is usually of a laxer texture.

The emitting of sparks by hair has given rise to many quaint superstitions amongst savage tribes. It is said that certain monkeys—notably the little owl monkey of the Amazon—being very nocturnal, and often hunting in family parties, give out waves of light as they make their way through the tree-tops. The marauding bands, bent upon rifling birds' nests, bring their long hair into frequent contact with dense vegetation, which literally combs them, and thus accounts for the electric display.

About half a dozen species of fish have harnessed electricity to their needs. By far the most notorious of these is the electric eel of the swamps of Brazil and the Guianas. The fish is exceedingly abundant throughout the greater part of North and South America, and may measure up to ten feet in length, of which the head and body complete but one eighth of the creature's entire length, the rest being all tail. Its general colour is slatey blue, a lurid red suffusing the under surfaces of the head. The eyes are so small as to be all but indiscernible.

The huge tail of the electric eel is practically one big battery, the electric organs extending along both sides in the form of longitudinal bands. These batteries consist of peculiarly adapted muscular tissues, and are composed of thousands of very small cells, full of a jelly-like fluid. Analysis shows them to be miniature galvanic jars in which each jar is richly supplied with nerves in communication with the fish's brain. They are thus all under direct control. It is said that this eel, which can give a shock equivalent to 300 volts, attains its best results when the head and tail are brought into direct contact with the victim—thus forming a circuit. The current produced runs from the tail to the head, which is curious, since in all other electric fish the flow is in the reverse direction. At least one Zoo keeper has been temporarily incapacitated by the creature, and its method of attacking the fish offered it for food throws a lurid light upon its lethal powers.

According to Humboldt, the natives at one time drove their horses and cattle into streams infested by electric eels, causing the eels to discharge their batteries until exhaustion supervened. The eels, conscious of their weakened condition, then sought the shelter of the banks, where they were easily harpooned. Humboldt actually closed certain forest paths, because of the electric eels swarming in the streams crossing them. It has been observed of captive specimens kept in aquaria that a long period of rest and plenty of feeding up is necessary to recharge the batteries, once they have been thoroughly exhausted. Electric eels are said to be good eating by the few Europeans who have made the experiment.

In a review of electric fishes, the electric ray or torpedo should really be entitled to prior mention, since it is one of the comparatively primitive fishes, which came into being long before the electric eel and other electric fish were evolved. The electricity in this fish is produced by two kidney-shaped organs situated on each side of the head.

Nature's Electricians

W. S. Berridge

ELECTRIC EEL THAT PRODUCES A THREE HUNDRED VOLT SHOCK

Most notorious of Nature's electricians is the electric eel of the swamps of Brazil and the Guianas. This formidable eel may be as much as ten feet long, and in colour it is slate-blue with a vivid red on top of its head. It is said to give a shock equivalent to three hundred volts, touching its victim with its tail and head so as to form a circuit. An idea of the current produced is obtained by remembering that the ordinary electric light mains work at a little over 200 volts. A fine specimen of electric eel has been exhibited in the Aquarium at the London Zoological Gardens.

Figuier in his Ocean World has given an interesting account of a demonstration, conducted by Dr. Walsh, a Fellow of the Royal Society, of the electric powers of the torpedo.

" Dr. Walsh placed a living torpedo upon a clean towel ; from a plate he suspended two pieces of brass wire by means of silken cord, which served to isolate them. Round the torpedo were eight persons, standing on isolating substances. One end of the brass wire was supported by the wet towel, the other end being placed in a basin full of water. The first person had a finger of one hand in this basin, and a finger of the other in a second basin, also full of water. The second person placed a finger of one hand in this second basin, and a finger of the other hand in a third basin. The third person did the same, and so on, until a complete chain was established between the eight persons and nine basins. Into the ninth basin the end of the second brass wire was plunged, while Dr. Walsh applied the other end to the back of the torpedo, thus establishing a complete conducting circle. At the moment when the experimenter touched the torpedo, the eight actors in the experiment felt a sudden shock, similar in all respects to that communicated by the shock of a Leyden jar, only less intense.

" WHEN the torpedo was placed on an isolated supporter, it communicated to many persons similarly placed from forty to fifty shocks in a minute and a half. Each effort made by the animal was accompanied by the depression of its eyes, which, slightly projecting in their natural state, seemed to be drawn within their orbits, while the other parts of the body remained immovable.

" If only one of the two organs of the torpedo were touched it happened that, in place of a strong and sudden shock, only a slight sensation was experienced—a numbness, or start, rather than a shock. The same result followed with every experiment tried. The animal was tried with a non-conducting rod, and no shock followed ; glass, or a rod covered with wax, produced no effect ; touched with a metallic wire, a violent shock followed. Melloni, Matteucci, Becquerel, and Breschet have all made the same experiments, with the same results ; Matteucci having ascertained that the shock produced by the torpedo is comparable to that given by a voltaic pile of 100 to 150 pairs of plates."

Electric rays are abundant in most warm waters, and are tolerably common off the west coast of Britain. They swarm in the sandy bays off Portugal and anybody who has been aboard a Portuguese trawler cannot but have been greatly impressed by the indifference with which the barefooted fishermen tread upon mounds of electric rays, without suffering apparently any inconvenience. Like the electric eel, this ray is esteemed as food—by a discriminating few. The torpedo is probably the best known of electric fish in Europe, and Pliny, Aristotle and many other old writers describe its habits most graphically. In Roman times, it was employed to cure gout and rheumatism, many of the ancient specialists having built up their reputations by an advocacy of torpedo treatment. The patient—(or victim)—was recommended to stand barefooted on the fish and to 'stick it' until its power was exhausted. The electric ray is a much flattened creature of a dull grey or brown, according to the colour of the ground upon which it lives. It feeds on live fish, being especially fond of the defenceless grey mullet. When one of the latter fish, all unsuspecting, approaches, the ray at once rises from the sea bed, and throws himself against the mullet, who falls an easy prey. The creature brings forth its young alive, the baby torpedoes being of a typical dogfish shape at birth, and taking several months in which to assume the flattened aspect of their parents.

Certain bottom haunting fishes of American waters allied to the common weever, and popularly known as star-gazers, have electric organs situated near the head, and innocent sea wanderers that

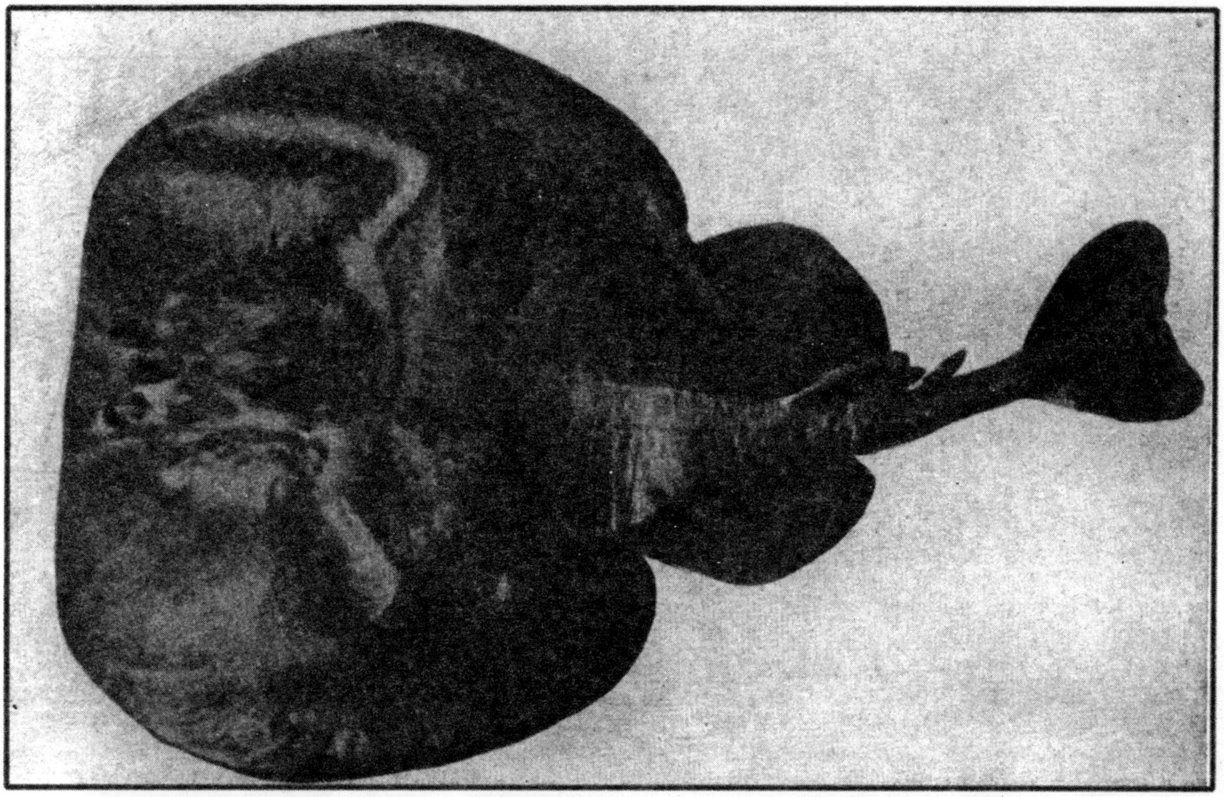

chance to snap at the fish's upturned eyes come into contact with the "live rail," meeting a speedy death. The living batteries of this fish are composed of a modification of the eyeball muscles.

It may be assumed that all electric organs in fishes are merely developments of the muscular system, certain cells of the body wall, having by some mysterious process developed electric powers, and obeyed the dictates of the fish's brain—such as it is. An extraordinary exception is exemplified in a Nile catfish, in which the organs are formed by abnormal developments of various glands, sheathing the entire body in a cuirass of highly-charged batteries. No portion of the fish can be regarded as insulated, and the apparatus is controlled by a single nerve on each side of the body. The shocks produced by the electric catfish, although considerable, are not so severe as those caused by the electric eel or ray. The fish called "raad" by the Arabs, a name meaning "thunder," employs its electric powers by sidling up to other larger fish, shocking them, and then devouring the partly digested food which the shock has forced them to bring up.

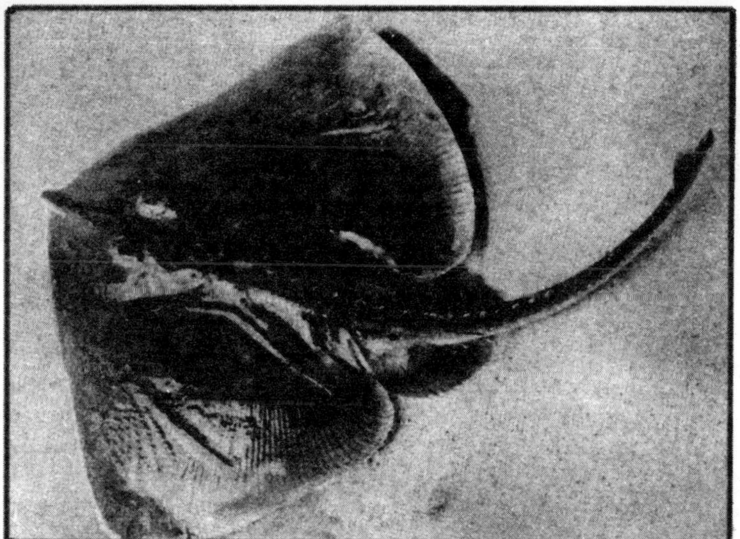

W. S Berridge

SKATE, AND THE RAY ONCE AN ELECTRIC CURE FOR GOUT

Early in its development the ray had found out how to give shocks. The lower photograph is of a skate, one of the ray family, which gives a shock, though a very slight one. Above is the electric ray or torpedo, common off the West Coast of Britain In Roman times, gouty patients were made to stand on the fish as cure.

We are naturally lead to ask, "What is the working value of an electric fish?" Could it be harnessed to a train or electric chair? The answer is "Yes." It could, provided you employed enough fish. If there is any truth in what our master electricians tell us, 10,000 electric eels might keep a District Railway train running for a couple of minutes. The train would then stop for 24 hours until the eels had recuperated their powers.

WONDERFUL EXAMPLES OF REALISTIC ART: BULL FROG IN THE AMERICAN MUSEUM OF NATURAL HISTORY

Originally the Greek word from which we get " museum " meant a temple of the Muses. Later it came to be applied to a building devoted to learning of various kinds. But now it signifies a place where antiquities or natural history specimens are preserved and displayed for study. As time has gone on the standard of efficiency whereby the specimens in a zoological museum are displayed for public inspection has become higher and higher until nowadays, and especially in the United States, where ample funds are available, the most wonderful things are done. Above we see one of the fine groups in the American Museum of Natural History in New York. The realistic effect is the result of years of study.

Chapter CXXXIX

Some Marvels of the Museums

By Henry Neal Milligan

Zoologist of the Horniman Museum

How many of us could answer the question, "What is a museum ?" Probably there are not many, even amongst men of learning, who would care to reply off-hand to such an inquiry. Some people might say, quite innocently, that it is a place where curiosities are kept, but (notwithstanding that there have been places of which this might be a very fair description) the men who are charged with the care and arrangement of museums would indignantly repudiate such a definition.

Readers of WONDERS OF ANIMAL LIFE are not likely to take alarm at the sight of a Greek word, and so we may begin by explaining that *mouseion* was the name anciently given to a temple of the Muses. Later it came to be applied to a building devoted to learning of various kinds. An institution of this latter sort was that famous one (a compound of learned academy and temple), one of the glories of the ancient world, founded in the palace at Alexandria about 280 B.C.

Nowadays the name museum is used of a building (or, it would perhaps be better to say, of the building and its contents) in which antiquities, works of art, and specimens of natural history are preserved, studied, and displayed. Very often the works of art are kept separate from the other objects, in what is then called an art gallery; but such distinctions need not here concern us, for in the following account we shall be dealing only with the zoological part of museums.

It will be well to note the order of the words, "preserved, studied, and displayed." Perhaps it may be thought that this is wrong, and that they should read, "preserved, displayed, and studied," because to show the specimens must be the first and only important thing. But that is not altogether the case. It usually comes as a very great surprise to most people to be told that the great national museums (such as the Natural History Museum in the Cromwell Road at South Kensington) may be regarded primarily as places (the case is rather different with the smaller or local museums) for the accumulation, study, description, and naming of specimens of natural history, and that it is only a relatively small series of examples which ought to be displayed to the public.

If a great central museum were to set out all its specimens for public exhibition it would need to have a very big building indeed. It would in any case be imprudent so to exhibit them, for most visitors to museums neither want nor need more than typical representative specimens. What a bore a museum would be if it showed all its mice, all its shells, all its flies, all its moths, and so on, in long, long rows! A great central museum, however, must have all obtainable specimens in its store-rooms, available for study and comparison when required. An example of what may have to be done in the way of first studying and naming specimens is to be found in the "Catalogue of Birds," a magnificent and learned work, published by the authorities of the Natural History Museum, in twenty-seven volumes, without knowledge of which no man can rank as an ornithological expert.

SAND-FLY MODELLED IN WAX

To study such insects as flies a greatly enlarged model is necessary, for there could not be much satisfaction about a stuffed fly. Here is a model of a sand-fly in the Natural History Museum at South Kensington. About 2,000 hairs have been placed on it.

Still, the function of properly displaying specimens for the delight and instruction of the public is of the very highest importance, and very probably it is the only one about which the non-professional reader will care to be told. What, then, are those wonders which a visitor may expect to see in a zoological museum—in a large central museum, that is, for we are not now speaking of smaller institutions, which may have specialities of their own.

To describe, or even briefly to indicate, all the museum wonders would here be beyond our power, and so we shall write only of the romance of that sort of exhibition which has come to be called the "museum group." Not, be it noted, such groups as lions and tigers fighting, with

They are in consequence more the prerogative of the larger than of the smaller museums, but this neither was nor is always the case, and some of the pioneer work of the kind we are discussing was done in small museums. There was, for example, the well-known collection of British birds, founded in the middle of the last century by a remarkable private collector, Mr. E. T. Booth, who, to quote his own words, endeavoured " to represent the birds in situations somewhat similar to those in which they were obtained; many of the cases, indeed, being copied from sketches taken on the actual spots where the birds themselves were shot." Mr. Booth's collection, which is now public property, is in the museum in the Dyke Road at Brighton.

plenty of teeth, talons, and streams and gouts of sealing-wax blood (exhibits fit only for a " show "), but really beautiful and instructive preparations which correctly show the creatures' forms and attitudes, and illustrate their modes of life, their seasonal changes of colour, their courtship dresses, their homes, their young, and so on.

Any old-style animal stuffer might set up a group of the first sort. Those of the latter sort are the work of highly-skilled men whose life-work is that of preparing museum exhibits. Such exhibits must be prepared not only with scientific accuracy, but also with sympathetic understanding of the wants of the visitor, and they must be labelled and explained in such a way that the visitor will naturally desire to see more of what the museum has to show. Does not every true teacher (and the museum official should be one) know that his function is not merely to tell, but also to excite the desire to know?

Museum groups are difficult to prepare and costly to install.

American Museum

PROCESSES IN THE MAKING OF A MUSEUM ANIMAL

In the old days animal skins stuffed with some material may have satisfied people, but nowadays the museum scientists insist on accuracy in every detail. Life-size models, anatomically correct, are made, and the skins of their living counterpart put over them. Here we see (bottom) a plaster mould being made and (top) a frame being covered in clay for a model.

It was not until some twenty years after Mr. Booth began to work that the national Natural History Museum, London, installed cases of birds each of which should illustrate a species in a natural position and in its natural surroundings. It is said that the first of the species thus to be installed was the well-known British bird called the coot. Others soon followed. The very tree on which the woodpecker was at work was hewn down and part of it used in the construction of the surroundings, the foliage being prepared and modelled with the greatest care. And now we can boast of that splendid series of cases in the Bird Gallery at South Kensington, justly regarded as among the best of that institution's exhibits. There are probably few persons who have inspected these cases and failed to receive much pleasure in doing so.

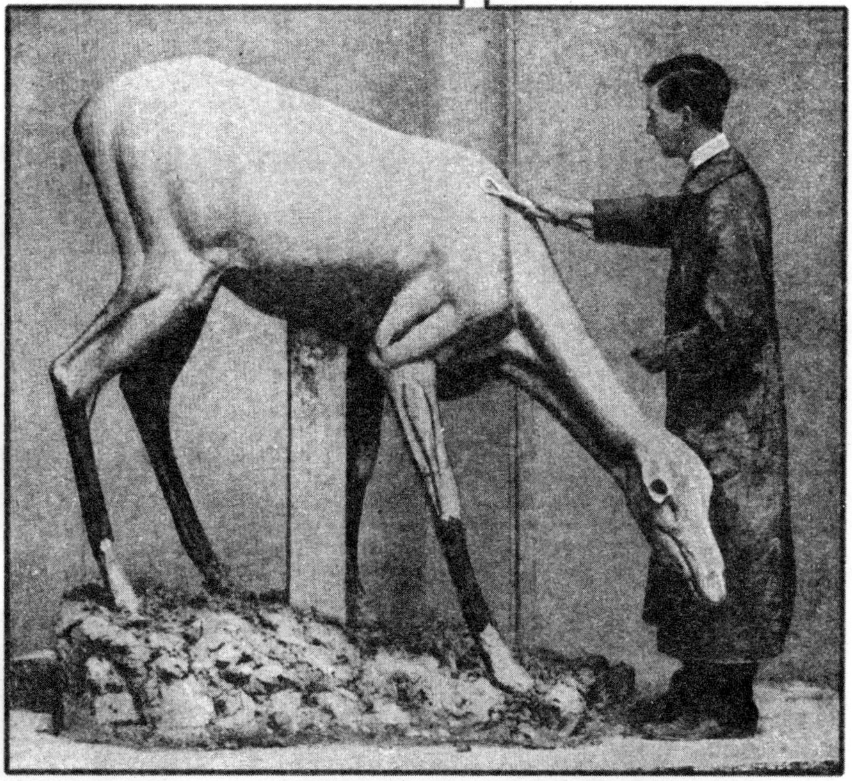

TRYING ON A SKIN AND MOUNTING AN ELK MODEL

The men who construct the animals in modern natural history museums have to be zoologists and sculptors at one and the same time. In the lower illustration we see a skin being fitted over a model, while above is the model of an elk being mounted. Both photographs are from the American Museum of Natural History in New York.

Of late years some of the principal American museums (like the one in New York, the American Museum of Natural History), which are as a rule much more lavishly provided with funds, by private benefaction and otherwise, than are European museums, have been able to carry installation of large groups to a very high pitch of perfection. Many of these groups are the direct work of members of expeditions who have gone out from the museums, or in connexion with the museums, on purpose to get the necessary specimens and the particulars about them. A recent series of yearly expeditions has gone, at the instance of an Englishman, Mr. Vernay, from America to India, for the express purpose of collecting Indian animals for the New York museum : expeditions which have received the enthusiastic assistance of Indian officials and native princes.

Few people have any conception of what has to be done before a group, on the thorough-

THE PROGRESS OF SEVENTEEN YEARS: GROUPS OF 1914 AND 1897 COMPARED

In the lower photograph we see the last group mounted by the famous Carl E. Akeley of the American Museum of Natural History. The group shows African buffalo and is a masterpiece of work which is the result of experience of living, as well as of museum, animals and real artistic skill. The upper illustration shows the first group ever mounted for the museum in 1897. The animals are lesser kudu, African antelopes that inhabit Somaliland. The hide is a handsome rufous brown and banded with white.

going modern American scale, can be placed on exhibition in a museum. First, the animals must be studied and obtained in their natural haunts. And to do this there must be a well-equipped expedition, led by an able, trained zoologist, who must know not only his animals but the anatomy of his animals. He must have with him other men who can undertake such duties as those of taxidermists, artists, photographers (almost certainly with a "movie" camera), and so on, and a company of native guides, camp-servants, and bearers, with all the needful outfits. It is desired, say, to get a certain kind of animal for a group. A male, a female, and a young one will probably have to be obtained, especially in a case where there is a marked difference between the sexes (lion and lioness, for example) and also between the young and the adult. The

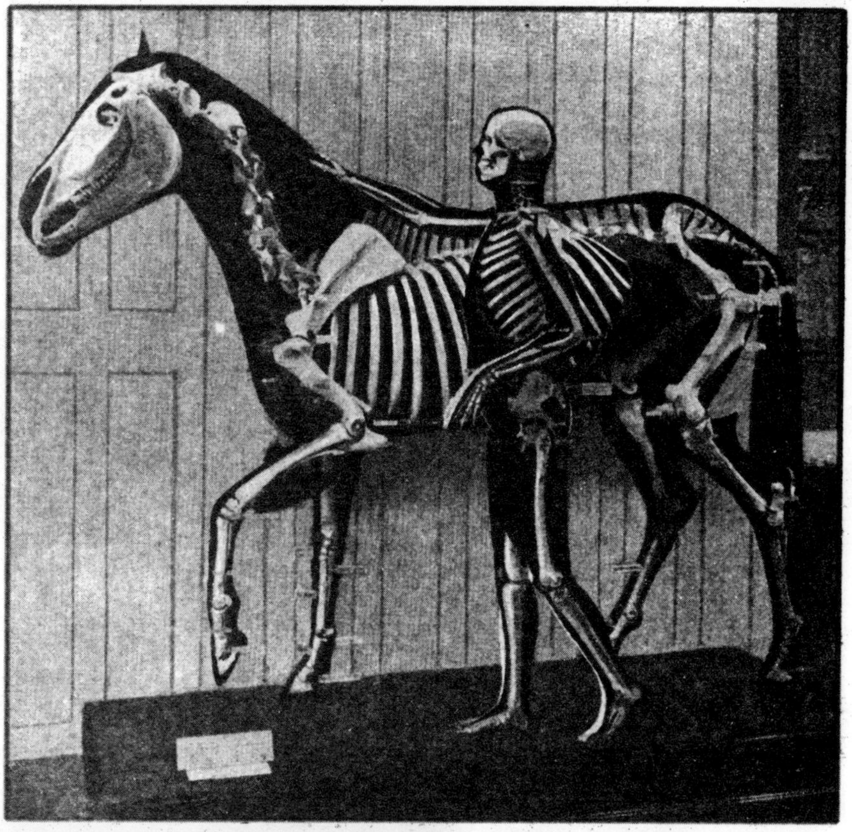

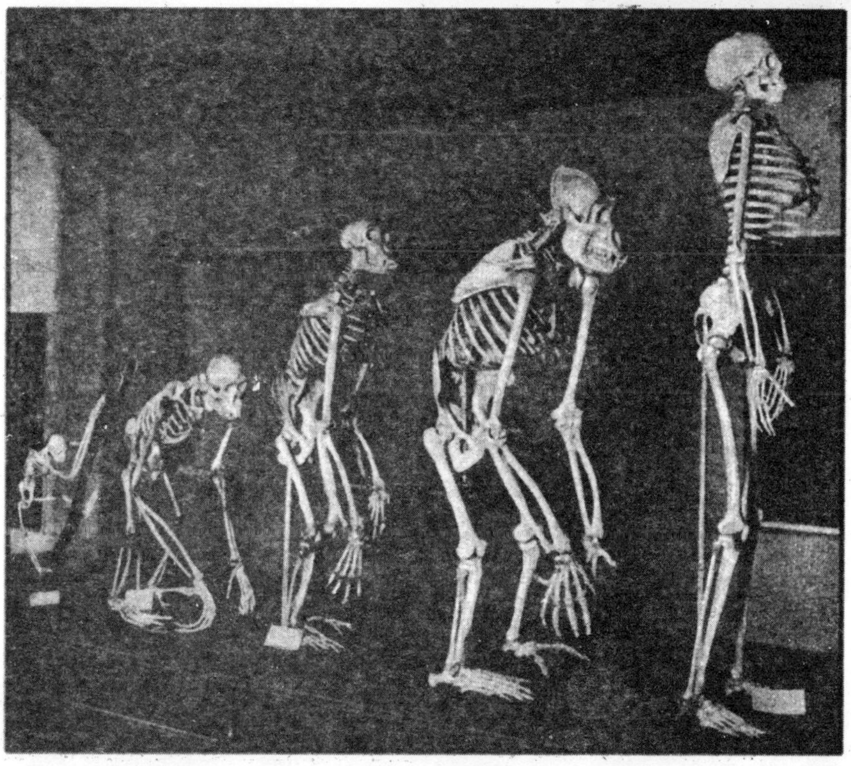

STRIKING LESSONS IN COMPARATIVE ANATOMY

Some convincing lessons in anatomy are revealed in these exhibits, at the American Field Museum of Natural History. Above the skeletons of man and horse are set up, side by side, to show the same basic structural foundation for these two very different bodies. Below is a series of anthropoid apes with a human skeleton, for comparative purposes, on the extreme right

animals must be discovered, stalked, and shot. They must be skinned, and their skins and skeletons preserved, a process which often involves an enormous amount of labour, particularly in the case of bulky creatures obtained in hot countries. The pencil and the photographic plate must make detailed records of the animals, and of their behaviour, and of their surroundings. Many details may even need to be recorded by means of casts. The worries incident to travel in wild country are matters of course, and need not be mentioned. Then, all must be transported home to the museum. It is often supposed by visitors to museums that the skins of all the animals are simply filled with straw or tow and the results arranged in artistic poses. No doubt there was a time when the process was not much more complex than this, but the creator of modern groups is not quite so easily satisfied. Here the

SOME OF THE MUSEUM WORK THAT GOES ON "BEHIND THE SCENES"

Museums contain far more than ever the public sees. A complete set of all the butterflies, for instance, such as a scientist needs, would take up too much room in the public galleries, and only be a weariness tc inspect. Again, only the finished products of months of work are on view. The putting together of exhibits is done behind the scenes. Below are skins being sorted and above some excavated bones of extinct animals being examined at the Museum of Science and Art, Los Angeles.

MUSEUM ANIMALS AS DISPLAYED BY THE EXPERT: TIMBER WOLVES AND WHOOPING CRANES

The function of the museum is to teach and, therefore, not merely to impart knowledge but to stimulate the desire to know. The exhibits have to be prepared by the museum staff not only from the point of view of the scientist but also from that of the public. The labelling and explanation of each exhibit, too, must be such that there is a desire to see the rest of what the museum has to offer. Here are two groups from the American Museum of Natural History showing timber wolves (bottom) and the almost extinct whooping crane (top).

American Museum of Natural History

IGUANA AND GILA MONSTER IN A LIFE-LIKE SETTING

Special expeditions are sent to all parts of the world to enrich the museum collections. The lower photograph shows an iguana as it was found in the Galapagos Islands. The surroundings and lighting effects are reproduced from exact local data. Above is a gila monster, a poisonous lizard found in Mexico and Texas.

particulars recorded in the field are employed with effect. The ways of setting up naturally vary somewhat with the different workers, but there is generally an exact model of each animal to be made in clay or other material, and the skin to be fitted upon it, or upon an ingeniously devised lightweight " manikin " got by moulding from the model. The man who can do such things must be a combination of naturalist, explorer, draughtsman, artist, and taxidermist! This is not impossible, for we have seen it in men like the late Mr. Carl E. Akeley, of American Museum fame. The re-creating of the surroundings (trees, leaves, grass, rocks, and what-not), every piece true to nature, is also a lengthy bit of work. How amazingly complex a modern animal group may be is shown by one of the groups in the Field Museum at Chicago, in which, it is related, no less than seventeen thousand artificial leaves were used.

Thus a townsman, who may never even have left his city, might now go into his museum and there see not merely stuffed skins, but the wild animals themselves in their native haunts. He may see, for example, a family of orang-utans (the great reddish brown, shaggy-haired man-like

apes) in the woods, or the African elephant in its jungle. It is difficult to believe that most of the progress in this sort of work in the American museums is the product of little more than a quarter of a century's experimentation. The interesting story has been well told by the late Dr. F. A. Lucas, of the New York Museum, a copy of whose "The Story of Animal Groups" the writer of the present article values as being a gift from Dr. Lucas himself.

It will be opportune at this point to speak of an exhibit, to be seen in the museum at South Kensington, which no doubt many of our readers would like to visit. This is a group of three African elephants—male, female and young—which have been installed by Mr. J. G. Dollman. The scene represents a part of the Knysna Forest, from which the vegetation for the group was obtained. Ingenious lighting was designed by Dr. G. F. H. Smith, and so arranged that on the pressing of a button the whole scene passes slowly from soft moonlight to full sunlight.

The mention of this lighting arrangement reminds us to point out that much of the success in revealing the beauty of American museum groups is being obtained by the use of electric

MARINE IGUANA AND DESERT TORTOISE AS AT HOME

Out of the wonderful group in the American Museum of Natural History which shows marine iguanas of Galapagos we reproduce a very vivid corner (bottom) where an iguana is sunning itself and a scarlet crab is just emerging from a crevice to pull the ticks from the iguana's skin. Above is a desert tortoise amid its native cactus.

THE MINUTE AND THE ENORMOUS HAVE BOTH TO RECEIVE THE SAME SCIENTIFIC CARE

In mounting a butterfly (bottom) or a whale (top) for public exhibition in a natural history museum the same principles obtain. The exhibit must satisfy the scientist and excite the interest of the man in the street. The work involved is often tremendous—whether it is concerned with the little intricacies of the butterfly or the enormous bulk of the whale. Notice the table of apparatus being used in the lower illustration. Above we have the framework on which a life-size replica of the earth's largest mammal will be built up.

MAKING A WAX CAST OF AN ANIMAL FROM AN EXACT MODEL

One of the ways of making an animal for a museum exhibit is to construct an exact model in clay or some other material and then to take a cast from the model. In this way a much lighter figure is obtained. A real skin is fitted over the cast and the exhibit is ready for setting up amid the details of its natural environment. Here we see (bottom) a wax cast of an animal in a mould and (top) the cast and the plaster mould almost separated.

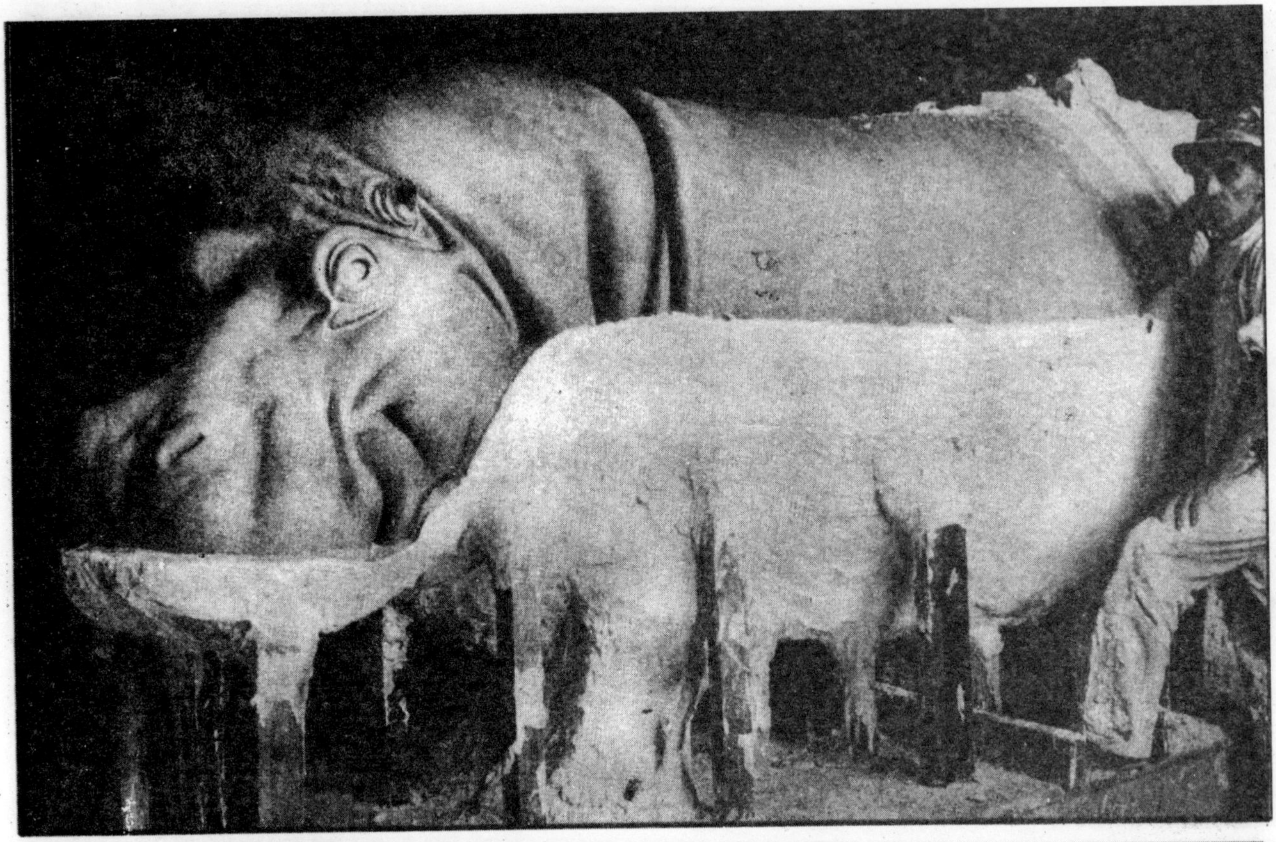

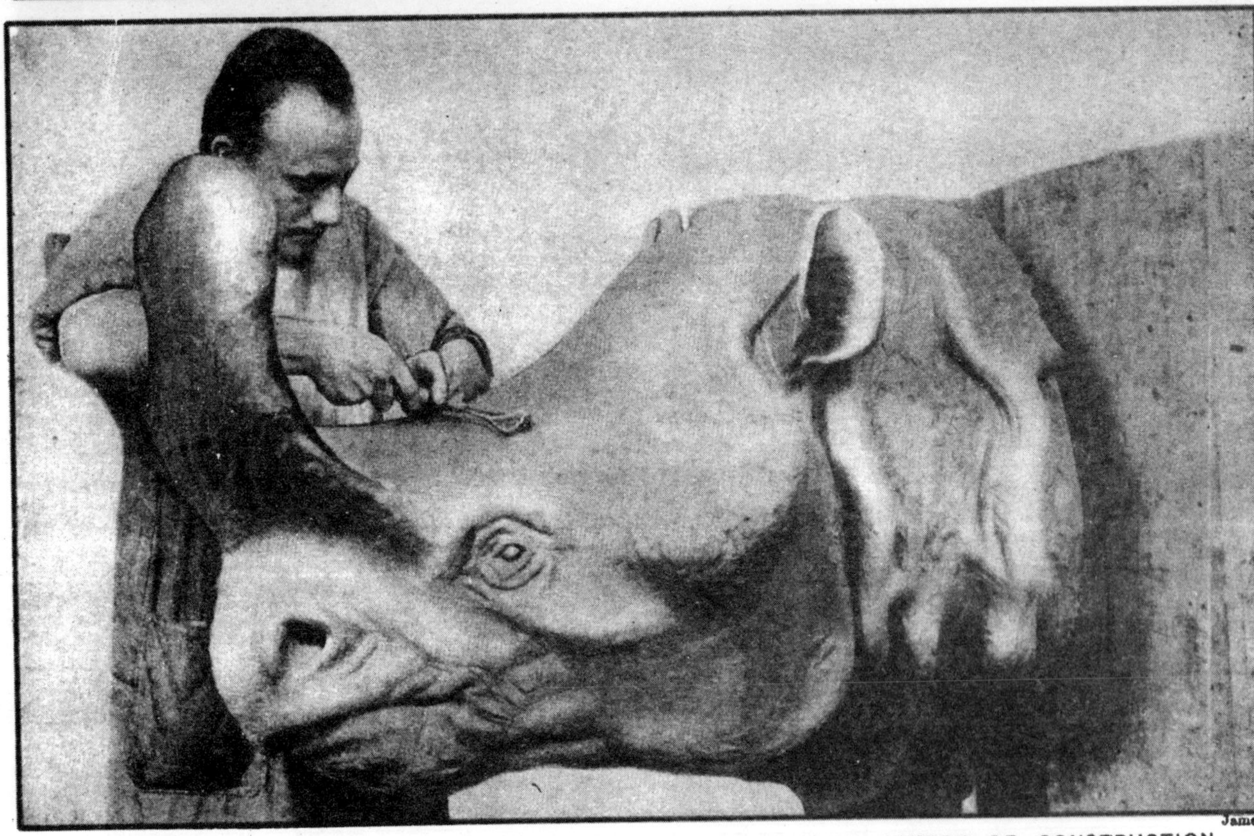

James

PREHISTORIC RHINOCEROS AND A LATTER-DAY HIPPOPOTAMUS IN COURSE OF CONSTRUCTION

Modelling a rhinoceros that lived before man appeared on the earth is only one of the many wonders achieved by the modern museum. In the lower photograph an expert is engaged on the task. Above we have the clay model of a hippopotamus, constructed in the museum, from the most carefully worked out details. From this clay model a plaster mould is made and from the mould a cast is taken which will be clothed in the actual skin of the animal originally shot and measured for the exhibit.

FITTING ON SKINS TO A FIGHTING GROUP AND MODELLING A LIZARD

When the model has been made for the mould the skin has to be fitted over it and any alterations necessary in the figure made. When there is more than one figure—as is the case in the lower photograph—and the figures are touching, this is a matter of some complication, as may be imagined. The representation here is of two wild boars fighting and the attitudes of the madly struggling beasts are fine examples of captured energy. Above we see a lizard being modelled.

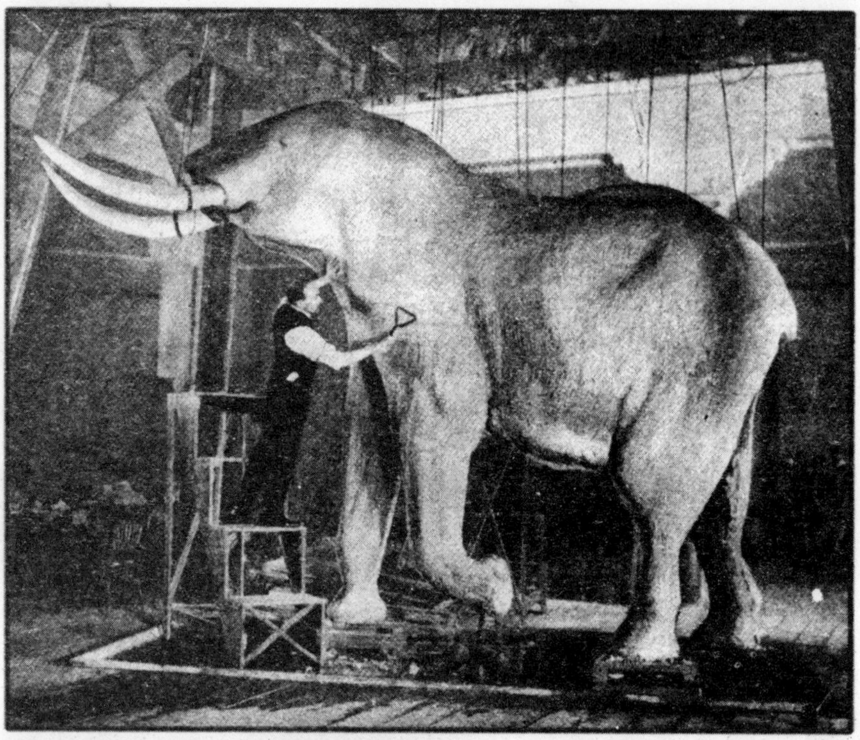

lighting cunningly managed. Things impossible to older forms of illumination are capable of achievement with the newer appliances.

We have so far been discussing exhibits composed of the larger animals (those technically known as mammals) and the birds. But, of course, there are other sorts of creatures which may be made the subjects of groups. Everyone acquainted with museums knows how difficult it is to preserve and adequately display specimens of the smaller and softer creatures, such as the sea-snail, the octopus, the sea-anemone, and the jellyfish. Even with the best methods of preservation such animals are almost certain to lose their shapes and their colours. To represent them by means of models is an obvious way, though in practice it is an extremely difficult way, and also a very expensive way. Still, the difficulties have in some instances been overcome; and the question of expense has seemingly been no deterrent to some of the American museums with large staffs and large incomes.

American Museum of Natural History

FINISHED ELEPHANT GROUP AND AN ELEPHANT IN THE MAKING

The camera, the sketch-book and, sometimes, months of travel are necessary before such a group as we see completed in the lower photograph can be set up. The man who arranges the group must know his animals from personal experience. It may take months or even years to make a single group. Above is an elephant model almost ready for its skin.

In the New York museum to which we have several times already referred there is a most interesting group of marine animals, modelled in glass and wax. One sees masses of mussels, with their blue-black shells; sea-anemones, with their beautiful long tentacles, resembling underwater flowers; sponges; sea-squirts, each one with its two water-carrying tubes; some small fishes; a glorious jellyfish, resembling, one might fancy, a fairy parasol as it pulsates through the water; and other creatures. All the animals thus modelled are represented as attached to, or close upon, the wooden piles of a wharf. The whole exhibit is now well known under the name of "The Wharf-Pile Group."

We must mention the latest production of this same museum. First, it should be explained that there are certain aquatic animals, called rotifers, some of which may be one-eighth of an inch long and some of which may be one five-hundredth. They are so small that they are not to be seen properly except with the aid of a microscope. The word rotifer means wheel-bearer, and the name has been given because typical rotifers have each one or two circlets of minute hair like organs—called cilia—on the front part of the body, and these cilia being in constant motion the circlets strongly suggest revolving wheels. The cilia lie around the mouth, into which they sweep, during their motions, minute food-particles. Some rotifers are enclosed in a hard, transparent case, open at both ends. By means of a bifid process at its hind end a rotifer can attach itself to a water-plant or some such object.

It is plainly impossible to exhibit such tiny animals, at all events in an adequate way, in a museum. It can be attempted, however, by means of models, and this has been excellently done in the New York museum. The rotifer group, to quote the official description, "enlarges a cubic half-inch of their watery habitat to one hundred diameters, or, cubically, one million times, so that it occupies a space measuring fifty inches, or more than four feet across. The front of the exhibit is constructed to represent a huge magnifying glass, through which the visitor peers into a jungle of water plants peopled by hundreds of tiny animal forms." There may be seen the comb-armed rotifer, a voracious trapper of other animals; tube-building rotifers; a rotifer which pursues and springs upon its prey like a tiger; vegetable-eating rotifers; swimming rotifers; creeping rotifers; and others. The installation of this remarkable group, like the wharf-pile group, has been done by Dr. Miner, curator of lower invertebrates, with a staff of expert assistants.

American Museum

A WONDERFUL MUSEUM EXHIBIT: THE HALL OF BIRDS

Groups of birds in the old-fashioned glass cases are apt to look a little stuffy and unnatural, however beautifully presented are the tints of their plumage. But, as seen here, the birds are mounted as though in flight and, against a cleverly painted background, seem indeed to be flying over the heads of the visitors. Thus does the new way in museum work supersede the old.

Exactly how long these men took to make their rotifer group we do not know, but it may be pointed out (what is perhaps new to many people) that the beginnings of work of this sort cannot be determined. We all know the story about the artist Whistler, who, when asked, during a famous trial, whether he was justified in charging a "long" price for a picture which was not long in the making, replied that he valued the picture as the result of a life-time of study. We might, if we were asked how long the rotifer group took to build, reply that we could say that it was one of the fruits of a life-time of study on the part of Dr. Miner and his colleagues—and of the men who, before them, had studied rotifers and thus paved the way.

Of course, in looking at such models there is the drawback that one is thinking always that they are but models after all, not the real things. There is a drawback, too, to the larger groups of mammals and birds, for one is in danger of thinking too much about the surroundings of the animals, and of the skill displayed in their installation, rather than of what the creatures themselves have to tell us. Still, there never are great advantages to be had without some sort of attendant disadvantages.

An important biographic purpose is fulfilled by the great museums in their elaborate model exhibits. As Dr. Henry Fairfield Osborn, President of the American Museum of Natural History, declares, their intent is the preservation and lifelike presentation of the manifold forms of both animal and plant life threatened with reduction or actual extinction. The Eastman-Akeley expedition to East Africa in 1926-1927 reported that "where once the great game herds ranged in tens of thousands, to-day tragically enough, they have practically vanished." Some are now represented in the great African Hall of the American Museum.

ENTERPRISE AND SKILL COMBINED TO MAKE AN IMPRESSIVE DISPLAY

The lower photograph shows one of the four deer groups in a museum representing the animals as they naturally appear in Spring, Summer, Autumn and Winter with the appropriate surroundings. The group shown here is the Autumn one. Above is a beaver group. The logs and branches used in the setting come from an actual beaver dam in Colorado. The background is artfully painted and joined to actual objects so cleverly that a real effect of natural distance is obtained. Subtle lighting, too, helps the illusion in such groups.

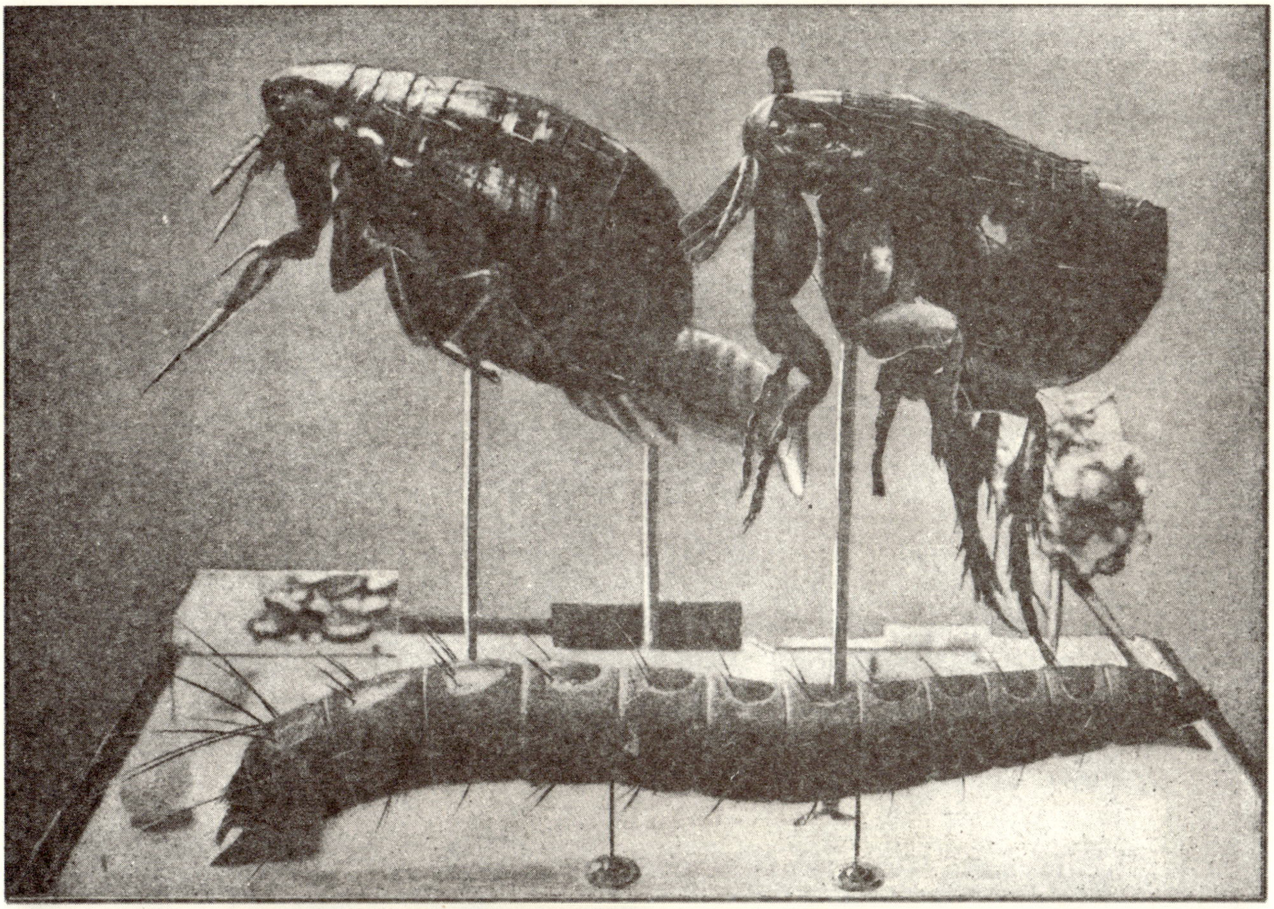

BLUE SHARK GROUP AND MODELS OF TROPICAL RAT FLEAS

Not only have the modern experts discovered how to set up land groups of all sorts and birds in flight, but even the depths of the sea are represented truthfully with their denizens. Below we see the blue shark group in the American Museum of Natural History at New York, showing some of the dread scavengers of the sea. Above are models, many times life-size, of tropical rat fleas with their larvae. They are displayed in the Natural History Museum at South Kensington, London.

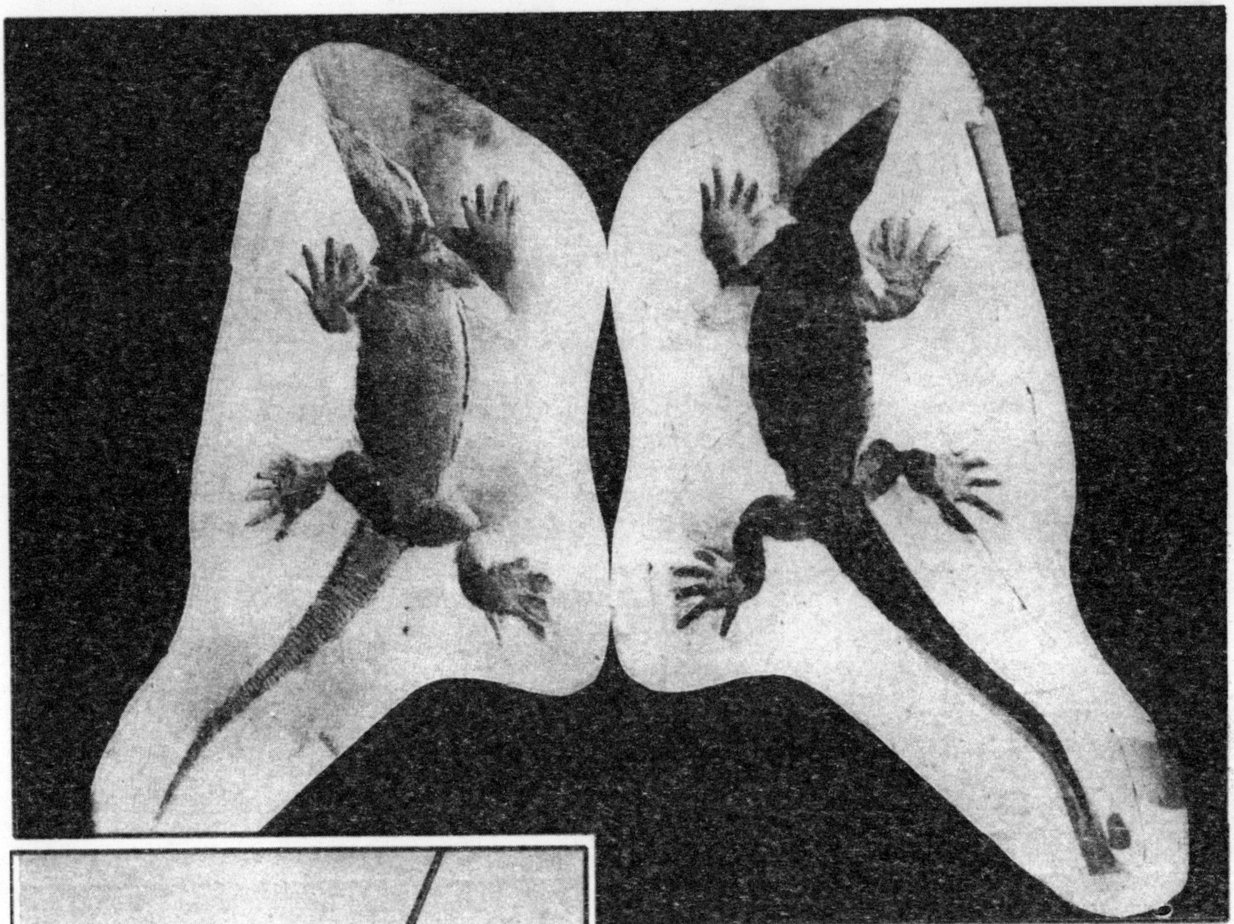

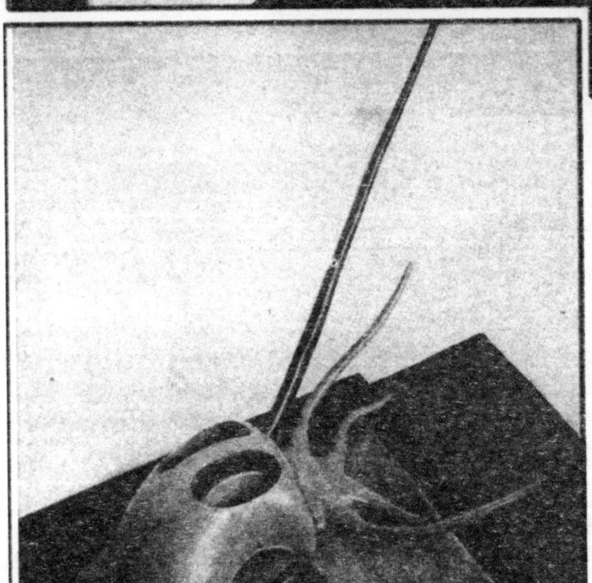

MARVELS OF BREATHING AND A LIZARD MOULD
This model shows the three-fold breathing mechanism of a gastropod that can take oxygen either by means of its lung, while on land, or by a syphon protruding from the water or by gills from the depths Above are the two halves of a mould made from a dead lizard

Much more could have been said about the building up of museum groups had space allowed; and very much more might have been said about other sorts of museum wonders. We might have spoken for example of strange fossils; or of the method of restoration of great extinct monsters; or of the wonders of animal skeletons; or of the weapons and armour of animals; or museum specimens which illustrate evolution. But let us return to where we began.

By this time we shall all probably be in a position to understand the indignation of those in charge of museums if their institutions should be defined as places where curiosities are kept. Museums are something other than that. A museum is a place for the delight and instruction of our people (of all ages, not of children only, despite a melancholy superstition to the contrary), and each of its exhibits will " tell a story " to anyone who cares to know.

Oliver Wendell Holmes, pleasantest and wisest of breakfast-table companions, explained long ago how we were to see the British Museum, referring to the institution at Bloomsbury. We were, it seems, to take lodgings next door, and to pass all our days in the museum until the age of three score and ten. Few of us, it may be presumed, will try to carry out this counsel of perfection. But we can go often to the nearest museum, and let it help to refresh us with the sight of beautiful and wonderful things.

Chapter CXL

Cradles of Animal Life

By Sir William Beach Thomas

Author of "The English Year"

THE ancients had a pretty belief that fine, still weather was sent for a short period in the spring in order to give a fair voyage to a sort of fairy cradle. The kingfisher, which Tennyson calls "the sea-blue bird of March," was supposed to build a floating nest that itself was rooted in "the cradle of the deep." So this period of fine weather has ever since been called halcyon, after the Greek name of the bird.

This particular tale has no more foundation in fact than the tale of the phoenix, the fire bird that arises from its cradle of flame and ashes; but a host of animals are cradled in a host of strange fashions, on and under water or land. If fact is not actually stranger than fiction, it is much more various and quaint.

Kingfishers do not build floating cradles, but the surface of the sea is the most populous of all cradles. Millions of fishes' eggs float there almost invisibly. Millions of odd creatures are born there, and the comparatively few who survive become fish. On the day of birth a great number of fish as of reptiles and insects bear very little likeness to the animal into which they will finally change. A rather surprising general rule may be laid down on this subject, though there are exceptions. It is that if the egg holds sufficient food in it, the young are born after the likeness of their parents. If the egg contains little food they do not develop into their final form till they have foraged for themselves, like the tadpole or the caterpillar. And when the young are of a different shape, the parents as a rule pay no attention to them. Indeed most insects, though they prepare the cradles with great care, never see their young. The ants and bees, which take such good care of the grubs that will be ants and bees, are quite exceptional. The fish vary in a most remarkable manner in the attention that they pay to the nursery. One of the model parents is the most familiar of all fish, the stickleback. Not only does the male make a nest, not so very different from a bird's nest, and guide the mother fish into it, but he spends the last days of his life in defending the young, who swim round about their cradle, from any fish-like enemy that dare to approach.

Some fish, and frogs, go further. They use their own mouth as the home of eggs or young, sometimes of both. The strangest example is a fish found in Brazil (*Geophagus scymnophilus*). The family when young keep near to the parent, who darts yet closer when any danger threatens, and if it is imminent the whole brood of thirty or so take refuge in its mouth. Some frogs and fish and bats, too, have pouches, like the kangaroo. There is a sort of sea louse which carries the young on its antennae—a rocking cradle indeed—and one of the shrimps is named after the opossum because it carries its young in a "brood-pouch" very much after the opossum's pattern.

J. J. Ward

FLY-CATCHER'S CRADLE OF MOSS AND FEATHERS

Cradled softly in a little structure of twigs, grass and moss lined with feathers and wool, the young spotted fly-catchers spend their first days before they acquire the art of flying in warm comfort. This nest has been built snugly in a hollow tree.

What may be called travelling cradles of this sort are indeed not uncommon in many classes of living creature. One sea urchin carries the young on its back, and most of us have seen big mother spiders carrying about, generally on the underside of the body, a bag made of the very finest silk. In the bag are scores of baby spiders, who can live, it is thought, for many months without food. M. Fabre believed, though he was probably too imaginative, that they could feed

Arthur Brook.

MALLARD AND EIDER DUCK THAT BOTH LINE THEIR NESTS WITH SOME OF THEIR OWN SOFT DOWN.

Usually near the water and always well concealed, the nest of the mallard, commonest of the British wild ducks, is almost invariably built on the ground, though occasionally up a tree. This cradle for the young is placed among sedge or reeds or in some thick undergrowth, the materials of the nest being rushes and grass, with an ample lining of warm, soft down from the bird's breast. From eight to twelve ducklings find room in this pleasant cradle and, unlike most fledgelings, leave and return to it many times before they are ready to go out into the world. The eider duck (right) breeds on the Northumberland coast and thence northward to the Orkneys and Shetlands. This bird also lines its nest, of grass and seaweed, with down on mere sunshine for as long as eight months. After being carried about like this at their mother's will, they one day break out and are driven by their instinct to climb the nearest upright grass blade or bush or post, or what not; and from there they leap into the air on a silken streamer that they have made themselves. So many, on occasions, are the young using their air-planes that whole fields gleam and shimmer in the October sunshine with the gossamer that has helped to spread the young spiders broadcast.

It is a general rule that the more numerous the family the more deadly are the perils run by the young. There are fish that lay millions of eggs, some to float on the surface, some secured to the floor of the sea or river. Others lay a few hundred, others no more than a score or two. On a much smaller scale such differences are seen between various sorts of reptile and bird; but the biggest broods do not always produce the biggest adult population.

The past masters in cradle making are the birds, and though the structure is for the most part firm, and well wrought and well designed, some of the cradles (or the crannies substituted for them) often look so dangerous that you would think neither egg nor young at all likely to escape destruction. Life looks dangerous enough for young buzzards or young ravens. The nests are built, as a rule, on some cliff ledge—though both often build on high trees—and any undue restlessness in the young must mean a fatal fall. Some of the buzzards who build in trees make a sort of flat or platform round the edge, and you may see the young birds struggle on to this, but their instinct, as a rule, is a complete safeguard. So far they go and no further, and though the wind rock tree and nest till the birds might be dizzy, even then a fall is rare.

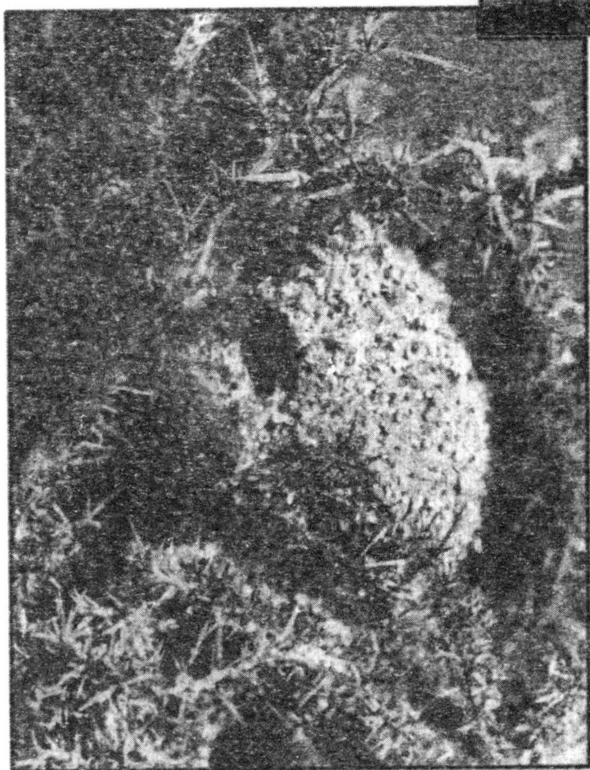

J. J. Ward

CRADLES OF TIT AND WILLOW WREN

This long-tailed tit's nest is made of hundreds of feathers, pieces of moss and cobwebs so woven together that they form a snug pocket for the eggs and young to rest in. Above is the nest of a willow-wren made of leaves and dry grass

The young of these great birds, as also of the eagles and peregrine falcons which build in similar places, seem to have a stronger instinct of safety than the birds that build in colonies. Young rooks not infrequently fall headlong and many a pet has been made by this accident, for though the instinct may be a little imperfect the bird is one of the cleverest of all and takes to domestic life very kindly. Immensely solid and well built though the nests are they are not so safe in the tree-tops as the yet bigger nests of raven and buzzard. In all these high and mighty cradles the eggs at any rate are tolerably safe, for the cups are deep and well lined. They are safe from

Oliver Pike

BLACK-THROATED DIVER'S NEST CLOSE TO THE WATER'S EDGE

An untidy-looking heap of water-weeds and moss forms the nest of the black-throated diver, the rarest of the three divers that visit Britain. The bird breeds in the Outer Hebrides though not in large numbers, and is usually found nesting on some unfrequented island in a fresh-water loch or else along the loch shore—but always very near the water's edge.

most enemies and from weather, though it happens now and again that a squirrel will climb into a rookery and destroy both eggs and young. Yet this is rare, and of the babies born in such airy nurseries a very large proportion are successfully reared. The percentage of successes is probably as high as in any other bird or animal.

Among the cliff-nesting birds the greatest danger, to all appearance, is faced by some of the gulls and the guillemots. The egg is often laid without any manufactured hollow or even platform on a narrow ledge jutting out from a steep cliff. Those courageous bird-nesters who allow themselves to be suspended by a rope over the edge of the cliffs (say at Bempton, in Yorkshire, which is one of the most populous nurseries on the English coast) find eggs laying within a few inches of the edge. The eggs are curious in many ways—some are cream-coloured, some green, some blue. Some have curious scratchings all over the surface, some have thick black patches concentrated at the thicker end; but if one may say so, the most curious part of the egg is the exaggeration of its oval shape. The thin end is very much pointed and the thick end very round. When a gust of wind strikes it, the egg is in little danger of leaving the little circle of space where it is laid. It spins round, and that is all. The guillemots have survived only because their eggs have this shape, and doubtless nature has selected for survival those birds whose mothers laid the most pointed eggs.

Few better examples of Darwin's theories can be quoted. It is really astounding that birds so cradled and so constructed can survive at all. The eggs and young occupy this precarious perch, open to the worst of weather and to any winged enemies. Such enemies are common. When you look down, say, from the towering cliffs of Ramsay Island in South Wales, you may see scores of eggs or young in the crowded hatcheries of the guillemots; and it is tolerably certain that you will also see some greedy gull devouring an egg. Probably you will find an egg or two on the beach, where it has been dropped by one of the thieves. And the bird does not lay a dozen or so eggs like a duck, or nearly a score like a partridge; nor even five like a thrush or robin or blackbird, but as a rule just one. However, when one is destroyed the bird lays another almost at once and its persistence wins, though the bird has little power of self-defence and is a poor flier.

It is a curious contrast in the choice of breeding places that while some gulls, such as herring-gulls (white headed, grey backed, with dainty black tips to the wings) like to nest on cliffs, others such as the black headed, the species which especially delights in London and the Thames Embankment, prefer to nest rather like moorhen in grassy marshes often far inland. The more lofty cradle is probably the safer. Few animals suffer heavier losses than young moorhen and duck. The ducks' nests, though they vary much in structure and in locality, are often delightfully warm and snug, and well-hidden; and as soon as they break from the green-grey eggs the young can swim; but where the waters are haunted by rats or pike the toll taken of the youngsters, while yet they are of an age when other young birds would be lying naked and

Arthur Brook

ROUGH-LOOKING NURSERY BUILT BY THE THICKET-LOVING JAY

Though the nest of the jay looks very rough from the outside, the interior is cleverly contrived into the shape of a cup and lined with hair and pieces of roots. The outside materials are sticks and twigs, woven and knit together with grasses. The jay is a lover of thick copses and spinneys and builds on the summits of thick bushes or else at the top of saplings. In this safe hiding place among the branches some half a dozen green-blue eggs are laid, mottled with brown.

helpless in their cradles, is pitiful. But the families are very large; the mother duck and moorhen are wonderful parents, and both species multiply where man permits their multiplication. The moorhen takes a special precaution very nearly peculiar to herself. She has two or even three or more cradles. Besides the nest where the ten or dozen are hatched, another nest is often built where the young are brooded. Sometimes the young themselves when grown a little more capable, will help in constructing this additional home. As a rule it is deeper, has more material in it, and is higher out of the water than the first cradle. But there are curious exceptions. The writer has found many a nest awash and has seen another—though this is certainly exceptional—eighty yards from any water and well off the ground.

Birds' cradles are of a variety beyond all description. It would take long even to sum up the different classes. Some are models of the neatest and daintiest of structures, such as our English chaffinch or long-tailed tit, constructed of lichen and moss and bits of spider silk. Like them are the minute cradles of the humming birds of South America; and superior to them in ingenuity of workmanship the pendulous tit of the South of Europe. At the other extreme are the guillemots on the cliffs or the green plover on the English tilths, which is content with a mere scoop and a blade or two, trusting for protection to the "protective coloration" of both eggs and young birds. The terns that nest in great colonies on spots of sand—such as at Blakeney in Norfolk—cradle their young as simply and trust to the same device of protective coloration.

Some utterly freakish cradles are made. The most surprising, perhaps, is the nest of an Australian turkey, which is a hot-bed as well as a nest, and designed to hatch the eggs by its own spontaneous warmth. It is curious that some English people believe locally that the greater crested grebe follows the same device. Like the partridge and the dabchick it covers up its eggs when it leaves the nest and sometimes uses a green water-lily leaf. The eggs certainly keep wonderfully warm beneath it, but the mother bird does not trust to the decaying leaf to hatch her egg. The writer recently saw almost side by side a pretty contrast in cradle-making. A crested grebe's nest (with three eggs carefully covered up by a reed) lay like a circular raft on the water. Close by a sedge-warbler had hung up her neat nest on three reed stems. The one nest was nearly flat, the other so deep in the cup and narrow you could scarcely have thought the bird would have sat there. The young would certainly be in no danger of falling over the edge. The nest was quite as deep as a long-tailed tit's, and this tiny bird is often so contracted for room

J. J. Ward

YOUNG THRUSHES AND SEA-BIRD'S CRADLE

Below we have a nest of young thrushes, while above is a wonderful cradle of life. This is Cape Kidnappers, at the south end of Hawkes Bay, in the North Island, New Zealand. Tens of thousands of sea-birds nest here annually.

that the tip of the tail protrudes as the mother broods her many little eggs.

We find some curious likenesses among creatures that have small likeness to one another, between mammals and marsupials and birds and fish and insects. That queer Australian animal the platypus broods its egg in a nest very much like a bird's in appearance as in reality. The mother earwig has often been compared with a hen brooding her eggs. In several continents live animals of the nature of the opossum also provide the oddest sort of cradle. For example, that pretty, tame, attractive animal the koala, which the Australians call a tree bear, makes a cradle of its own long soft hair. The youngster clings on to this as naturally and surely as a young monkey clings with tail and hand to a bough in the swinging cradle of the trees. An American opossum makes of its own tail a sort of rail over the cradle of its own back, and the young wind their own tails round it. Could there be a quainter, more peripatetic cradle than this? And it is very effective, like all the cradles.

Other opossums have a pouch very much like a kangaroo's or a wallaby's; and this sort of cradle may be said to be the most popular; that is, it is used for a longer time than other cradles. The young are cradled in it while they are still undeveloped, blind and naked. They jump forth from it to be practised in running and jumping about the wide Australian plains with their parents; but till they are a good size—as big, say, as a muntjac or barking deer—they jump back into the cradle when danger threatens and are swung about with a vigour that would upset most other cradles and damage the bodies of most other babies. This cradle that is the peculiar mark of the marsupials, which especially flourish in Australia, is at first like a mother's womb. Then it is a sort of nest and lastly a cave of retreat.

It is a little surprising how few birds imitate the kangaroo and return to the nursery when once they have left it. The first flight generally means complete desertion of the nest. The nests, where thrushes and blackbirds were cradled, later become the storehouses of mice and sometimes the sleeping-place of stoats—to quote one particular experience. Kestrels use the old nests of rooks or crows. But there are exceptions. A quantity of Jenny wrens will sometimes resort to an old nest if the winter is severe; and with the tribe of swallows who find roosting places a difficulty, the young will return every night to the nest almost till the time of the long migration is imminent. For the first few days they practise flight and are fed in the nest. Then they are fed on the wing and lastly learn to feed themselves.

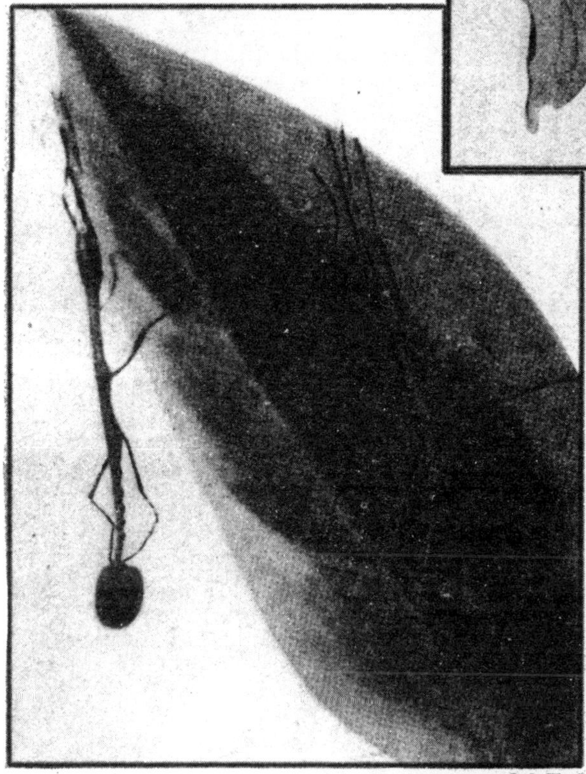

J. J. Ward

WHERE INSECTS BEGIN THEIR LIFE

Insects have some strange-looking cradles. The Indian stick insect emerges from an egg-shell (bottom) and the holly blue butterfly (top left) has the same kind of cradle. But the cuckoo-spit spends its early hours in a mass of froth (top right).

How very different are the first days of life among animals that may closely resemble one another in most respects! The young moorhen can swim on the day it is born, the young raven does not fly for six weeks after birth. The young rabbit is half developed and helpless, the young hare lively and alert; and in these animals the birthplace exactly suits the development of the young. The mother rabbit first makes a warm and snug nest, often largely made of her own fur (as some duck use their own feathers). It is placed in a specially dry but short hole with only one opening, generally at some distance from the bigger burrows where the parents have chiefly lived. When she goes foraging the doe rabbit closes this up so carefully and cunningly that it deceives the sharpest eye. Tame rabbits in quite small enclosures have made such holes and tended their young till they could look after themselves and yet entirely escaped the notice of their keepers.

Young hares, on the other hand, are born in the open; and are much more advanced at birth. They resemble in this almost all the hoofed animals, except the deer. The mother has a habit, very rare in other races, of separating the young and keeping them in different concealments. She does not like to have all her eggs in one basket! In the degree of development at birth the rabbit resembles the dog and the hare the cat. Certain differences appear among bats; but in most sorts the young are born blind, and are often carried in a pouch by the mother, but even in this apparently helpless state they show a certain activity and will leave the pouch soon after birth and cling to the mother's back, or, a little later, cling to any convenient support. Bats fly about with their young, and have a likeness to the Australian marsupials in this respect; but squirrels, even so-called flying squirrels, prefer to build nests like birds. On the other hand, certain flying lemurs carry their helpless and single young one, like some of the bats, not in a pouch but attached to their body.

C. Reid

MOUNTAIN GOATS THAT FOLLOW THE MOVEMENT OF THE SNOWLINE ON THE HIGH PEAKS

As one climbs higher and higher up the mountain side, the tree-line or zone where the forest gives way to open land, and where only stunted bushes and heath grow, is reached. Above this belt, where vegetation gradually fails, the snowline begins. This line varies its position with the seasons. In some cases it is at quite different levels on the different sides of the peak. The mountain goats, living between the forest-line and the snowline, advance and retreat as their territory alters in extent with the seasonal changes.

Chapter CXLI

Animal Life at High Altitudes

By R. I. Pocock, F.R.S.

Of the Zoological Department, British Museum

One of the most important factors in the struggle for existence is competition for territory. So keen has this been that every habitable acre of the world is occupied by living things, and since warmth, with requisite moisture, supplies conditions most conducive to the development of animals and plants, and cold, whether wet or dry, is to a corresponding degree unfavourable, we find the greatest luxuriance of species and the largest and most numerous individuals inhabiting the tropical forests, and a steady decline in those particulars as we pass northwards or southwards from the Equator, until in the neighbourhood of the Poles life to all intents and purposes ceases to exist.

A phenomenon, precisely comparable but on a smaller scale, is encountered during the ascent of high mountains. There is a gradual decrease in the richness of the fauna and flora as we proceed up the slopes from the forests or jungles at the base to the snow-capped summit, a barren waste practically devoid of life.

The so-called " snow-line " above which manifestations of life are at most scanty is not capable of precise demarcation. On a mountain under the tropics, where the seasonal changes are comparatively negligible, the snow-line is tolerably steady throughout the year and is at a great height, although it may vary on opposite sides of the peak. To the north or south of the tropical zone the snow-line sets in at lower and lower levels, according to the latitude of the range; but it varies to a great extent both locally and seasonally on the same range.

In the Alps, for example, the snow-line may be set in some places at about 8,000 ft.; in others at 9,000 or 10,000 ft. In the Himalayas its average altitude is much higher—from about 15,000 to 19,000 ft. or 20,000 ft. The " tree-line " above which the vegetation is represented by shrubs passing upwards into heaths, lichens and mosses is similarly variable. In the Himalayas it is at about 11,000 or 12,000 ft.; higher, that is to say, than the snow-line of the Alps. Since animals are dependent upon plants, the altitudinal extension of the fauna of mountains is as variable as that of the flora, both being dependent on the latitude of the range. Herbivorous species, for instance, which flourish at 10,000 ft. on a mountain within the tropics would die of starvation in a week at that altitude in the Alps.

The fauna of the Himalayas, the loftiest range in the world, with a height up to 29,000 ft., may be taken as an illustration of animal life at high altitudes. To the south these mountains slope gradually down to the low-lying plains of India, but to the north they pass into the table-land of Tibet, which itself stands at an altitude of from 10,000 to 17,000 ft. above sea-level. It is from this comparatively waste and barren area that the animals adapted to the heights of the Himalayas have been mainly derived.

The largest animal is the yak, a species of wild cattle domesticated by the Tibetans, which may range in summer as high as 20,000 ft. and as low as 10,000 ft. in winter. The bharal, a peculiar kind of goat, and the Himalayan ibex, have a similar habitat. The argali, the largest wild sheep, is found only at slightly lower levels, while the Tibetan gazelle and the Tibetan antelope, or chiru, ascend to 18,000 ft. These herbivorous animals feed on the stunted vegetation which also supports several species of rodents, hares, pikas, or mouse-hares, and mice living at from 15,000 to 20,000 ft., voles at 17,000 and marmots at 16,000.

Of carnivorous species which prey upon the hoofed animals, and upon the rodents and birds, the most noteworthy are the snow leopard, or ounce, which ranges from 9,000 ft. in winter up to 20,000 ft. in summer; the lynx, which is always above the tree-line at about 14,000 or 15,000 ft.; wolves and foxes, which are met with at 21,000 ft. on Mount Everest; and weasels, which were seen on the same mountain at over 15,000 ft. Even the brown bear in the Western Himalayas occurs as often as not above the tree-line at about 12,000 ft. The mammals, hitherto mentioned, have unquestionably invaded the heights of the Himalayas from Central Asia lying to the north. As an illustration of the fauna, which has probably invaded them from the plains of India to the south, we may cite the grey monkeys, or langurs, which have been observed leaping amongst the snow-clad pine-trees at 12,000 ft. near Simla.

Characteristic birds of the high Himalayas are the Tibetan snow-cock, found up to the snow-line; snow-finches and Alpine hedge-sparrows, resident at that level; wrens and dippers, seen on Mount Everest at 17,000 ft.; while the camp established at 20,000 ft. by the exploring expedition of this mountain was visited by ravens, two kinds of choughs, kites and hoopoes, and a lammergeier was seen flying overhead at 25,000 ft. This expedition, to which the highest records of animal life are due, discovered a lizard at 17,000 ft., and brought back beetles and grasshoppers from 18,500 ft. But the occurrence of insectivorous birds, like the hoopoe, at much higher altitudes attests the existence of insects, spiders and no doubt worms at 20,000 ft., or more.

The Alps, with a mean altitude about half that of the Himalayas, and with the snow-line and tree-line at considerably lower levels owing to their more northern situation, have a fauna similar in many

with a characteristic fauna, over the greater part of Europe, and to the survival of the species referred to in the high Alps with the passing of the cold and the return of a temperate climate to the central plains of Europe.

The fauna of Ruwenzori, an equatorial African mountain rising to a height of 16,815 ft. between Uganda and the Semliki Forest, will serve to illustrate animal life at high altitudes in the Tropics. The vegetation zones, considerably higher on the eastern than on the western flank, consist of tropical forest up to about 8,000 ft., followed by bamboos up to 9,500 ft., tree-heaths and moss to 12,000 ft. and groundsels and lobelias to 14,000 ft., the summit, from 14,500 ft. marking the snow-line, being composed of bare rock and snow supporting lichens and mosses amongst which the only apparently resident animals are a few worms. Butterflies, moths and flies may, however, be seen on the snow up to 16,000 ft., but they are probably blown there by the wind.

respects to that of the Asiatic range, although some of the larger and formerly characteristic forms, like the ibex and northern lynx, are verging on extinction. The chamois, however, which ranges from the Pyrenees to the Caucasus, still holds its own, extending from the forest belt up to the snow-fields and glaciers. Foxes, martens and stoats are found above the forest belt, and a species of marmot, hare, vole and shrew occur close to the snow-line. Familiar birds are the ptarmigan, snowfinch, Alpine swift, the raven, lammergeier and many others seen in the Himalayas, and the Alpine chough occurs in the loftiest mountains. Peculiar to the range is the black salamander, which goes up to 10,000 ft.

An interesting feature connected with the Alpine fauna is the resemblance in many particulars it shows to that of the north of Europe. The ptarmigan, lynx and hare belong to species also found in northern Scandinavia but not in the intervening low-lying country. Similar resemblances are observable between the insects and spiders of these widely separated areas; and a small fresh-water crustacean, which swarms in the icy pools of the highest Alps, lives in similar situations at low levels in the extreme north. These likenesses are believed to be attributable to the former prevalence of sub-Arctic conditions,

.S A.

ALPINE CHAMOIS IN THEIR LONE AND LOFTY HOMES

Chamois range from the Pyrenees right across Europe, via the Alps, to the Caucasus Mountains. Their old rivals, the ibex and the lynx, are now almost extinct. In the Alpine regions, where the above photograph was taken, the ibex, related to the antelopes, occupy the tracts between the snowline and the point where the forests end. Under man's protection they still hold their own.

The fauna of the mountain is essentially African and has been derived mainly from the surrounding lowlands. It is abundant up to the forest line, but scanty above that point; but the situation of the mountain almost on the equator enables large, typically lowland animals to maintain themselves at much higher altitudes than would be possible in temperate latitudes. The chimpanzee, for instance, ascends the slope into the bamboo zone, almost up to 10,000 ft. A little antelope, the duiker, lives in the tree-heath zone at about 11,000 ft. The leopard and a wild cat, probably the serval, go still higher, being found in the groundsel zone at about 13,000 ft., where also occur a species of bat, as well as rats and shrews and a coney or hyrax, the last as high even as 14,300 ft.

The principal birds are hawks, crows and doves up to 14,000 ft., as well as fly-catchers and swifts, attesting abundance of insect food, the swift nesting on the cliffs at that height, as high as the summit of many of the lofty peaks of the Alps. A sun-bird, also insectivorous, is restricted to this groundsel zone; but a warbler and a seed-eater, observed in it, were probably, like the leopard, stragglers from the tree-heath zone below. A species of chameleon, common at lower levels, lives at 10,000 ft., and a frog, also found in the plains, up to 9,000 ft.

A tolerably similar fauna inhabits the Birunga volcanic range to the north-east of Lake Kivu in tropical Africa. Here, too, the leopard and the coney ascend to 13,000 ft.; but the most interesting animal of this range is the shaggy-haired mountain gorilla which has been seen in the bamboo forest as high as 12,000 ft.

FETCHING CAPTIVE CHAMOIS

Here we see mountaineers bringing chamois which they have captured down the mountain. The upper illustration shows a halt for refreshment, with the animal taken out of the stretcher in which it is carried to avoid self injury.

ALTHOUGH animal life extends to high altitudes in the Andes, the fauna of South America contains very few animals of large size comparable to those of the northern hemisphere. No wild goats, sheep or chamois are to be seen on the mountain peaks, the sole representatives of the ruminant hoofed animals being the wild llamas, the vicugna which inhabits the barren tracts almost up to the snow-line in Peru and Bolivia, and the huanaco which replaces it in similar districts at lower levels farther south. In Ecuador, it is true, there is a so-called mountain tapir; but this species is essentially a forest form and does not appear to extend above 8,000 or 9,000 ft. in the Cordilleras.

Of the large carnivora the only species which ascend to a great height is the puma, whose tracks

Neville Kingston

ft. Insects pass above the limit of bird life, beetles, butterflies, grasshoppers, plant bugs and flies live at 16,000 ft. or over; and stick insects above 13,000 ft. Centipedes and woodlice occur at the same altitude, and earthworms close upon 15,000 ft. The snow-line of these mountains, rising to 20,000 ft., is approximately at 15,000 or 16,000 ft., and many of the insects occur amongst stones imbedded in blocks of ice. The same species of insects, too, it may be noted, live at similar heights on peaks sometimes many miles apart, but not in the intervening valleys.

Since the mountain-tops have been invaded by animals derived in the main from those found at lower levels in the particular continents of which the mountains form a part, it cannot be claimed that a uniform high-altitude fauna exists in the world. The animals of the summit of Ruwenzori in tropical Africa,

have been seen in the snow on Mount Cayambe in Ecuador between 14,000 and 15,000 ft. up; and the small bear which in the same country may occur as high as 12,000 ft. or more. Rodents and other smaller mammals may live at much greater elevations. A species of mouse, for instance, has been captured at close upon 18,000 ft. in Peru. In the river valleys leading up to Aconcagua, which is over 23,000 ft. in the Argentine, rodents were not seen above 9,000 ft., and Azara's fox occurred at the same level. The condor, ranging from sea-level up to about 16,000 ft., may be regarded as the characteristic bird of the Andes; but bird-life in general is abundant practically as high up as food is procurable. In the Aconcagua valleys seed-snipes occur at 14,000 ft., milvagos, a kind of hawk, at 13,000 ft., miner birds, doves and dippers at 12,000 ft., swallows, finches and tyrants at 11,000 ft., and humming birds up to 9,000 ft. Toads, lizards and scorpions also live at about 9,000 ft.

But in the Andes of Ecuador, by reason of their situation on the Equator, a similar fauna exists at much greater elevations. Lizards, for example, occur at nearly 12,000 ft., snakes at 8,500 ft., frogs and toads at over 13,000 ft., and scorpions at 12,000

E.N.A.

MOUNTAIN SHEEP AND LYNX

Below are some African mountain sheep from the highlands of Tripoli. Above is a specimen of the northern lynx, now rare in the Alps, though occurring in Scandinavia. Indeed, there is a definite link between the fauna of these two European highlands.

E.N.A.

ANIMALS THAT LIVE AND LABOUR IN THE LOFTY CORDILLERA OF SOUTH AMERICA

The breed of huanaco known as llama inhabits the immense mountain ranges called cordillera in Peru and Bolivia, and is found almost up to the snowline. The llamas actually trained for man's use are indeed his only means of transport in most places, the animals being adapted in temperament and physique to high altitudes and the special conditions of rarified air, besides extremes of cold and difficult going. The upper photograph shows a donkey pack-train on its way over the high paths of a mountain range of Venezuela.

E.N.A

BIG AND LITTLE ANIMALS THAT FIND A LIVELIHOOD AMONG THE HIGH PEAKS OF SNOWY MOUNTAINS

There is no uniform fauna confined to high altitudes throughout the world, but there is definite connection between the faunas of the different ranges, though these last may be hundreds of miles apart. The Alps and the uplands of Scandinavia, for instance, have certain animals in common, and what the Alps lack is due to man's interference, not to Nature. Resemblances can be traced between animals of the Rockies and those of the Andes which are in this respect a zoological as well as a geological continuation of the same system into the Southern Hemisphere. These photographs show (bottom left) Parry's souslik from the Rockies, (bottom right) a Rocky Mountain goat, (top left) a marmot from Switzerland and (top right) a llama from the Andes.

for example, are quite different from those found in the high Andes of South America. But where a continuous mountain chain, or adjoining mountain chains, stretch across a continent from east to west or from north to south, there is generally close similarity between the species inhabiting the different peaks, more particularly in the case of birds and insects which can voluntarily travel or be carried by prevalent winds from one peak or range to another. The same applies to spiders, which, when young, are frequently blown long distances through the air on their gossamer webs. Even mammals, owing to their capacity for adaptation to life at varying levels, pass from mountain to mountain by means of the intervening valleys. Thus, it comes about that the mountains of Europe and temperate Asia, together constituting a continuous mass of land, possess a tolerably similar high-altitude fauna, which is known as "alpine." Throughout the Rocky Mountains also, which extend from north to south, the fauna is very similar at great heights, and resemblances are even traceable between this range and the Andes, which, in a measure, are linked to the Rockies by the highlands of Central America.

E.N.A.

BRITISH COLUMBIAN MOUNTAIN GOATS UPON A CRAG

Adaptations to a life in the mountains are extremely interesting. Though one might expect to find, for instance, specially adapted lungs for withstanding the rarefied air which causes so much distress to humans, there is no such thing. The adaptations seem to run entirely to hair. The coats of high-altitude animals are thick, and the feet have certain hairy modifications. The hoofs of the mountain goat enable the animal to cling to places with the smallest foothold.

Although several species of animals, like the yak, the snow-leopard, the argali and the snow-cock of the Himalayas, are found only at high altitudes, there are not many groups so restricted. Several, however, may be cited as characteristic of hilly or mountainous country. Ibexes and other wild goats, for example, are found mainly in the mountains of southern Europe, of Asia and of north Africa; but the common Persian ibex may descend the hills to places only a little above sea-level. Wild sheep, too, range from comparatively low levels to the highest peaks; and the "bighorn" of the Rockies extends from Alaska to Mexico. The Rocky Mountain goat, which belongs in reality to the chamois tribe, varies its habitat from sea-level up to the snows and its ally the European chamois passes from the forest zone to the snow-fields and glaciers of the Pyrenees, Alps and Carpathians. We have mentioned only a few of the more familiar animals, usually regarded as restricted to high altitudes, to show that they frequently occur at comparatively low levels, having great powers of adaptation to varied conditions.

Animals living at high altitudes exhibit adaptive structural modifications similar to those exhibited by related species living under similar conditions elsewhere. To withstand the cold at the mountain-tops, the wolves and foxes, for instance, have thicker

YOUNG CONDOR WHOSE PARENTS SOARED AMID THE ICY PEAKS OF THE ANDES

Photographed when about eight weeks old, this young condor weighed, at the time, more than six pounds. The condor is found in the Andes up to a height of about 16,000 feet. The enormous wings bear this, the greatest of the vultures, soaring over the grim ravines and awful heights of this vast wilderness of mountain and snow. But life in the Andes is prolific, even humming birds being found up to 9,000 feet. For long hours of sunlight warm the tropic regions of this range, counterbalancing the effects of altitude with its snow and ice.

furry coats than those of the warmer lowlands; and for traversing snow-fields their paws are overgrown to a greater extent with hair. In these particulars they resemble the foxes and wolves of the North Polar region. So, too, are the hoofs of mountain goats and sheep compact and strong so as to maintain a secure footing on bare ledges and peaks, just as are the hoofs of some African antelopes frequenting the rocky hillsides of sub-tropical Africa. No mountain ungulates, however, have the hoofs broad and widely separable to prevent sinking in the snow, such as are well known in the reindeer; and no modifications in the structure of the respiratory or circulatory organs to obviate the troubles experienced by mountaineers from the reduced pressure of the atmosphere and its attenuated supply of oxygen are known to exist in mammals habituated to life at high altitudes. The same applies to other animals. Birds, indeed, can drop in a straight and rapid course from 20,000 feet or so to sea-level without evincing any signs of discomfort.

In mountains, like Ruwenzori, upon or near the Equator, there is no marked seasonal change; the snow-line remains at approximately the same level throughout the year and no occasion arises enforcing a change in the mode of life of the animals to meet alternating periods of heat and cold. But in the Alps, Himalayas and other high ranges in temperate latitudes there is a great contrast between winter and summer and the animals living on their heights have to adapt themselves accordingly; and they adopt the same methods as those inhabiting the colder lowlands of north temperate and sub-Arctic districts.

TAKING the Himalayas as an illustration, we find that the marmot and Kashmir brown bear, for instance, retire to winter quarters in the autumn and lie dormant until the return of spring. Others, like the shrews, remain active even beneath the snow, feeding upon the spiders and insects which, like the reptiles, frogs, toads and other cold-blooded animals, pass through the cold period in winter sleep. But most of the large mammals, such as the sheep and goats, descend the mountain slopes to warmer levels where food is still available; and they are followed by the large predaceous beasts, such as the wolves and the snow leopards. Nowhere, indeed, do mammals exhibit the phenomenon of seasonal migration more manifestly than in high mountain ranges. The birds also move to lower and warmer

Life at High Altitudes

MOUNTAIN SHEEP AND TIBETAN YAK

Below is a flock of mountain sheep among the high snows of the National Park of Colorado in winter. Above we have a specimen of a Tibetan yak, a long-haired ox found 2,000 feet up when the Tibetan summer drives the snowline towards the sky.

levels in search of food, and this movement is precisely analogous to the southward migration of the cuckoo and swallow from England to Africa in the autumn, the only difference being that in the latter case the movement is measured by miles in longitude, whereas in the former it is measured by feet in altitude. Climatically they are exactly similar.

Similar, however, as are the conditions of existence at high altitudes in temperate and even tropical countries to those of the lowlands in high latitudes, there is one great difference that must be borne in mind. In Arctic and sub-Arctic climes the daily winter sunshine is at the best weak and of short duration or may be altogether absent, whereas in the latitude of the Alps and Himalayas it is comparatively powerful and of long duration, compensating in a measure for the coldness of the night. Nothing comparable to the repetitions of the long, cold winter night of sub-Arctic latitudes is inflicted upon the animals which in temperate and tropical countries live at the loftiest altitudes.

Arthur Brook

SWANS THAT HISS, SOMETIMES TRUMPET BUT NEVER SING

Swans were anciently supposed to sing before dying and, from this it was held that swans were tongue-tied except during their last moments. In fact the species most commonly found in England is called the mute swan and the only sound it is usually heard to make is a petulant hiss. In its ordinary semi-tame state the bird does not seem to produce any more interesting sound than this but when really wild it trumpets most stridently when mating time comes. The hiss, by the way, reminds us of the reptilian ancestors from which all birds evolved.

Chapter CXLII

The Language of Birds

By Dr. C. J. Patten

Professor of Anatomy, Sheffield University, Author of "The Story of the Birds"

How delightful it is to learn, at the outset, that the birds best known to us are just those which have most to say for themselves! Our studies of bird-language will be all the more delightful! Yes; our familiar and favourite garden-companions are furnished with quite an extensive vocabulary. Therefore we shall devote special attention to their utterances.

These birds belong to the highest order. Their vocal machinery reaches the acme of perfection; in habits of life their intelligence, vivacity and responsiveness reach high-water mark. When we remember that birds, structurally and developmentally, show definite affinities with reptiles—those cold-blooded, taciturn, irresponsive creatures—we cannot but pause and wonder! A general survey of ornithology, however, tells us that gradations can be established between the loquacious house-sparrow and the speechless stork, a bird so mute that his vocal addresses to his prospective mate can only be made known by the sound of his snapping jaws! The heron shows little desire to acquaint himself with human society. Watch his silent, stealthy figure! See! he remains at times quite motionless. Of a sudden he uncoils his long, slender, flexible neck, and secures his quarry with the speed of a serpent's strike! A subtle movement, surely reptilian in character!

Birds, however, as a class, have departed widely in temperament and modes of life from their silent reptilian ancestors. But we still wish to know how it has come about that our little feathered friends have, in so large a measure, grown so loquacious. Because it must always be borne in mind that for countless ages our planet was inhabited by voiceless living creatures. Millennium after millennium rolled on ere such incipient sounds as the stridulations of the grasshopper or cricket, the croak of the frog, the snort of the crocodile, or the hiss of the snake arose. The reign of the reptile lasted an immeasurable time, in which were evolved many specialised forms; nevertheless, in these vertebrate creatures the faculty of producing vocal music lagged behind.

From a curious reptilian ancestry birds eventually emerged. Then, for the first time, voice played a prominent part in evolution. With the tide of life flowing breast-high; with hot blood and body temperature exceeding that of mammals; with vitality geared to its highest pitch; birds, vivacious, beautiful in form and engaging in manners, could no longer restrain their highly-developed emotions in silence.

Birds—essentially denizens of the air, and capable of accomplishing immense journeys, might easily have become separated from their fellow-travellers to a dangerous degree, were they not endowed with far-reaching utterances. It seems hardly surprising, then, that musical sounds (which we know carry a long way) should have developed as a prime factor in bird language. We shall see presently why musical utterances are particularly indispensable. Birds, however, endowed with musical talent, can at times proclaim their state of mind by harsh, stridulent, or otherwise unpleasant utterances.

We are now in a position to ask—what, then, is the purport of bird language? In those types in which the vocabulary is fully developed, bird language may be said to serve a threefold purport. In the first place we can interpret certain utterances which are beyond doubt emitted for purposes of warning, alarm, challenge, and even battle. All these sounds are conveniently distinguished as the alarm-notes. They are not necessarily musical; far from it, they are often harsh and permeated with overtones. Nor is their carrying power necessarily far distant, seeing that they are most vigorously poured out when the enemy is being engaged close by.

It is noteworthy that the message of warning can be interpreted readily by many species. It serves as an "international code," which is taken up and relayed by one bird or group of birds to others. The effect is astoundingly prompt. When the common enemy appears, even afar off, what seems to us like a babel of sounds soon rends the air; the feathered communities far and wide being all intent on baulking the plunderer.

The language used in engaging the common enemy is, as a rule, similar to that adopted when rivals of one species come into close grips in disputing their rights of territory. The pugnacity of male birds when pairing in spring is notorious. At that season we frequently hear angry feelings expressed in the language of furious battle-cries. Notes of warning, alarm-notes and battle-cries all come into one category. Their chief feature consists in monotonous repetition. We see elaboration from the primitive single squeak (which is still retained by the hedge-sparrow in an angry mood) to the quick, repeated chatter of the angry missel-thrush. The alarm-note of the chaffinch, though repeated, is rather disjointed; in other words, it lacks rhythm. In its evolution it may be said to form an intermediate stage between that of the hedge-sparrow and missel-thrush. The squeak, though primitive, evolved from a toneless puff, snort, or hiss; utterances which are clearly indicative of rage. Beyond these utterances reptiles have not advanced; perhaps the hiss of the enraged snake is most familiar. Some birds also hiss and puff, notably in defence of their eggs

G. W. Teager

STARLING THAT HAS A VERY LARGE REPERTOIRE

With head feathers slightly erected as though with the effort, the starling sings, squeals, hisses, chatters and even makes a noise like laughing. It can also give vent to a sharp "kah" when annoyed. This bird has an extraordinary repertoire of vocal effects and is about the most versatile of British birds.

If we bear in mind that birds are essentially creatures of the air, and owing to their swiftness of flight might readily become separated from their companions to a dangerous degree, it is evident that the possession of far-reaching utterances must have become a *sine qua non.* Then again, birds have enormous appetites, and are obliged to trek far and wide in search of food. Individuals, therefore, of a large foraging party find it much to their advantage to maintain conversation. On migration, the leaders of the companies keep the vanguard in touch by their wild, musical cries. In the spring the male keeps in touch with his partner by frequently calling aloud to her when they forge ahead in search of tree or shrub, suitable for a nesting-site. The helpless nestling must needs have a voice powerful enough to send out messages soliciting food, warmth, and protection. The far-reaching voice of the parent brings comfort to the infants, who anticipate her return post-haste. Such are the call-notes (the mainstay of bird language) poured forth under many conditions, yet associated with the duties of every-day life.

These notes present well-marked features. They are essentially musical in character, and their tones are so pure that they carry a wonderfully long distance. They are usually plaintive and melodious to an exquisite degree, and full of sympathy. Many call-notes are composed of two syllables; the second being pitched a third or a fifth higher than the first. These strains seem all the more expressive because the intervals in pitch follow closely those in the diatonic scale. We are familiar with such intervals both in melody and

and young. The tiny blue titmouse can almost strike terror into the mind of the egg-robber when she vehemently lets go her sibilant notes from the little dark cavern in the old stone wall. The loud hiss of a brooding duck, goose or swan, is really quite menacing. Most of us are familiar with the blowing and puffing sound which nestling-pigeons exercise when suspicious of danger.

The development of squeaks or other clear cries from the toneless puff or hiss no doubt took place very gradually. Alarm-notes have their cradle of origin in breath-sounds, which naturally became exaggerated and sibilant in character when produced in a strained and hurried way, following combat. "Natural selection," finding these menacing breath-sounds to serve a useful purpose, has made them the founders of manifold alarm-notes with which we are now familiar.

in the building up of harmony. Consequently they fall very tunefully on our ears.

There is a well-known call-note, syllabled *you-ee,* common to many of our small birds, more particularly the warblers. While these syllables vary in pitch and tone according to species, they are astonishingly melodious, and enter into the formation of the unique "water-bubble" trills and rolls of the fully-developed song. Let it be clearly understood, however, that there are birds in which the song, in its strictly technical sense, has not evolved; in other words, it forms no part of their language. Nevertheless, these species possess most plaintive and sweetly melodious call-notes. Several of our familiar shore-birds, including the curlew, redshank, greenshank, and ringed dotterel, are thus endowed. In these denizens of the sand-flats and soblands, devoid of cover, the call-notes, in a large measure, indicate

BROWN OWL OF THE WOODS WHOSE LANGUAGE SHAKESPEARE RECORDED

From the densest parts of wood and spinney there comes at dawn and dusk the loud "hoo-hoo" of the brown or tawny owl, as it is sometimes called. Shakespeare in one of his songs "When icicles hang by the wall" makes the "staring owl" sing "tu-whit to-who." The younger birds give vent to a hoarse "che-wick." Of all the British owls this one seems to dislike the sunlight most of all and those who want a sample of its language must either wait till dark—or else try robbing its nest.

alarm-notes. The grand, wild, musical cry of the curlew affords a notable example. No doubt this whistle plays the part of a multiple code.

The third purport which the language of birds serves is that of the song. This part of the vocabulary is developed only in certain species known as "song birds," which constitute the highest orders. Here, the vocal machinery reaches its highest development; muscles, in addition to those present in the lower orders, work the delicate vibrating membranes.

We have seen that the alarm-notes have undergone elaboration when compared with the toneless puff, hiss, or snort so characteristic of reptilian utterances. The same may be said in regard to the call-notes. More particularly still is the composition of the song a product of evolution. This phase of bird language has been derived from the alarm-notes, and more particularly from the call-notes. These, expressed in rapid succession and subjected to variations, are primarily responsible for the building up of the song. Many of the more simple stanzas, for instance those of the hedge-sparrow, yellow bunting, and others afford evidence of being conversation-notes strung together. Among the premier vocalists this synthesis is elaborated by the introduction of many new notes and phrases, together with greater and more varying degrees of modulation, pitch, colour-tone, rhythm, and other matters of vocal technique, which, in many cases, is associated with varying degrees of emotion.

G. W. Teager

YOUNG STARLING ASKS ITS MOTHER FOR MORE

Compared with the parent bird seen in the opposite page, this young starling is rather a drab object. It is a uniform grey-brown on the back and sides and whitish below. Just as its plumage gives no hint of the brilliance that will develop later, so its voice gives no promise of the amazing range that will come when the bird comes of age.

AMONG some species, mimicry is manifestly a dominant factor in the elaboration of the song. Inanimate as well as animate musical sounds are often reproduced. Whatever may have been their source in ages far remote, they are now handed down to the offspring and reproduced, generation after generation, without tuition. It is true that in certain phrases of the best singers, for instance the song-thrush, linnet, goldfinch, and others, the notes of other birds are often reproduced with extraordinary exactitude; nevertheless, the foundation of the vocal theme of each species is distinctly prescriptive. The spirit and manner in which each species sings, despite borrowed notes, always retain their individuality. The most varied and accomplished song of any one of our major vocalists cannot baffle the practised ear of the listener.

Singing in birds is an instinctive act and, from the physiological standpoint, is as compulsory as eating or drinking. Birds must tune up when the season approaches: they have no choice in the matter! In spring they pour forth their joyous melodies under adverse circumstances. Behind prison bars, where they have hardly room to turn, domiciled in grimy city-slums, they sing with the same zest as their companions under the open firmament. How oft have we heard the skylark caroling joyously when standing on the floor of its cage, far too meagre in dimensions. Even from birds when migrating at night, under a canopy of inky darkness, a burst of song may be heard o'erhead. Hosts of skylarks, thrushes, blackbirds, robins and warblers of various sorts, emerging from the impenetrable gloom in thick weather and coming under the subtle influence of the dazzling beams of the lighthouse, will at times carol tunefully to the night-air. The song of birds is for the most part poured forth with the greatest zeal. Though often intensely melodious, it is true that on analysis it conveys no expression whatsoever of sympathy.

A. H. Willford

THE CURLEW OPENS HER CURVED BEAK TO CALL HER MATE TO THE NEST

If disturbed at its feeding grounds on the foreshore where it seeks shell fish and sand-worms at low water, the curlew is off like a flash and crying loudly all the time. But it has several variations of its characteristic "coor-lee" besides the alarm note. Here we have a hen bird on the nest calling loudly to her mate to come and take a turn at sitting on the eggs while she goes to get something to eat. When this photograph was taken the cock bird was actually within a few yards though not in focus with the nest.

What then can be the purport of this joyous and passionate rhapsody? Plainly it is an expression of emulation, of rivalry, of defiance, and, in a large measure, of pugnacity. Two robins, having come into such close grips that feathers were sent flying, and having let go, closely approached and immediately sang at each other in most defiant attitudes! Song is not solely a message of love addressed to the expectant mate. It is also a proclamation to a rival suitor, warning him to keep within the bounds of his rightful territory and not to trespass! Apart from a definite challenge which may, or may not, invoke combat, male birds in the pairing season vie with each other in their vocal powers. They may be seen perched on the topmost branch of a tree or other vantage spot, singing antiphonally in the most passionate strains.

In courtship and wooing song plays a most important part, in which the females are much interested. The partner, full of combat, full of vigour, full of subtlety, persistent in his love-antics and dances, and lusty in song, becomes the successful competitor. During the early period of wedlock the lyric is continued with unabated energy—an assurance to the patiently brooding female that all goes well. Later, when the eggs are hatched, and food must be sought all day long, with little or no intermission, to satisfy the prodigious appetites of the youngsters, the male is deprived of his leisure and the woodlands and hedgerows lapse into silence.

In the British Isles, the finest vocalists are, with few exceptions, modestly attired, and possess little or no contrast colours in their plumage. The nightingale, blackcap, garden-warbler, reed-warbler, willow-warbler, skylark, woodlark, and others, follow this rule. But the goldfinch, chaffinch, robin, and redstart are examples of a few which are gaily robed. Some charming songsters, however, clad in rich and beautiful garbs, are not uncommon in far-off lands. Among these may be enumerated the pie-bald white-backed shrike—as large as our rook—the magnificent crimson cardinal of North America, and the lovely snowy-plumed bell-bird of South America.

The nightingale, peerless minstrel of the summer nights, is a small brownish bird, hardly exceeding in size the robin, though a trifle longer and more slender. If the smooth, drawn-out phrases, deliciously melodious, and reminding us of the sighing cadence of the night wind's gentle whistle, descending through almost imperceptible gradations of the chromatic scale; if the fervent whisper of the tiny brooklet, or if the shimmering of delicate foliage, offer stanzas tinged with melancholy, surely this is soon eclipsed when the famous minstrel lets loose a succession of chattering notes, silver-toned yet defiant, subtle as they wane, mystic as they seem to float away on the night-air, thrilling as the passionate theme rolls back with dramatic suddenness upon our ears. This marvellous composition, even when heard by day amid a chorus of other strains, cannot be confused by the listener well-versed in bird language.

Nightingales sing freely by day in certain districts, especially in southern counties where they happen to be common. Nevertheless, little or no attention is, as a rule, given to their voice until after sun-down, partly because the vocal activities of several other

Oliver Pike

HARSHLY CAWING CARRION CROW AND THE WHISTLING EAGLE

Carrion crows are not so rare in England as is generally supposed. Their scarcity would be less believed in were it not so difficult to distinguish them, at a distance, from the rooks. If near enough the observer may readily note the absence of the bare white patch on the base of the beak that marks the rook. The carrion crow goes singly or with its mate and never in flocks. The cry is rather like the rook's but even harsher in tone. The bird is fond of cliffs, especially where there are woods near by. The upper illustration is of a whistling eagle.

A. H. Willford

LAPWING, SKYLARK AND PIED WAGTAIL CALLING TO THEIR MATES AT NESTING TIME

When the lapwing's eggs are hatching or when the fledgelings have begun to squawk in the nest, the parent birds are always on the look-out for danger. If an enemy appears the male goes through a series of the most astonishing aerial acrobatics, hurling itself about, thirty feet or so above the field, and calling madly so that all attention is distracted from the nest, and directed on those mad antics. The lower left-hand photograph is of a hen lapwing calling her mate. Her call is the familiar "pee-a-wit" whence the alternative name of peewit is derived. The skylark sometimes calls his mate to join him in soaring into the blue. Here (bottom right) we see one of the birds about to leave the ground. The upper photographs show pied wagtails.

Arthur Brook

Oliver Pike

BUZZARD THAT UTTERS A PLAINTIVE MEWING AND THE JACKDAW WITH AN IMPERTINENT VOICE

The common buzzard makes a melancholy mewing noise as it mounts the heavens in slow and beautifully traced spirals Its note may well be melancholy for, except in the West of England and especially in Devon, where there is plenty of woodland left, it is rapidly disappearing. Its persecution seems unjust, for it preys almost exclusively on vermin and never pursues other birds, being of a sluggish disposition. Field-mice, rabbits and an occasional grasshopper form its usual fare and, if it gets a bird it is by surprise, not pursuit. The jackdaw (right) on the other hand, is abundant wherever there are cliffs. It cries " jack " sharply or else " jock." Often found with rooks it is to be distinguished from them by its smaller size and by its grey nape.

A. H. Willford

COMMON TERNS SCREAMING WILDLY ABOUT THEIR NESTING PLACES

Having prevailed upon its mate to leave her nest and take some time off for a little fishing, the hen tern (bottom) gives a parting scream as she flies away. It is now his turn to sit on the eggs. The common tern makes a sound like " kree-kree " often repeated. This bird is found all round the coasts of Britain save in the North wherein its place is taken by the larger Arctic tern. In the upper left illustration we see a number of common terns returning to their nesting places. Here too (top right) is a male bird calling to its mate.

O. Pike

RAVEN, RENOWNED FOR ITS HARSH CROAK

Very fond of sea-cliffs as a site for nest-building, the raven is often seen in Scotland, though now rather scarce in England. It is a sturdier and heavier bird than either crow or rook, and its language can either be a sort of growling or else a harsh exclamation like " kerk " as it sweeps ponderously over the moor. The raven has long been considered a bird of ill-omen.

species cause distraction, but mainly because the idea is still very prevalent that the nightingale bides his time until nightfall before he tunes up.

This idea is so deeply rooted that many birds (some with far inferior voices) which happen to burst into song at night, are credited with the performances of the famous minstrel. The song-thrush, the blackbird, the whitethroat, and more particularly the sedge-warbler, may be heard from time to time singing in the hours of darkness. In Ireland, where the nightingale has as yet not been recorded, the sedge-warbler is named in many rural districts the " Irish nightingale." It is also a prevalent idea that the nightingale sings only when ambushed. As a matter of fact its " platform," even in broad daylight, is often represented by an elevated, naked sprig ; one which commands the full view of an observer ! The blackcap, smaller than the nightingale, and also quietly attired — although he dons a smart little skull-cap—possesses that enchanting quality of voice which emulates the babbling of the brooklet. Nothing can exceed the beauty and flexibility of his so-called " water-bubble " phrases. True, his compass is limited, and yet, as his music flows from out the depths of the thicket, he seems to set the chords of the inmost soul of the wild-rose vibrating. We must be prepared to watch, wait, and listen in silence, because this superb vocalist is exceedingly shy and retiring, and will cut his song short on the least suspicion that his home and family are being betrayed.

At the head of the list we should certainly place our beloved blackbird for his rich, flute-like tone, his rhythm, his regularity in time, and motif. The voice of the song-thrush is a melodious rhapsody—wild, buoyant, and decisive—expressing the very acme of joy. The indomitable energy of his vocal powers stamps him as leader of the feathered choir. He oft repeats his verses, embellishes his own sweet notes with many borrowed from other vocalists, and seems ever in the " limelight."

The skylark's faculty of pouring out an unbroken melodious carol while he ascends spirally on pinions beating several hundred times a minute to a surprising altitude, is a performance which seems beyond our comprehension. To understand it, and, indeed, bird-language in general, we must study the anatomy and physiology of the respiratory, vocal, and muscular systems, which in birds have undergone special development.

Stupendous power, amazing to comprehend, is the grand feature in the bird's voice. In many species a veritable cascade of sound gushes forth through minute air-passages. A wax-match would easily distend the wind-pipe of a nightingale. Think, then, of the extraordinary volume of pure, musical, far-reaching sound, which can be emitted through this tiny tube! A skylark can be heard distinctly at a distance at which the human voice would be quite inaudible. Here, again, it may be pointed out that a match would block the wind-pipe of this marvellous minstrel! The corresponding air-tube of man admits the finger of a grown person! What a contrast!

A YOUNG sparrow, feathered but not yet able to fly, when taken from the nest and placed on the carpet, startles the household by the clarity of its vociferous call-notes. This chirp is given forth without a moment's hesitation—indeed, with marked attack and precision; truly an object lesson for the student of human song! No animals have their bodies fully permeated with air like birds. This pneumaticity is certainly unique. Bubble-like, thin, transparent sacs (which we regard as direct extensions of the lungs, and with which they are in direct communication) appear in every region. They burrow under the skin, the muscles, and the vital organs, and in many species they actually form a lining for the hollow chambers in some of the bones. The air-sacs lend their aid in the production of voice, especially in birds whose powers of song are highly-developed.

By a special muscular mechanism a great volume of air can be driven swiftly and under high pressure, not only from the lungs but also from the extensive system of air-sacs, into the "song-box." As a result, the delicate vocal membranes are set vibrating. The "song-box" of the bird is called the syrinx, and it is situated at the bottom of the wind-pipe where it immediately branches into the two bronchi. At this spot a vertical elastic membrane projects upwards. It acts after the fashion of a reed, causing the air-column to vibrate in its passage up the wind-pipe. The latter is remarkably long, and so highly elastic that, when fully stretched, it almost doubles its length! The succession of rings, which constitute its framework, can approach and recede with amazing rapidity and suddenness. This mechanism is responsible in the main for the marked resilience which simulates joyous, tinkling, bell-like tones. The wind-pipe is also capable of considerable extension, and, as the tube steadily contracts to regain its normal diameter, vocal utterances gain in duration and steadiness.

HERE the mechanism may be likened to the gradual emptying of a toy-balloon to which a mouthpiece is attached. Every little schoolboy is familiar with this prolonged, steady, mewing sound! The tracheal tube or wind-pipe may be compared to a long reed instrument, such as an oboe, which we know produces delightfully rich, mellow, fluty tones. By the contraction and relaxation of the muscles, not only those attached to the wind-pipe but also to its branches—the bronchi—a variety in pitch and tone, almost unlimited, can be produced. The human trachea is short and relatively inelastic. Moreover, it is voiceless, because the "song-box," known as the larynx, is situated above it. Human utterances, therefore, are denied the flexibility which culminates in the exquisite rolls and trills of bird language. Human voice-sounds are formed just a little below the floor of the mouth. Here the passage of a column of air, impinging upon two horizontal elastic membranes—the vocal cords—sets them vibrating. The voiced column is consequently very short, and, in endeavouring to escape through the mouth, may be partially imprisoned in one or more "pockets" in the throat or it may be blocked by the fleshy tongue, soft-palate, uvula and tonsils, if these be not skilfully kept out of the way. Faulty voice-production, giving rise to throaty or tight effects, is therefore apt to occur.

In man, singing is a fine art, and the voice requires most careful cultivation and manipulation. In birds, song is instinctive and requires no tuition. No obstructions are offered to the free passage of the outgoing voiced current of air. Directly it emerges from the wind-pipe into the open mouth, it is wafted into the atmosphere without loss of clarity or purity of tone. Birds when singing are not bashful, or self-conscious. They do not elect to sing to any special assembly, and know nothing of expectant criticism! They "broadcast" their music to every creature within the range of hearing, caring naught whether their exposition gives pleasure or dissatisfaction.

WE are proud of our song-birds, and rightly so; they are many and of the first order. With Goldsmith, we can join issue in saying that in the British Isles "Gentle music melts on every spray." It is quite a popular error to think that the distribution of song-birds is restricted, and that outside the British Isles (more particularly in lands afar off), melody falls away or is even quite hushed to sleep. Many glorious minstrels, for the most part migratory—some, indeed, gaily attired—are to be found extending over a wide area of the temperate regions of both the northern and southern hemispheres, and in both the Old and New World. The birds of the Tropics migrate but little. Indeed, it may be said that, on the whole, they are stationary. Far-carrying musical utterances are, in a large measure, supplanted by shrill, discordant screeches and screams, which, though ear-piercing when heard close by, have, owing to their overtones, very limited carrying-power. However, they furnish a code, quite sufficient to protect the short lines of communication of these stationary species.

The males of many tropical birds are provided with strikingly handsome liveries, decorated with long, wavy plumes, crests, and other appendages. These birds delight to show off their grandeur to the females. Indeed, the factor of "display" in courtship here strikes a dominant note. In many other tropical birds, however, both sexes are brilliantly coloured, and their plumage harmonises so closely with the gaiety of the tropical vegetation that they are afforded adequate "protective coloration." Hence, in the Tropics, bright, gaudy colours, not proving dangerous, have largely persisted.

THREE WARBLERS AND A LINNET, ALL THE MOST INSISTENT SINGERS Oliver Pike

The warblers in general are apt to make themselves very much heard though all of them are not particularly pleasant hearing. The sedge warbler (bottom left) which haunts river banks and marshes makes an almost incessant noise both night and day, the voice being rather harsh as a rule. The willow-warbler (bottom right) rushes up and down the scale and then ends almost in a whisper. The garden warbler (top left) is a fine songster with low melodic notes. Lastly, we have the linnet (top right) which ejaculates " tit-turrow " and " chit-chit."

Arthur Brook

GEESE WHOSE GAGGLING IS AS EFFECTIVE AS A WATCH-DOG'S BARK

Farmyard geese are presumed to be descended from the grey lag goose which used to breed in Norfolk but which, in a wild state, is now only a migrant to Britain. But the domestic breed is a very old one and has probably had an admixture of wild grey lag from time to time. The voice of the farm goose is much like that of the grey lag—a harsh gaggle with a kind of creak in it. Here we have a "close-up" of a happy family waiting for the inevitable time when the demands of Michelmas shall end its days.

In the British Isles, and in other temperate climes, Nature protects many of her feathered children by robing them in modest attire to bring them into line with their more sombre surroundings. The males of many who have forfeited their attractive dress to the greatest extent have become endowed with most glorious thrilling voices. Pushing "display" and "antics" somewhat into the background, these famous "artists" set out to win the hearts of the females by their superb incantations.

It has been pointed out that, in some species, mimicry is a dominant factor in the elaboration of the song. Our familiar song-thrush affords an example. In captivity, elaboration often proceeds much further; we find not only the notes of other captives, but also snatches or even complete lines of tunes reproduced. The bullfinch is an apt pupil and soon picks up snatches of a song whistled by his owner. But there are birds which do not sing in the technical sense; nevertheless, they carry mimicry to a greater pitch of perfection.

Parrots copy faithfully the calls of many other birds, but their powers of modulation are developed to such a marked degree that they can also reproduce

G. Hearn

A. H. Willford

OYSTER CATCHER AND THE NIGHTINGALE, KING OF THE BIRD SINGERS

Places on the coast where there are rocks interspersed with sand and shingle are the favourite haunts of the oyster catcher (bottom) which, by the way, lives on limpets and mussels which it levers from the rocks at low tide. When anyone approaches, the birds all set up a loud and complaining " keep-keep " frightening every other bird in the neighbourhood. The nightingale is well known as the most lovely of bird singers (top). But it is seldom noticed although it often sings on an open branch. It looks like a large robin with a grey breast.

G. W. Teager

"milk - lapping," "sharpening the carving-knife," "pulling corks," and so on, seems certainly very wonderful.

It is true that in parrots the tongue is thick and fleshy, and it has been suggested that this organ may therefore lend an aid in the production of articulate speech. On the other hand, birds of prey have also a tongue which is built on similar lines, and they are the last class of bird one thinks of attempting to teach to speak. Then again, the tongue in the crows, mynahs, and others, which can reproduce phrases of speech, is thin, dry and horny. In other words, it is the form of tongue typical of hundreds of species which make no attempt to extend their more or less stereotyped vocabulary. The wonderful repertoire an African grey parrot can build up is purely a matter of mimicry. It is quite suggestive that the faculty of mimicry arose

E.N.A.

MOCKING BIRD AND THE MELLOW BLACKBIRD

Common in the U.S.A. and the West Indies the mocking bird (bottom) is an expert at imitating the language of its feathered fellows. The same term is applied to the icterine warbler which occasionally arrives in England. The blackbird (top) is a brilliant singer but adopts a hard "chuck" or "chink" if alarmed

most diversified sounds with astonishing fidelity. The African grey parrot, with his red tail, perhaps the best of all feathered impersonators, can give many "star turns" in mewing, barking, grunting, lapping milk, sawing wood, drawing corks, and so on; to say nothing of ejaculations and even a considerable variety of short expressions of human speech!

OTHER members of the tribe also acquit themselves with marked ability; for instance, the green "Amazon" and the sulphur-crested cockatoo. Members of the crow family, including the raven, hooded crow, carrion crow, magpie, jackdaw, jay, and chough, also our common starling and the mynah, or grackle, of India—with its curious face appendages—the mocking bird of America; the lyre bird of Australia and others, pronounce words and other sounds with considerable but varying degrees of accuracy. Their repertoire, however, is, on the whole, more limited than that of the parrots.

It is a prevalent idea that the vocal machinery has undergone specialisation in certain directions in order to facilitate the reproduction of human words This is a fallacy. The faculty of producing human words is only part of the performance, and it is questionable whether their reproduction demands as much skill as many weird imitations of inanimate sounds. The vocal mechanism involved in "purring,"

in certain birds in order to put the enemy off the scent. The desire to practise any accomplishment is one which is tenacious and readily elaborated by encouragement. Hence, in captivity, feathered mimics of the first order become famous.

Do parrots and other birds, which appear to use speech knowingly, know what they are talking about? If the phrases of human speech or other sounds which they have been taught to reproduce have from the beginning been intimately associated with appropriate actions, then some conception of association of ideas cannot be denied. A parrot heard and saw corks of beer bottles being drawn at dinner-time. With little or no delay, and quite spontaneously, he started to

" draw corks " with wonderful success. Observing astutely that beer drinking was a regular habit at dinner, he was obliging enough sometimes to " open " the bottles a little in advance! Indeed, when he saw the dining-table fully equipped he often " pulled several corks " before the diners sat down to their meal! On the other hand, if a parrot be taught to say " Good-morning " in the evening, and, for the sake of experiment, the phrase of speech be carefully withheld during the rest of the day, then it is just as likely as not that the clever mimic may refrain from wishing a visitor " Good-morning " before the sun has dipped below the horizon! Other experiments of this nature which can be easily contrived will give similar results.

Daddy, with a tomato in his hand and accompanied by his small son " Billy," confronted their pet magpie. The bird was clearly shown, but prevented from seizing, the desired tit-bit, until he had heard the boy's name repeated a dozen times in succession. The experiment was carried on for several days. The sagacious impersonator, however, was not long in completing his education. He soon commenced to call aloud " Billy—Billy—Billy—Billy ! " the very moment he espied a tomato in the hand of either father or son. Surely a clear case of association of ideas. But whether the magpie was conscious of the fact that Billy was really Billy, there we must stop—and leave the verdict open.

G. W. Teager

THREE BIRDS EASILY RECOGNIZED BY THEIR VOICES

Largest of the British gulls, the great black-backed gull (bottom) has a particularly querulous call which consists of a kind of cackling. The mistle thrush (top) persists in song through the winter months. The song-thrush (top right) has a fine, varied voice.

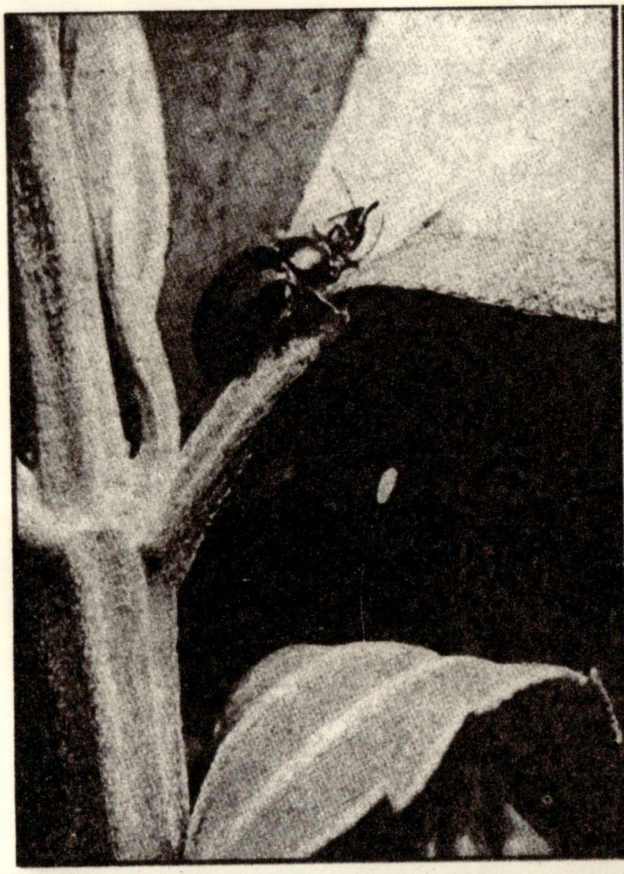

LADYBIRDS IMPORTED INTO MANY PARTS OF THE WORLD TO FIGHT MAN'S BATTLES

In England, California, Palestine and South Africa, the ladybird beetle is fighting man's battle with the insects that are trying to multiply at his expense. The lower photograph shows ladybirds on an apple branch destroying the larvae of greenfly. Above are (left) a magnified photograph of a ladybird eating a greenfly and (right) a photograph from the U.S.A. This shows thousands of the little beetles collected in the mountains where they congregate in the winter. They are taken down to the warm valleys where they prey on fruit tree pests

Chapter CXLIII

Insects that Fight for Man

By N. D. Riley

Joint Secretary, Entomological Society of London

NEW countries, virgin soils, rich crops are no less attractive to insects than they are to man, not only on account of their intrinsic values and potentialities, but also in the escape they offer from the bondage of old-established civilizations and associations. One can perhaps hardly regard insects as appreciating the latter considerations, yet their escape is none the less real. The old-established balance of nature is for them a very real and effective bond, from the loosing of which man has suffered severely on many occasions.

The pine beauty moth has a caterpillar that feeds upon the needles of pine and fir. It is moderately common in England, but seldom so plentiful as to cause any considerable damage. On the continent of Europe, however, the caterpillars occur in such abundance at times as to present a really serious problem. An investigation made a few years ago during one of these outbreaks, and not intended to be by any means exhaustive, showed that these caterpillars were parasitised by no fewer than fourteen other different kinds of insects, either of the small blow-fly type (*Tachinidae*) or wasp-like creatures, mainly of the family ichneumonidae, and generally known collectively as ichneumons. In addition, another ichneumon attacked the eggs, a polyhedral disease attacked the caterpillar, and, of course, numerous other creatures attacked them in more obvious fashion. Against this should be set the fact that certainly six insects (hyperparasites) preyed upon the primary parasities, although naturally not immediately neutralising the work of the latter. Imagine for a moment the effect upon the pine beauty moth of its removal to a paradise free from all these enemies, and provided with an abundance of food in the form of a limitless pine forest!

All insects, if left to multiply unhindered, would in a relatively short space of time overrun the whole of their available food supply, only to perish in the end from the lack of it. Normally a balance is struck between the rate of increase and the rate of destruction, so that the numbers arriving at maturity fluctuate little from year to year. It is only when an insect spreads to some new area and escapes from its natural enemies, a process that is usually due to accidental transportation by man, that it can give rein to unhindered multiplication. This happened to the cottony cushion-scale, or fluted scale, in California.

RATHER handsome, and of comparatively large size, this scale insect was first noticed clustered along stems of an acacia in 1868. Later it spread to the citrus and other plants, but little attention was then paid to it. Some years afterwards it was discovered on another acacia in New Zealand, recognized as being nameless and described as *Icerya purchasi*. In the meantime, it had continued to spread in California, and by 1887 the head of the United States Bureau of Entomology lamented that " the pest has come to stay. No human endeavour can exterminate it." Indeed it appeared to be so, for in spite of all attempts to control it with the means at that time available, it really looked as if the citrus industry of California was doomed to perish from the attacks of this seemingly insignificant creature.

Artificial control having failed, it was inevitable that thought should turn towards the re-establishment of natural control. The insect was known to be a native of the Australian region, and, further, it was well established that there it did very little damage. So it was resolved to send an entomologist to Australia to discover the insect's natural enemies. Administrative difficulties—how could Congress sanction a scheme so manifestly absurd?—were eventually overcome, and in 1888 Koebele reached

H. Bastin and E. A. Botting

PUPA, LARVA AND ADULT LADY-BIRD

There are about two thousand different species of lady-bird, forty or so being found in Britain. Here are a pupa (bottom left), a larva (right) and an adult insect (top left). The adult is compared with the eye of a needle, the photograph being highly magnified.

Australia and at once set about his task. In spite of misfortunes that overtook the consignments of insects, eventually both parasitic flies and lady-bird beetles arrived safely at Los Angeles, and by May, 1889, it could be asserted that the latter at any rate were well established on a few trees and showing great promise. By the following June a grower was able to report that the beetles had "multiplied in numbers and spread so rapidly that every one of his 3,200 trees was literally swarming with them." Success was remarkably complete, and to-day it is possible to assert that the fluted scale as a serious pest of citrus trees in California is virtually a thing of the past, and for this a lady-bird beetle is to be thanked.

The immediate success that attended the use of this insect in California to check the ravages of the fluted scale aroused high hopes for the future that were only dispelled by many rather costly failures. Nevertheless, it was another lady-bird beetle that again came to the help of the same citrus growers about the year 1916, when the trees were attacked by the *Critophilus* mealy bug. In this case, however, the ladybird (*Cryptolaemus montrouzieri*) is not able to pass the winter very successfully under local conditions, and, therefore, a large reserve has to be raised and kept in special insectaries so that supplies can be distributed and the trees re-colonised at frequent intervals. Results certainly appear to justify the labour and money spent upon the beetle; but it is fortunate that the other species are better able to look after themselves.

In the American Museum of Natural History in New York is a very cleverly arranged exhibit occupying an entire case devoted to showing these lady-bird beetles, these "insect friends of man," emerging from their winter quarters on a mountain top in Colorado. The number of individuals that gathers together in these rocky crevices on the very peaks of the mountains is often immense, the beetles flying long distances in order to congregate. Wherever they are, be it an orange grove in California, South Africa or Palestine, or a rose garden in England, one may be sure that the lady-bird beetles are doing their bit to help man in keeping the green-fly, mealy-bugs and scale insects in check. But there is one curious fact that often seems to allow the pests to gain a long start of them, and that is that they require a slightly higher average temperature than their natural enemies need to rouse them to activity. And hence in places, notably California, a practice has arisen of collecting them in their winter quarters, obviously somewhat remote from the haunts of their prey, before their normal time of awakening, and of transporting them to these already warmer or more sheltered areas. Efforts to establish some of these lady-birds in New Zealand are alleged to have met with little success, because, although they behaved satisfactorily during the summer, after retiring to the mountains for hibernation they never were seen again!

Some of the most remarkable experiments that have been carried out in the biological control of insect pests have taken place in the Hawaiian Islands. Situated some two thousand miles from the nearest land, and at the "cross roads" of the Pacific, this isolated group of islands forms in certain respects an ideal experimental laboratory. The clearing of the native forests and the subsequent spread of civilization, and also the chance importation in ships of many insects both beneficial and harmful, wrought far-reaching changes in both fauna and flora.

Owing to the rather special manner in which many crops are raised in the islands, and also perhaps in a measure to their great variety, it was early discovered that the orthodox "contact" methods of spraying, and so on, were locally of little avail against insect pests and consequently biological control was essential. In the efforts to establish it some of the most romantic chapters in the history of entomology have been, or might have been, written, most of them, too, like true romances, having happy endings.

The earliest work was an offshoot of the campaign against the cushion scale already referred to above, a stock of the lady-bird beetle (*Novius cardinalis*), being sent on to the Hawaiian Islands. It rapidly overtook the pest, and has retained it in a condition of virtual impotence ever since. During subsequent years no fewer than ninety different kinds of beneficial insects have been introduced from all parts of the world and successfully established; a far larger number failed to establish themselves, but the work is still being carried on. About the year 1900 a little insect called a leaf hopper—a small bug allied to the diminutive creature that causes the "cuckoo spit" so familiar in gardens—made its appearance in Hawaii, and as a result of its depredations in about three years the average sugar production fell by approximately fifty per cent.

Three years later a number of living parasites of other leaf hoppers sent from the United States, having proved of very little value, two Hawaiian entomologists set out for Australia and Fiji to search for other parasites. As a result, two minute wasps, that attacked the eggs of the leaf hoppers, were sent home, together with several other species, and these, in about eighteen months, very materially affected the situation. It appeared that the value of many of the other promising species imported was greatly reduced by the attacks of hyperparasites.

Further efforts were made, and finally in Fiji and Queensland Mr. Muir, from Hawaii, found a bug that lived entirely upon the eggs of the leaf hopper, sucking them by means of its beak—a carnivorous habit most unusual in the family of insects to which it belonged. It was therefore not without misgivings that consignments were sent home, for it was conceivable that this bug might at any time, by reverting to the normal practice of its near relatives, become a serious crop pest. However, the gamble was justified. Since 1920, when it arrived in the Islands, it has completed the subjugation of the leaf hoppers and is considered its most important enemy.

Insects that Fight for Man

A far longer search had to be made for insect aid in checking the sugar cane borer beetle. No accurate information existed as to the real home of this insect, so practically the whole of the East had to be ransacked. The first efforts, again by Mr. Muir, were made in the Malay States and Southern China. Thence he proceeded to Java and Borneo, on to Amboina and through the Kei and Aru islands to Larat, where finally the beetle was run to earth and studied for a while.

INSECTS THAT FIGHT INSECTS FOR MAN'S BENEFIT

By the formidable process of reproduction called polyembryony some parasite insects prey very effectively on destructive pests. A parasite of the tomato caterpillar (bottom), laid one egg in a caterpillar and from that single egg were hatched all the larvæ whose cocoons we see smothering the dead body. Above is an ichneumon-fly that attacks larvæ of the pigeon tremex.

Having learnt something of its habits, Mr. Muir, on his return to Amboina, was able to locate it there as well and to discover a tachinid fly, allied to the blow fly, that parasitised it. The real problem then became one of transport.

Attempts were made to send consignments to Hong Kong. The difficulties of keeping alive not only the beetles and their parasites but also a supply of the food plant of the former proved too great, however, and only failure was recorded. Another route had to be found. The beetle and its parasites were located in New Guinea, and with a large stock of both, Muir set out *via* Brisbane for Honolulu, but overtaken by typhoid at the former place, had to leave his charges unattended, and all perished on the way. In the end, intermediate breeding stations had to be established in both Australia and Fiji, and then at last the parasite was got through, the work having occupied four years. Results justified the efforts, however, for it was stated in 1926 that in many places indications of the borer beetle were then very hard to find, the tachinid fly having apparently got it well in hand.

The degree of control obtained over the Mediterranean fruit fly by the importation of parasites has not yet proved so great as in the foregoing cases, in spite of the fact that of the many brought in no fewer than four are fully established and widely distributed in the islands. On the other hand, the anomala beetle, another pest of sugar cane, has been most effectively controlled by means of a single species of large solitary wasp, *Scolia manilae*, sent by Muir from the Philippine Islands.

It is only recently that this particular family of wasps (*Scoliidae*) has been recognized as of value in biological control, as their somewhat specialised habits had escaped attention. They are not ordinary parasites. The female wasp burrows in the ground in search of beetle grubs and, on finding one, paralyses it and lays an egg on its under surface. The young wasp grub, on hatching, buries its head only in the body of the beetle grub, but nevertheless in time completely consumes it, except for the cuticle. The wasps seem to have an especial predilection for the grubs of beetles, and have already proved themselves of considerable value, not only in Hawaii, as mentioned above, but also in other places, as for example in Mauritius, where they are employed to check the ravages of the Oryctes beetle that attacks the sugar cane.

Of necessity most of the interest in the biological control of insect pests has centred around the United States of America, for their need has been greatest. It is refreshing to find, however, that of late years the study has been taken up with considerable enthusiasm in various parts of the British Empire, especially Australia and New Zealand, South Africa and Canada. One of the most successful experiments has been the introduction into New Zealand of *Aphelinus mali*, a minute wasp that attacks the woolly aphis or American blight of apple trees. This tiny creature lays its eggs inside the aphides, the resultant grub feeding upon and eventually killing the aphis, the cuticle of which thereupon hardens and turns black, rendering it easily visible. In order to obtain a strong and healthy strain of the wasp, and to rule out as far as possible any special traits that might have been developed by local races, such as were established by the tachinid parasites of the gipsy moth referred to below, stocks were obtained from three climatically very different sources in the United States, and crossed in New Zealand before being liberated. Whether these precautions were actually of value or not cannot now be determined, but the fact remains that the insect, when set free, proved most successful, quickly bringing the aphis under control throughout the Dominion. A supply of the New Zealand stock has since been distributed in parts of Australia, and there, too, it has already produced highly beneficial results.

There is one other field in which insects have already proved, in certain districts, of enormous benefit to mankind, and that is in the control of noxious weeds. It was in the Hawaiian Islands, where so much successful work of this nature has been carried through, that the first experiments were made. Lantana, an attractive tropical shrub, had been introduced into the islands for ornamental purposes about 1850, and by 1900 it had spread to such an alarming extent as to be a veritable scourge in low-lying pastures. A large number of species of insects that feed upon this plant was introduced over a period of years, and although it cannot be claimed that they have destroyed it, yet they have successfully prevented it from re-colonising areas from which it had been cleared. The most spectacular success, however, has been achieved in Australia. About the year 1920 it was estimated that the various species of prickly pear (*Opuntia*) which had been originally brought to Australia as botanical curiosities, had taken possession of some thirty million acres of land, mainly in Queensland, so effectually that it was impossible in places even to force a way through it. And it was further estimated that it was spreading at the rate of about a million acres a year—it needed only a very simple calculation to determine how long it would be before the whole of eastern Australia would become a vast wilderness of prickly pear.

Chemical methods having proved either too costly or ineffective, the help of insects was sought. The first species introduced was the cochineal insect, *Dactylopius indicus*; soon after liberation it entirely destroyed some thousands of acres of one species of *Opuntia*, but it had no effect on others; it has since itself been attacked by the lady-bird that was introduced to check the mealy-bug, but fortunately seems to be keeping ahead of it.

Other species of Dactylopius have since been introduced, and one of them at least has done very fine work, a permanent staff being engaged in distributing it to all areas that need it. The red mite, not strictly an insect, and a large plant bug (*Chelinidea tabulata*), a weevil, some long-horned beetles, and several caterpillars (one from the Argentine in particular gives great promise) have also been imported and liberated. And as a result it now really seems that salvation from the prickly pear will almost certainly come from the insect world.

That biological control of insects is seldom such a simple process as the earlier experiments seemed to indicate is well shown by the work that has been done in the United States in the endeavour to check the ravages of the gipsy and brown-tail moths, two European species introduced about 1870, the latter quite a rarity, by the way, the former now extinct in England. Up to 1926 over sixty species of parasites had been imported, of which, although sixteen had been established in New England, only about six could be accounted really important, namely, a predacious beetle, two tachinid flies, and an ichneumon attacking the larvae, and two minute wasps attacking the eggs. It should not be too hastily assumed, however, that the other fifty-four imported species will never prove of any particular importance. It took over twenty years for *Pleurotopis epigonus*, a parasite of the Hessian fly, to make good. This species, although imported into the United States between 1890 and 1895, was not met with again until 1917, yet since that date it has become one of the commonest parasites of the Hessian fly throughout Maryland, Pennsylvania, New Jersey and New York.

In the case of the gipsy moth, unexpected set-backs were met with. For example, on one occasion a number of gipsy moth caterpillars known to contain tachinid parasites was brought from Europe. The parasites duly pupated but produced only hyper-parasites, a species of Perilampus, whose origin was a mystery and whose introduction was the last thing desired. Subsequently it was discovered that the grub of the hyperparasite had a habit of lying dormant inside the grub of the tachinid, and only becoming active after the latter has left its original host and pupated. Later still it was found that the Perilampus did not even lay its eggs on the caterpillar in the usual way, but upon leaves, and that the minute grub, practically invisible to the naked eye, upon emergence had to find its way to a caterpillar, burrow into it and then locate inside it the grub of the tachinid. This fact accounted for the previous failure to detect the hyperparasite by the usual observational methods.

A curious result also attended the introduction from Europe of another tachinid parasite of the gipsy moth. In this case the European species was so closely allied to an American species as to be barely distinguishable from it, yet its American ally was quite valueless as a parasite. The two tachinids most unfortunately interbred, with the unexpected result that the parasitic power of the European parents was entirely lost in the subsequent generations.

Again, in the case of a small ichneumon (*Meteorus versicolor*), which appeared a promising species, all efforts to raise a stock were for a long time frustrated because nothing but males were ever bred under laboratory conditions. However, when finally it was decided to give up all attempts to raise a stock of them, the solution of the difficulty was actually discovered by accident whilst a small number of both males and females freshly received from Europe were about to be liberated in the field. The bright rays of the sun struck the glass container, and mating took place at once.

J. J. Ward

ICHNEUMON-FLY AND UNPACKING PARASITES' EGGS

The palisade sawfly attacks the leaves of the black poplar and defends itself effectually against ants (see p. 1589). But here (bottom) is a flying parasite that can get at it. Above, eggs of the Tachina fly from Japan are being unpacked for use in U.S.A.

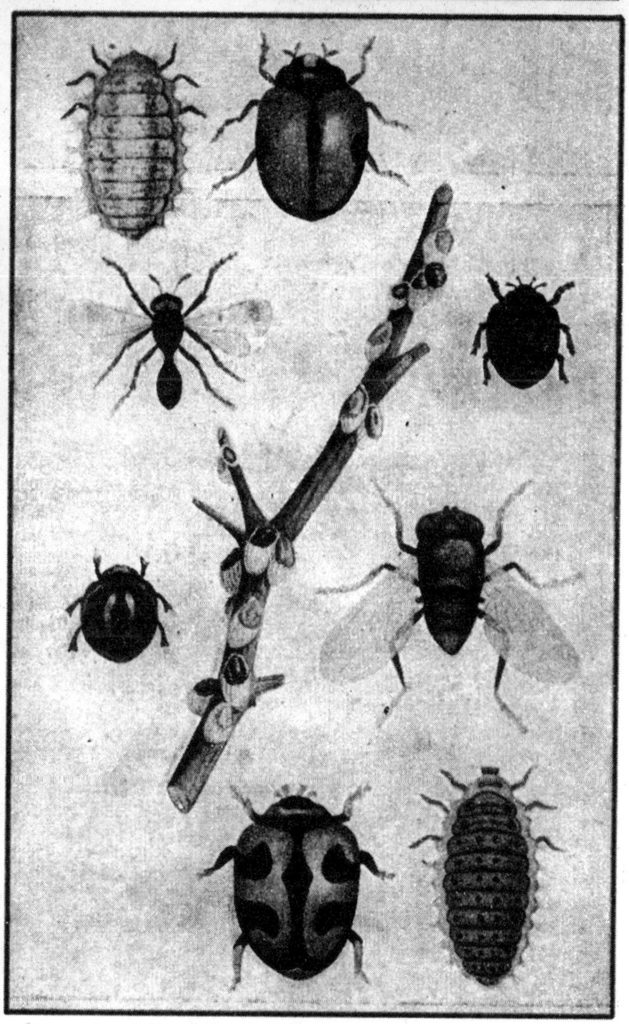

KILLERS OF CALIFORNIA'S PESTS

Here is a number of friendly parasites which attack the agricultural pests of California. These specimens are either ladybirds or parasites of the very destructive cotton cushion scale. The twig in the centre shows the scales attacked by some of these louse-like parasites.

From the standpoint both of guarding against the importation of dangerous secondary parasites (hyperparasites), and of the raising of beneficial primary parasites it is therefore of the utmost importance to have the fullest possible knowledge of the life-cycles and habits of every insect that falls into either of these categories, before introducing it to a new sphere of activity. For example, but for the introduction of a secondary parasite some twenty-five years previously, the habits of which were imperfectly known, it seems probable that the recently introduced primary parasite, *Aphycus lounsburyi*, would have proved an almost perfect control of the black scale in California. Nowadays, therefore, the most elaborate precautions are observed at all entomological stations working upon problems of biological control, for one small gap in the knowledge of the habits of an insect may make all the difference.

WILD BOARS, ENEMIES OF CULTIVATION AND SO OF CIVILIZATION

Everything retreats before the herd of wild boars when it appears. The pig family is a pugnacious one and the boars know very well how to cooperate against an enemy and to drive all competitors away from their feeding ground. We see a herd here descended from the hill to feed in the valleys. As they root about they raise clouds of dust and all vegetation round them will be ruined. Woe to any agriculturist whose carefully-tended land they come across. In an hour all may be destroyed.

Chapter CXLIV

Animal Enemies of Civilization

By Dr. William J. Dakin

Professor of Zoology, Liverpool University

ONLY a generation ago it was not very obvious that there were animals which seriously menaced civilization. The schoolboy of that time, if asked to name the serious animal enemies of man, would probably have thought of man-eating tigers or the dreaded cobra of India with its huge annual toll of deaths. He might also have realized that plagues of locusts were not exactly to be regarded as harmless to the people of the Mediterranean countries, although in this case the danger would arise through the destruction of crops.

Now, however, the situation is entirely different. We read that a beetle—the boll weevil—destroys upwards of 400,000 bales of cotton in the United States per annum. The name of the animal becomes quite familiar on the Liverpool and Manchester Cotton Exchanges. The total losses in the United States alone from injurious insects have been estimated at the almost incredible figure of £400,000,000 per annum. We give the United States figures because probably no other country has made such an organized attack on insect pests.

Even more serious than attacks on man's products are the animal enemies of his health. Not so many years have passed since it was usual to apply the term "White Man's Grave" to parts of the Tropics Pioneers and buccaneers paid with their lives for their invasion of the West Indies, Central America, the West Coast of Africa, and so on. Malaria and yellow fever, or "Yellow Jack," as it was called, were the dread diseases of those regions, and the inability to find their cause made them no less terrifying.

The mystery of these diseases is clear to us now and the Panama Canal stands as the finest memorial to our discovery of the part played by the mosquito in their causation, for did not De Lesseps leave the graves of 50,000 workmen in that very region where disease rather than lack of engineering skill robbed him of another triumph?

It needs very little investigation to show that the insects are our worst enemies. In fact, they are the only group of animals that we need at present fear in our contest for the possession of the earth. The competition lies then between the highest group of invertebrates and the highest group of the vertebrates. After a study of insect life one can thoroughly appreciate the remark that it is well for us there are no ants the size of human beings. Perhaps, if there had been no limits to size in the insect group, there might have been no higher groups at all. This, however, is pure speculation. What is certain is that they make up in numbers for their small size and they show every conceivable adaptation to life in the air and on land, but are curiously restricted from life in the sea.

H. Bastin

COTTON PEST

Cotton has played a tremendous part in civilization and the cotton boll weevil (grub, bottom, adult form, top) is always at war on the cotton crop.

THE first of the really great tropical diseases to be traced to its source was malaria and Sir Ronald Ross, one of the most brilliant scientists, played a foremost part in the discovery. Malaria was supposed to be due to a deadly miasma—some emanation from marshes and swamps—and it was assumed to be most deadly in the early morning or at dusk. Yellow fever might run through a ship, striking down one after another of the crew, and so the contents of the hold—bilge water and various sorts of cargo—were also supposed to produce miasmas. Then came the discovery that the actual cause of malaria was a microscopic blood parasite which destroyed the red blood corpuscles. It remained to find where this came from and how it entered human beings. More than once the suggestion had been made that mosquitoes were to be associated with both malaria and yellow fever, and, of course, these suggestions fitted in quite well with the old miasma superstitions, for mosquitoes are certainly more abundant in the neighbourhood of marshes, and many species only bite at night or in the dusk of early morning and evening. It was not easy, however, to bring the proof. The disease germs were microscopic and the entire anatomy of a small mosquito would have to be searched for them. Besides this, they would only be present in mosquitoes which had themselves obtained them from somewhere else—probably an infected human being. Although it was not then known, the great "snag" lay in the fact that only certain kinds of mosquitoes could carry the malaria parasite and over 1500 species of mosquitoes have been described. Mosquitoes range from the Arctic latitudes to the Tropics and at least twenty-five kinds are found in the British Isles. Sir Ronald Ross, after long search, was successful in finding the parasite in the genus Anopheles. This anopheles mosquito is, to a layman, very like other species of mosquitoes—in fact, it takes an expert to name a mosquito.

Now the only sound method of wiping out malaria (and also yellow fever) is to destroy the mosquitoes. This is not altogether so difficult a task, because there is one weak point in the mosquito's

life history—its early stages are aquatic. The anopheles mosquito lays its eggs on the surface of still water, such as is found in small ponds, ditches, roof gutters, collections in old tins and buckets and water tanks, each female laying 40–100 eggs. Out of each of these eggs a little larva soon hatches. It lives an aquatic life, capturing and feeding upon microscopic particles of organic matter, but it *must* come up to the surface to breathe. We need not go further into details. After a period varying from days to weeks the larva changes to a pupa and from the pupa comes the winged adult, which returns no more to the water unless it be to the surface to lay eggs.

A thoroughly well-organized system of mosquito control would take over a district, drain it, see that all casual collecting places of water were destroyed, and water tanks screened. An additional method of attack is to put a small quantity of oil on the surface of water collections already infested by mosquito larvae. Even a delicate oil film prevents them from breathing and results in death. It is characteristic, however, of human frailty that really little has yet been done. The great success of the Panama Canal builders has not been continued in other places to the extent one might have expected. But notwithstanding this, the discoveries of Ross, Mawson, Grassi, and others must be credited already with saving hundreds of thousands of lives and probably enriching the world by millions of pounds sterling.

The disease-carrying propensities of the mosquitoes are equalled by those of the tsetse-flies of Africa. These insects belong to the same group as our house-flies, stable flies, bluebottles, etc., and at first sight look not unlike stable flies. They are blood-sucking flies, and attack not only man and his domestic animals, but also wild game and even such creatures as crocodiles. There are several species, and they are responsible for more than one disease, the best-known being a human disease, sleeping sickness (*not* sleepy sickness, a curious disease which has recently been receiving attention in the English newspapers), and the earlier known trouble called nagana, or "tsetse-fly disease," of cattle and horses. The role of the parasite, and of the tsetse-fly which carries it, was first proved conclusively as the result of the investigation of nagana by Bruce in Zululand in 1897.

The parasite in both these diseases is called a trypanosome, and it is found in the blood of infected animals. Some other trypanosome diseases are not

W S. Berridge

PUFF ADDER AND ALLIGATORS EVER RESENTFUL OF MAN'S PRESENCE

White men going out to exploit new territories have constantly been fighting the animal dwellers in their domains. One of the deadliest enemies of the pioneer has been the venomous snake, striking suddenly, unobserved. Below is a deadly puff adder. Above we have a group of alligators which dispute man's path when he reclaims the swamps.

conveyed by insects at all, but we are here concerned with the tsetse-fly and not with the parasite.

Sleeping sickness has resulted in the death of millions of natives of Africa, and also of many Europeans. It is often a disease of long duration, yet until quite recently there was little hope of any cure by the use of drugs.

Unfortunately, the tsetse-fly is not nearly so easily vanquished as the mosquito. It provides a very serious problem indeed in man's fight for dominance in Central Africa. The fly is active by day. Eight species are known to carry pathogenic trypanosomes, and they have a wide African range; but where common they are generally, though not always, found along definite tracts called "fly belts." The flies like cover in the nature of forest, bush, or something equivalent. They are infrequent or absent altogether from open plains. Some like to be near water, others are not so restricted. The great difficulty in destroying the tsetse-fly is the absence of a stage in which it could easily be attacked wholesale. It does not lay eggs at all. The females produce living and full-grown larvae, ugly yellowish, limbless maggots, one at a birth. These almost immediately seek a hiding-place and pupate. Destruction of the fly would therefore require an attack on the adult insects, an almost inconceivable task when one thinks of the numbers, the country where they are found, and the immense areas involved. In many regions the deadly haunts of the tsetse-fly still form a barrier to the advancement of tropical agriculture and colonisation. Clearing of the tsetse-fly areas has been attempted, and many other suggestions have been made to stem the tide of sleeping sickness. At the present, however, the only complete safety lies in the difficult avoidance of actual bites, and the only remedy of the unfortunate sufferer is the questionable efficiency of dangerous drugs.

WORK OF DEADLY FOES TO HEALTH-GIVING FRUITS IN HOT CLIMATES

Citrus fruits are a vital need in certain hot parts of the world, especially where fresh vegetables are scarce. Scurvy, the old scourge of the sea, was finally conquered by the juice of the lime. Here (bottom) we have a devastated orange grove in U.S.A. The damage was done by the Mediterranean fruit fly accidentally imported. Above is a grape fruit damaged by maggots.

Let us turn to an insect pest of man's vegetable products. The cotton boll weevil is certainly notorious enough for this short illustration. It is not only seriously affecting one of the biggest industries of the United States, but is probably playing some part in the success of manufactured products like artificial silk. *Anthonomus grandis* is a weevil about a quarter of an inch in length, a very near relation of the weevils which destroy grain and other food products. It is a native of tropical America, and it spreads gradually from there through Mexico and northwards. This should be noted. There is no question that had man not developed the cotton plantations, there would have been far fewer boll weevils in the world to-day. Probably its limits will now be determined solely by aridity and cold in winter. The beetle passes the winter in the adult state hiding in cracks

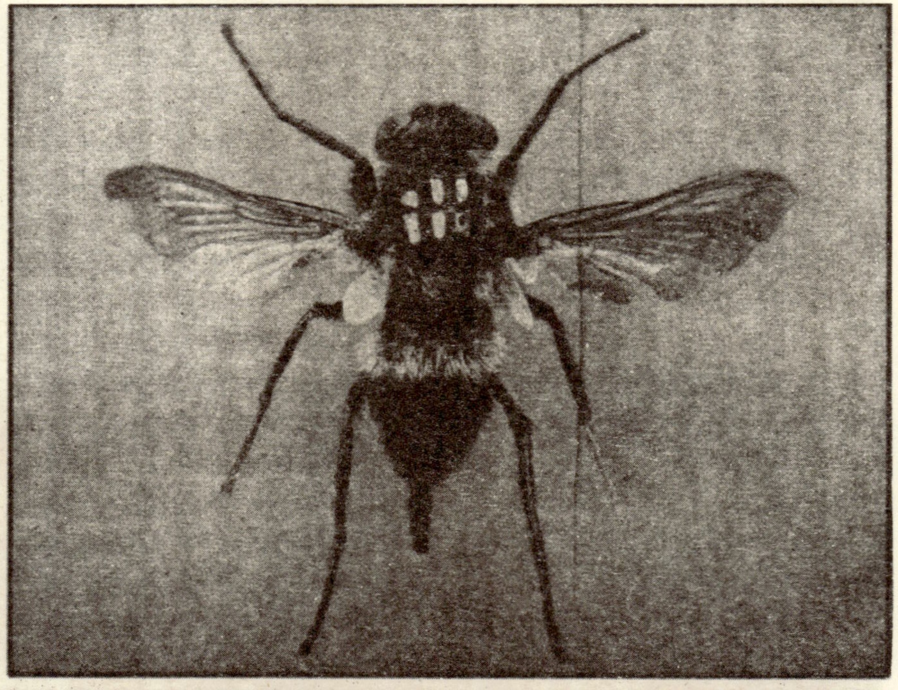

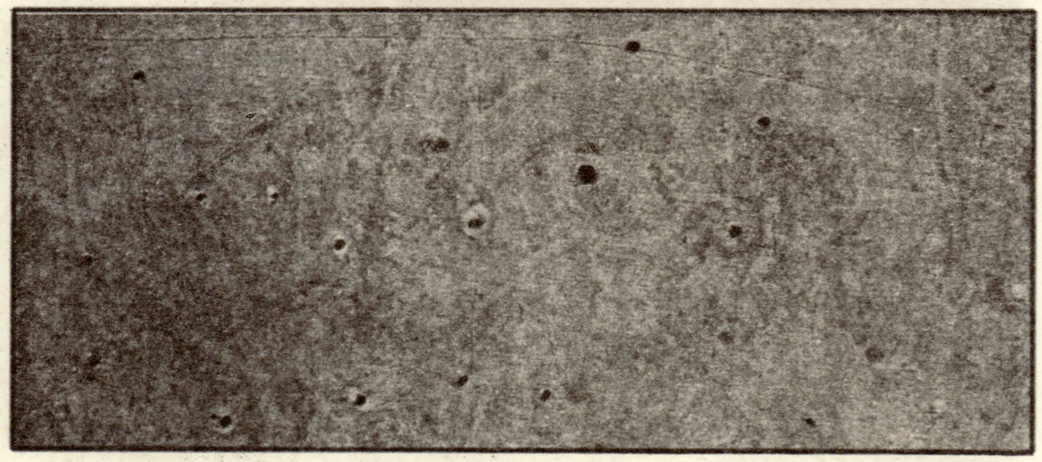

WARBLE FLIES THAT PREY UPON THE CATTLE MAN HAS RESERVED FOR HIS OWN USE

H. Bastin

Nature's law decrees that as soon as one kind of animal becomes very plentiful its enemies multiply and, when those enemies have multiplied up to a point, they, in turn, dwindle to normal as their food supply is reduced. But man constantly steps in and upsets this delicate balance to maintain that state of things called civilization. Man has decided to be the chief parasite of certain animals; the ox, for example. Therefore, he must fight all other things that prey upon it. Above are some of them—warble flies that lay eggs in the hides of cattle. Below (left) are three grubs and (right) a skin damaged by them. Above we have adult flies. The one on the right is a female with ovipositor partly showing.

B N.A

HOW THE DEADLY BOLL WEEVIL SETS ABOUT ITS WORK OF DESTRUCTION IN THE COTTON FIELDS

The boll weevil is especially renowned among agricultural pests because it is doubly dangerous. While moths, for instance, are only destructive in the caterpillar or larval stage the boll weevil devours the cotton plant not only as a larva but as an adult as well. Our photographs here show (bottom left) an adult weevil puncturing a cotton bud to deposit its egg; (bottom right) weevils puncturing partially matured cotton bolls; (top left) a larva at home in a cotton bud and (top right) the weevil in its pupa stage developing within a bud. The boll weevil gets its name because it attacks the bolls or seed-pods of its host plant. The problem of how to cope with it has been troubling American entomologists for years.

E.N.A

DIFFERENT DEGREES OF DAMAGE DONE BY BOLL WEEVILS TO MATURING COTTON

In the lower photograph are some cotton bolls in process of maturing. The largest has not been attacked and is in a healthy, normal condition. Compare it with the other examples which are in various stages of destruction. One is, in fact, totally destroyed. Above are a normal and a punctured cotton square—square being an alternative term for boll. The boll weevils that do all this damage are terribly fast breeders. It is estimated that by the end of the cotton season about 12,750,000 weevils could be produced from a single pair

in the ground, under rubbish, or in any other suitably sheltered spot. In spring, during the fruiting season of the cotton plant, the females deposit their eggs in little cavities made by boring into the fruit. In about three days the little grubs hatch from the eggs and immediately begin to feed. Seven to twelve days suffice to bring the grub to the resting pupal stage, and then three to five days more

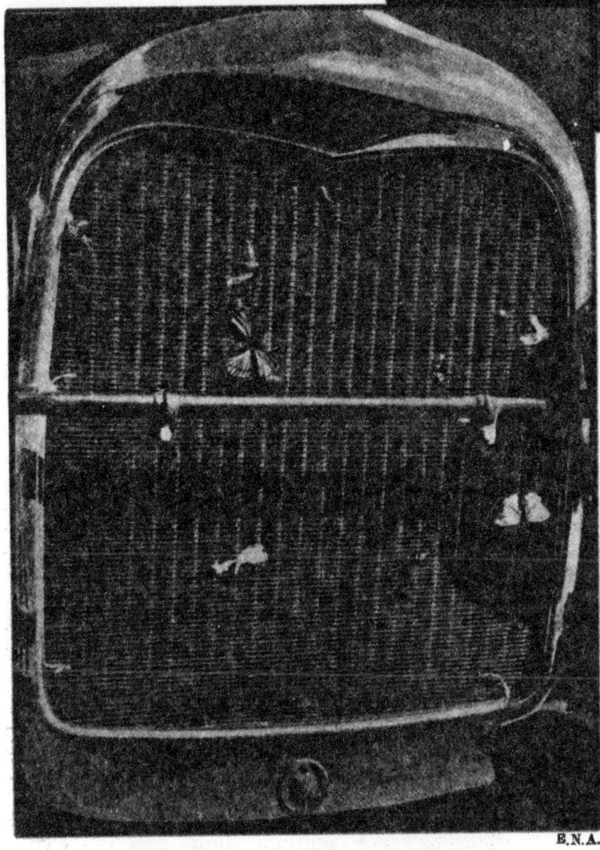

B.N.A.

NOXIOUS PESTS OF PROGRESS

A bonnet full of insects (bottom), many of them harmful, is collected by a car as it moves forward and, indeed, this is a symbol of the way in which human progress comes into collision with insect pests, such as the wood-boring beetle for instance (top).

see the adult out. In five days it may be laying eggs for another generation. The prolificity of these insects is amazing. It has been calculated that from a single pair of beetles at the beginning of the season there might arise 12,750,000 by the end. Our cabbage white butterfly only destroys vegetables during its larval stage, and this applies to many other insect pests like the clothes moths, for example. The cotton boll weevil feeds both in the larval and adult stages on the same plant. It is not surprising that the problem of its destruction has long been agitating the foremost entomologists of America, or that the danger of its spread to other and new cotton-growing regions should be fully appreciated.

Coming to Europe, one other illustration may be taken to show how a country's industries may depend upon the success or failure of a fight with an insect pest. The culprit this time is an aphis (a near relative of that annoying greenfly which spoils our roses) called *Phylloxera vitifoliae.* This creature is a native of America. In America, however, some degree of natural balance has been evolved, for American vines are more or less resistant to the pest. Somewhere about 1860 the Phylloxera reached Europe, probably by accidental importation with grapes or American grape vines. The European vine proved very susceptible to its attacks and, finding other conditions equally favourable, it developed to an amazing extent. The damage done in France and Italy was enormous. It cost France millions of pounds sterling.

This insect has a most complex life history. It exists in two main forms, one of which lives on the leaves, the other in the ground on the roots. It is the latter which is the dangerous form in Europe. Various preventive and destructive measures have been tried, but the most practical measure is the neat trick of grafting the European vines to the resistant American root-stocks, a curious but very rational sequel.

It is a point especially worthy of note that many of the creatures proving most disastrous to human life and industry to-day owe their power to a consequence of human enterprise, or of human carelessness. That consequence is the disturbance of "the balance of Nature." It is well illustrated by our mammalian pests—the rats and mice all over the world, the rabbit in Australia and, most recent of all, the fruit-eating bats of the same country. It is quite interesting, although it may be decidedly annoying, to see, too, how far some creatures change their

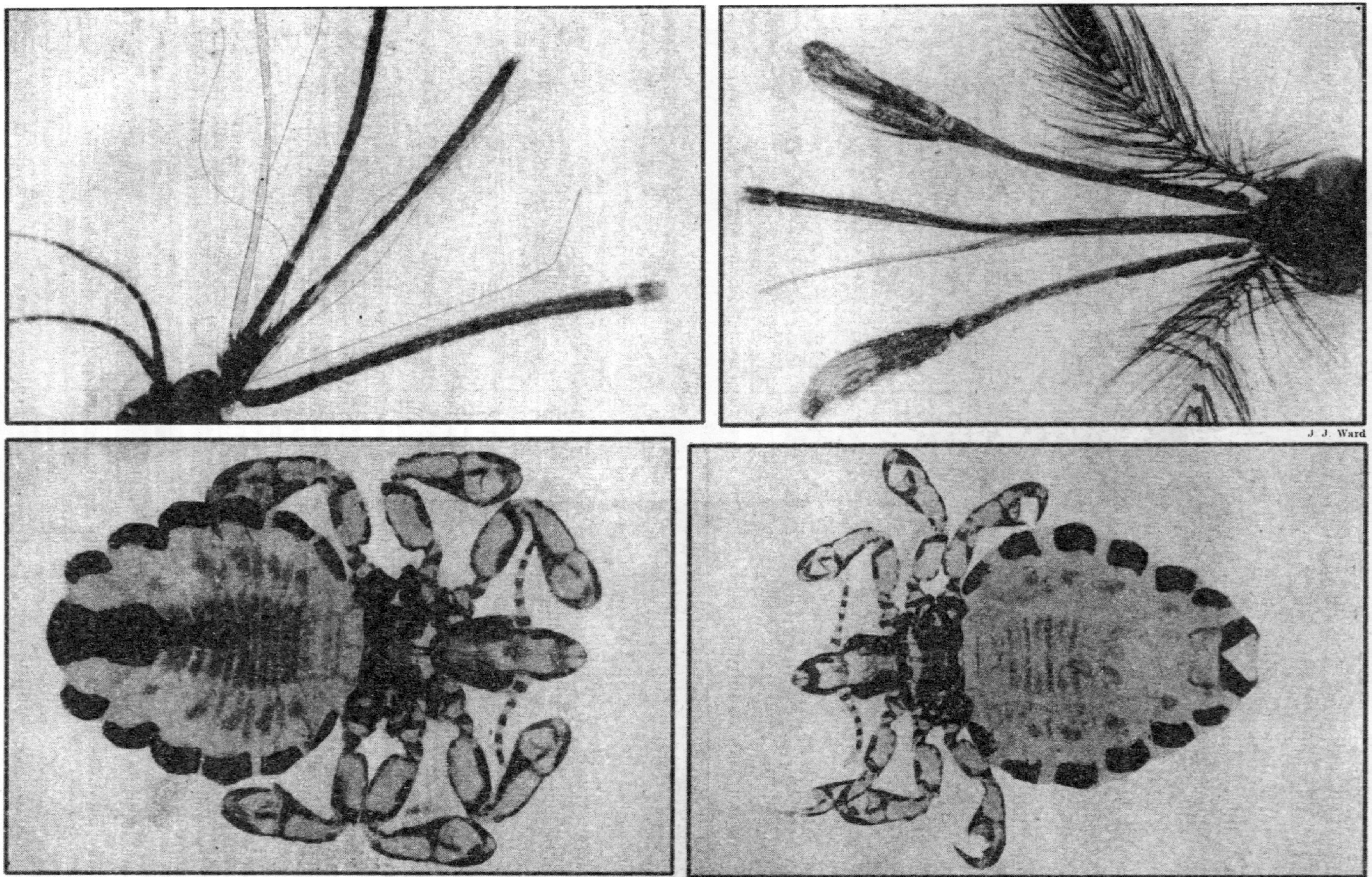

J. J. Ward

H. S. Cheavin

MALE AND FEMALE PARASITES OF THE PIG, AND THE MOSQUITO THAT SPREADS MALARIA AMONG MEN

The two lower photographs show the male and female forms of a troublesome parasite of the pig. Both specimens are very much magnified. Above we have the heads of (left) the female and (right) the male of the Anopheles mosquito also seen at a high magnification. It is only the females of this troublous creature that bite and they are provided with a minute case of lancets for piercing the skins of their victims. A mosquito really stabs rather than bites. The organism causing malarial fever is transmitted from the mosquito to man during the blood sucking process. Mosquitoes are among the most formidable enemies of civilization and they nearly prevented the cutting of the Panama Canal.

habits under such circumstances. Could anything have been more perverse than a bird, the kea, a parrot of the South Island of New Zealand, which fed upon seeds, fruit and insects until the sheep was introduced and developed? The creature then acquired the habit of pecking holes into the backs and sides of the sheep with its powerful beak!

We have provided rats and mice with excellent means of travel, we have supplied them with abundance of food, and we have reduced their enemies, the weasels, foxes, stoats, etc., in short, we have domesticated them. They have spread far from the land of their origin, and must be regarded as most serious pests.

Two species of rats are found in Great Britain, the black rat (house rat or ship rat) and the brown rat, but

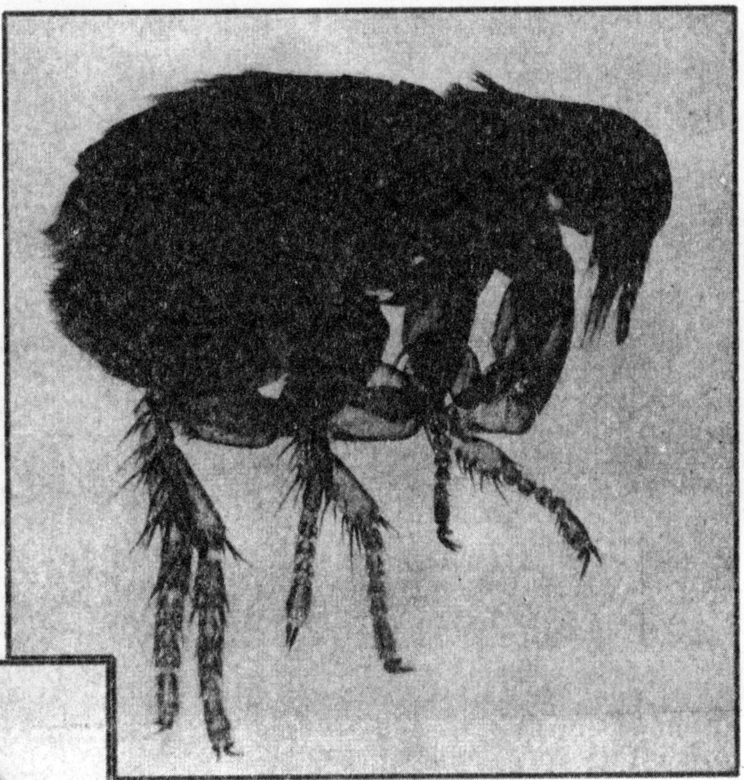

J. J. Ward

THE UBIQUITOUS FLEA

Found alike in temperate and tropical lands, the fleas are specially modified for a life of parasitism on their various hosts. This is a rabbit **flea.** The photographs of the whole insect (top) and of its head (bottom) are much enlarged.

the colour is not by any means a safe guide to the identification of the species. The first-named probably came from India; it is by nature an inhabitant of a more genial clime than ours, and that is why its existence is so closely associated with the shelter of our dwellings. Some authorities suggest it came back with the Crusaders. It is just as likely that its arrival was less romantic, perhaps a gradual spread like that of the rabbits in Australia. It soon became a terrible pest in Europe, and was responsible for those frightful outbreaks of plague such as the Black Death and the Great Plague of London whose descriptions provide such vivid pages in English history. The brown rat, too, was formerly unknown in Great Britain (its home is definitely the temperate parts of Asia), and probably did not reach Western Europe at all until about 1700.

The reproductive possibilities of the rats are surprising and it is not at all remarkable that a ship may be soon over-run with them. Indeed, the conditions so wonderfully depicted in "The Pied Piper of Hamelin" have actually been realized, for in a little town of Finland rats have actually "made nests inside men's Sunday hats," and even invaded the beds of the inhabitants.

Assuming that a pair of rats had six litters of eight in a year, and that the young were breeding in their turn when three and a half months old, then the progeny at the end of twelve months would be 880 rats (provided that sexes were produced in equal proportions, and no deaths occurred). There is an actual record of two females having 26 litters in 13 months, and producing 180 young. This would

Wheat stalks attacked by Hessian fly grubs

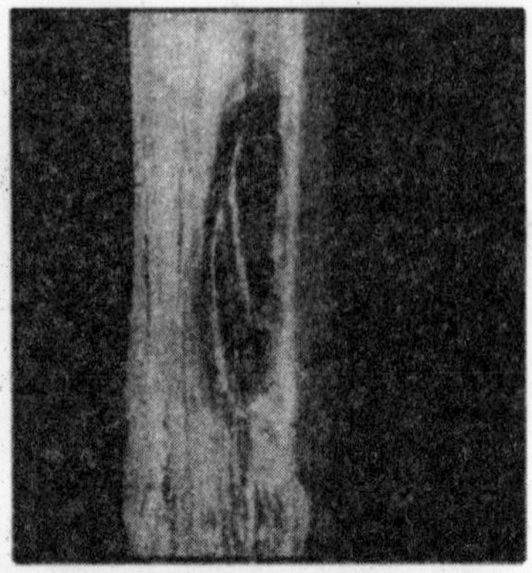

Grooves made by larva

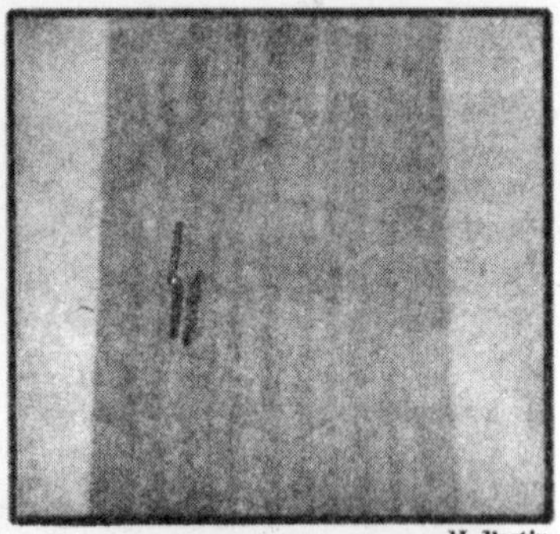

H. Bastin

Three eggs on wheat leaf

Top; Pupa of the Hessian fly—bottom; Flax seeds

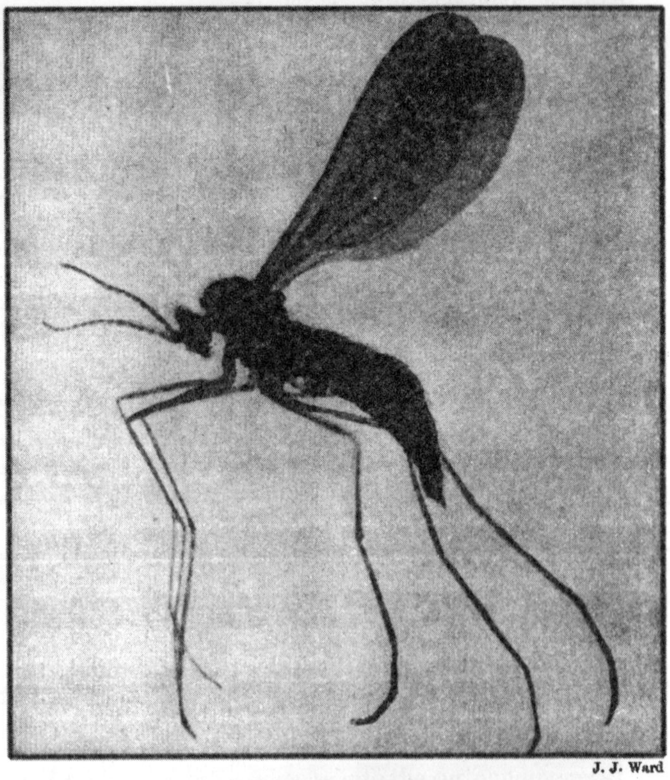

J. J. Ward

Hessian fly highly magnified

HESSIAN FLY, ONE OF THE WORLD'S VERY WORST FARMING PESTS

Belonging to the family of the gall-midges, the Hessian fly is like a very small gnat about $\frac{1}{16}$ in. long. As an adult it only lives for a few hours in which it mates and, if a female, lays its eggs. These are placed on the leaves of wheat and other cereals. On hatching the grubs bore into the wheat stalks and make their way down to one of the knots in the stem where they feed, at length destroying the life of the stem. Enormous damage is done in this way in America, but this fly has, luckily, not become a serious trouble in Britain.

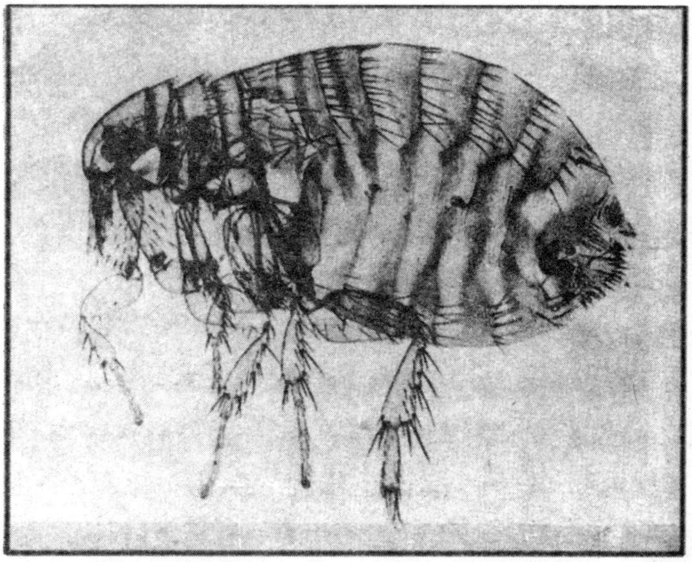

Bubonic plague flea of rat, female

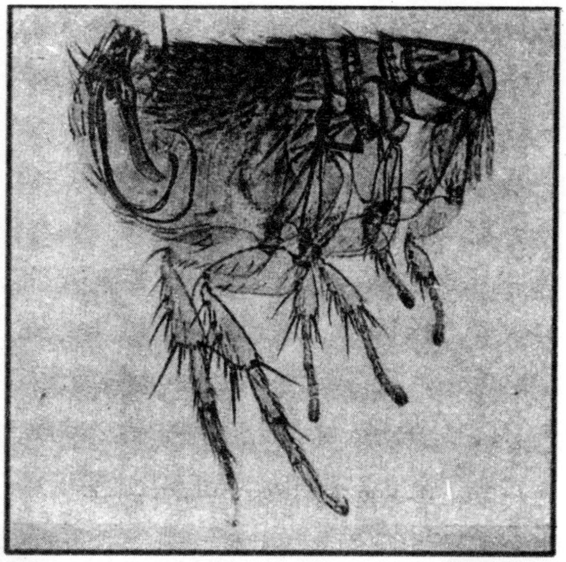

Male of rat flea carrying bubonic plague germs

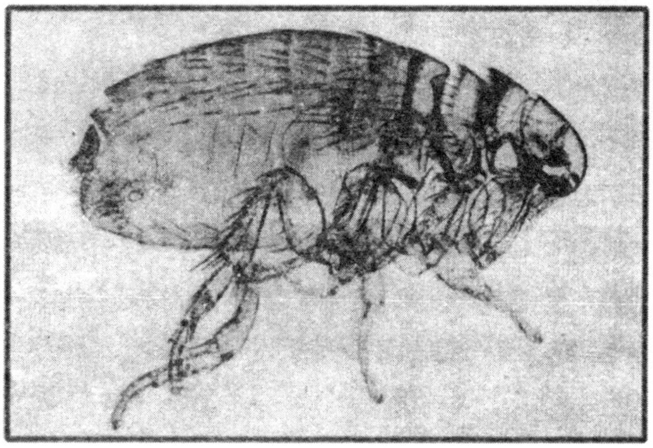

Dog flea, female

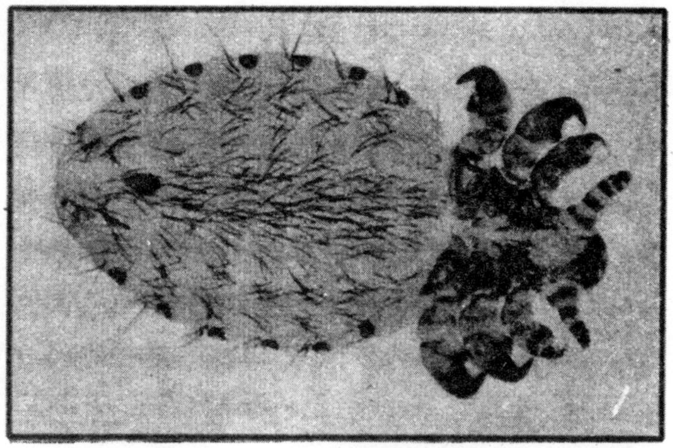

Common dog louse

Head and forepart of sheep tick

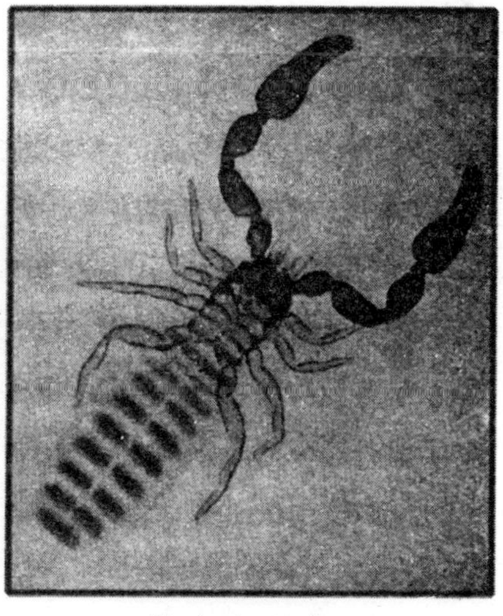

The book scorpion

PARASITES THAT PREY ON MAN, HIS PETS, FLOCKS AND BOOKS

These photographs show their subjects considerably magnified. All these creatures are concerned in the ceaseless war against the interference that man sets up in the natural order of things. The weird-looking thing in the bottom right photograph is a book-scorpion which sometimes infests libraries and museum collections. The long claws in front bear a superficial resemblance to those of the scorpion. Bubonic plague, the disease of the Black Death and the Great Plague of London, is caused by the bite of a rat-flea (top photos).

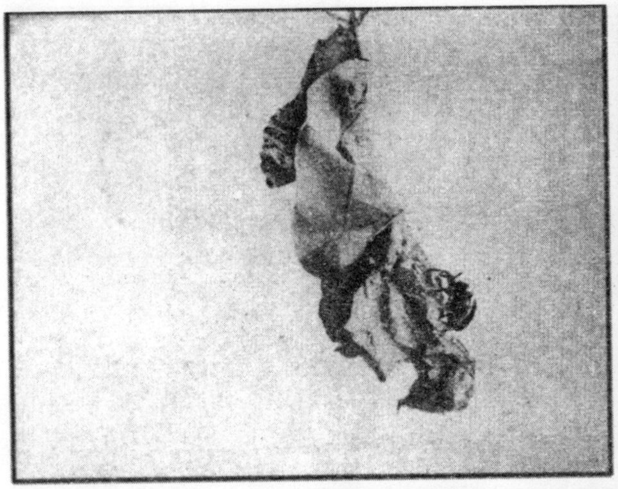

The weevil lays its eggs and rolls the leaf

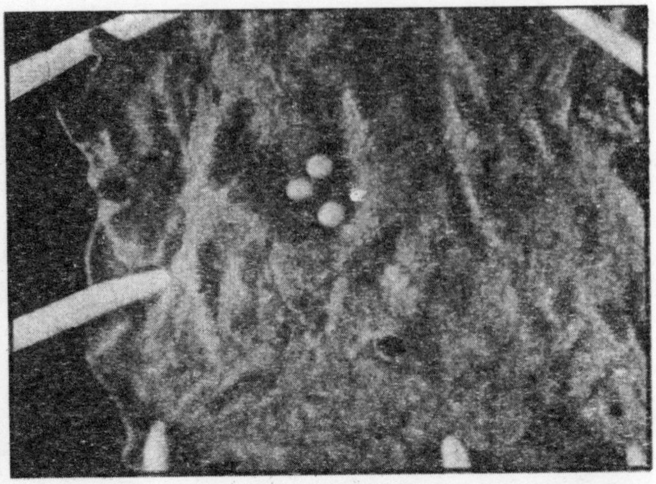

The leaf unrolled to show eggs

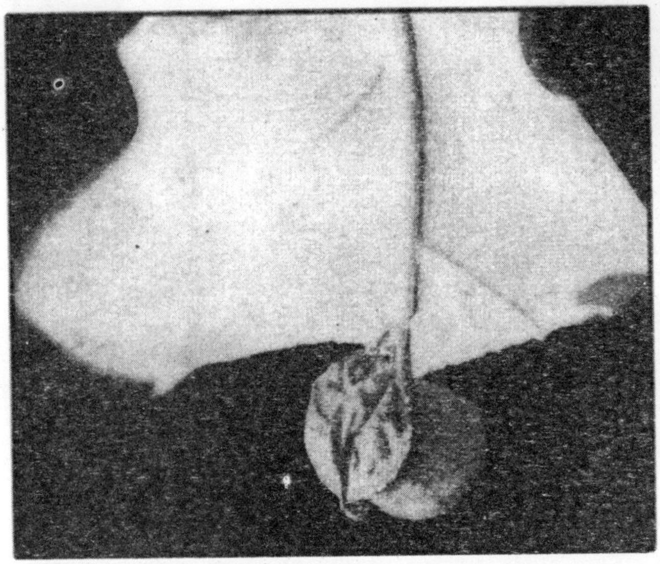

A finished " roll " magnified

" Roll " opened to show full fed larva

Searching for a suitable place

Terminal leaves are usually chosen for " rolls "

H Bastin

Leaves of hazel rolled by a similar insect

MINUTE ENEMY OF A BIG TREE AND A RELATIVE THAT ATTACKS LAUREL

Oak trees have an enemy in a small insect called the oak roller. It lays its eggs upon an oak-leaf and then proceeds to roll the leaf into a kind of cocoon for their protection and concealment. Inside this snug retreat the eggs hatch, and the larvae start to feed. Considering the comparative sizes of leaf and insect, the rolling is really quite a remarkable feat. The bottom right-hand photograph shows laurel leaves rolled for a similiar purpose by a member of an allied species.

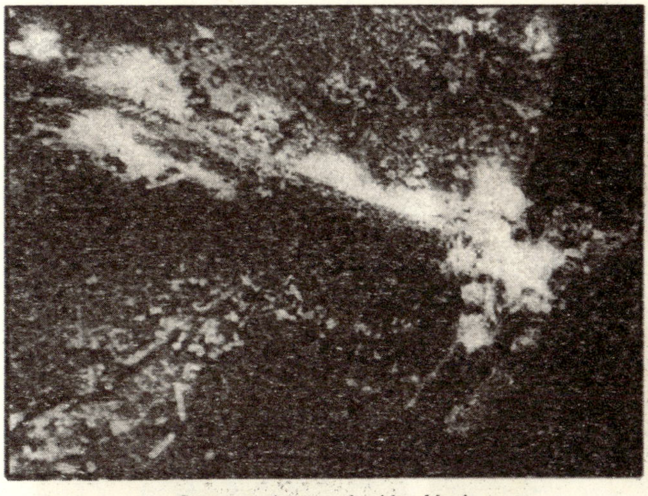

Orange scale on underside of leaf

Orange scale

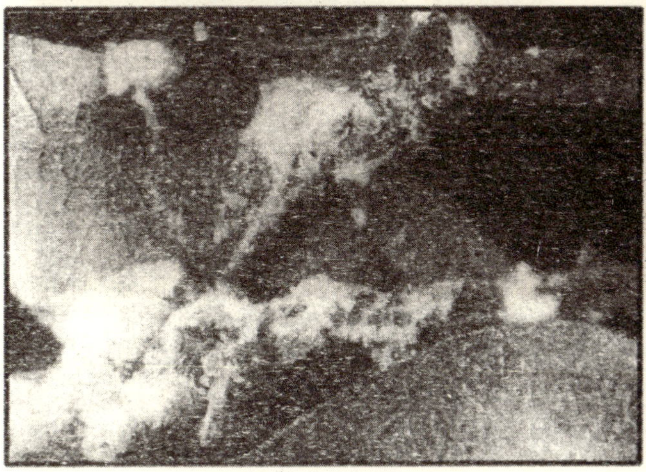

Another kind of orange scale

Cottony cushion scale

San Josè scale

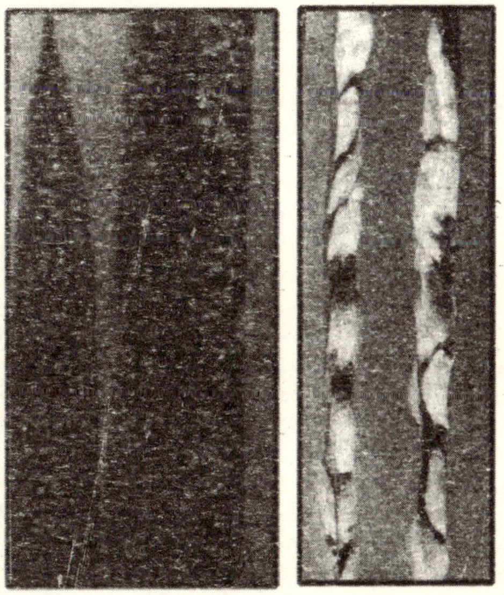

Scale on cycas in Ceylon and on pine needles in Corsica

H. Bastin

Oyster scale on apple trees

NOXIOUS SCALE INSECTS THAT SUCK THE LIFE JUICES OF PLANTS

Some years ago the orange-growing industry in California was nearly ruined by a massed attack of scale insects accidentally imported from Australia. There are various kinds of this pest. One, the cottony cushion scale, secretes a white, cottony substance as a wrapping for the eggs. In other species the female dies after laying and her shrivelled body acts as a covering. Scale insects suck the plant juices by means of beak-like organs. The males are incapable of feeding and die after mating.

H Bastin and J. J. Ward

RAVAGES OF WINE-CORK MOTH AND A GOAT-MOTH COCOON

The wine-cork moth lays its eggs upon the corks of bottles, utterly regardless of the preciousness of vintage. As we see here, a cork can become absolutely riddled with the burrows made by the feeding caterpillars. In the centre is the cork from a sherry bottle that has been ruined with disastrous results to the wine. On the right we see a goat-moth caterpillar making itself a cocoon of wood-dust. These big larvae do a great deal of damage to standing timber.

give twice as many as the above theoretical calculation. These powers of reproduction are not attained normally in nature, or else a pair of rats might give rise to something like 950,000,000,000 in six years!

Many people still simply regard the rat as a loathsome beast which may become so ravenous as to attack human beings. The real tragedy, however, in which the rat plays a part, is of far greater significance, for plague, a disease caused by a particular bacillus—the *Bacillus pestis*—is still a nightmare in crowded Oriental countries. During the present century it has slain millions of people in Asia. The rat is not the direct medium by which the dreaded germ is introduced into man. This part is played by a particular rat flea. And so we get the chain—plague-infected rats—fleas feed on blood of such rats—fleas invade human buildings or otherwise reach man.

JUST before the beginning of the War, plague invaded Ceylon. The spread of the disease southward in India had been gradually watched until it reached the extreme southern parts. Its first appearance in Ceylon was in the great port of Colombo, and here the first cases came from the neighbourhood of the grain warehouses on the harbour wharves near the very place where the rats disembarked after their unofficial voyage, and where they found food in plenty. The rat can actually be used as an indicator of the probability of plague, and it is common now for a regular rat examination to take place in dangerous localities so that the advent of plague in rats can be watched before it appears in man.

Rats are very good travellers, and plague occurs every now and then even in British ports. The devices employed to prevent rats going aboard or coming off ships are too often forgotten.

It must not be thought that plague is the only reason for rat or mouse destruction. Other diseases are rat-borne. Trichinosis, caused by a parasitic threadworm, and very probably foot and mouth disease are two which may be mentioned. Lastly, we must not forget the toll on agriculture. Grain is the chief and favourite food of rats, although their tastes are extremely varied. The average total rural damage per year in Great Britain has been estimated at £15,000,000. Probably this is a conservative estimate.

It is quite impossible to describe here the biological organization which is being built up to support man's fight against some of the lower organisms. The battle gains in importance as populations increase, and the world's demands for food and other natural products grow. It is a big problem, requiring the fullest use of the science of biology, for whilst none of the pests we have named can have much of a good nature said about them, there is always the danger that careless destruction of any one kind of creature may disturb the balance of nature and reveal or set going a quite unexpected circuit of other troubles.

Chapter CXLV

Winged Warriors of the Air

By S. L. Bensusan

Author of "Wild Birds Throughout the Year"

War in the air! We humans think at once of airships, aeroplanes and searchlights, of high firing shells, of bombs bursting and the terror of destruction on all sides. We associate it with night attacks on terror-stricken cities, with a blind, blundering destruction that knows not where it strikes, nor what it destroys, but aims first and last at creating fear or panic.

But there is another war in the air, one we may watch in ease, security and perhaps with a certain sympathy for its victims on cloudless summer days when to all outward seeming peace is the law of life. There are few who realize that strife is eternal, that Nature's hand is never relaxed, that she creates one form to be the victim of another, and is lavish in giving birth in order that those who can only live by destruction shall not fail of their sustenance.

Sometimes we see the destroyer at work; it may be the stately golden eagle of the mountains, it may be the insignificant shrike of the river valley, known to the schoolboy as the 'butcher bird,' but whether it be one or the other, the great or the small, the magnificent or the insignificant, we know that something dies lest the pursuer should go hungry, and that Nature will replenish the ranks of those who fall and perhaps even give them a little space of joy and sunshine before they pass to serve their appointed tragic end.

There can be no attempt here to set out the whole story of strife in the world of birds and insects, a struggle that will never find the solution provided by a peace conference. Space would forbid, and the writer can only tell of things that have come within the range of his vision.

At first sight it may seem a little inaccurate to describe the air as a battleground in times of peace and goodwill among men, but for some birds and insects it is no less dangerous. There are always warriors in wait for the unwary. The golden eagle, for example, most powerful of all our raptorial birds, appears to use its eyrie, usually on the ledge of a rock, sometimes the branch of a tree, as a jumping off ground for the pursuit of prey, and beyond all doubt the high places of the air are its observation ground.

From the near neighbourhood of cloudland it looks down upon the mountain hares, the grouse, sometimes the new-born lambs and fawns, and it is from the heights that death comes to them almost unawares. They know nothing more than the passing of a shadow across their light, the rush of wings, a moment's sense of danger and a swift end. With the best of good intention it is impossible to regard this king of birds as other than an enemy. The most that game preservers have found to say in his favour is that he rids the grouse moors of weak birds because they are the easiest to catch. But this will not make atonement for the destruction of lambs and fawns, or for the occasional swoop on babies, of which several cases are on record.

There are birds that chase and capture their prey in the air; the fast flying peregrine falcon provides, perhaps, the best example. I have seen a peregrine chasing a terrified company of wild pigeons over a long stretch of marshland, actually strike one down in flight and pick it up before it had fallen to the ground. It is a curious thing but one many observers will have noticed, that sometimes when a falcon swoops to its quarry and misses, it does not seek to recover and return to that pursuit, it goes on in search of something else, as though ashamed of the missed stroke. Hawks pursue grouse and partridges, and are used for this purpose by those who train hawks to fly at game. The merlin, sometimes flown at sparrows and larks, is also given to seeking these birds in the air on its own account. Hobby and sparrowhawk will do the same and the goshawk will chase and kill rabbits. Even snipe and woodcock are sought by these fast flyers; they contrive to take their quarry in spite of the irregularity of the flight, adjusting their movements with marvellous celerity.

The most familiar form of hawking in this country was, and is, at herons. This sport has been followed for many centuries in England; the hawk always tries to get above the heron and the heron to keep above the hawk, or to oppose its beak to the stroke. Hawking has been described by very many English writers from Spenser to Sir Walter Scott, and it is only dying down in England because herons are scarce. Sometimes the struggle between hawk and heron has been known to last as long as half an hour, but it generally ends with the heron's death. To-day herons are shot on sight in the neighbourhood of trout hatcheries; their love for game fish penalises them.

It is well to remember that the regulated pursuit of one bird by another did not originate in this country, it has been practised from time immemorial. In Asia falconry was certainly in vogue four thousand years ago, it came into Europe from Asia before the Norman Conquest. Nobody can state the precise date, but many of the French kings had falconries where birds were bred for sport. The Saxons trained hawks and the Norman conquerors of the country were great lovers of the falcon. In twelfth-century London sparrowhawks and goshawks were kept for hawking, and down to the fourteenth century there was a royal falconry at Charing, now Charing Cross, and then a village between London and Westminster. The fashion has been re-established in the past few years, and there are to-day many private estates where hawks are kept and trained. In the old days it was even said that birds belonged of right to certain classes of the community. Thus an emperor was entitled to hunt with an eagle, a prince with a falcon, an earl with a peregrine, a lady with a merlin, a yeoman with a goshawk, a priest with a sparrowhawk. There is a small dictionary of terms which falconers know by heart, and by the time a sport has its own glossary, we may be sure that it has captured a public.

We have to remember that all the raptorial birds are dependent for their food upon their prowess as hunters, and that where they pursue birds it is to take them in flight. Only the owl differs in this regard; it will frequently take sleeping birds off bushes after nightfall. When an owl seizes its prey, the grip drives a claw through the victim's body so that death comes quickly.

THE shrikes or butcher birds are often overlooked in rural England because of their alleged rarity, but their habits are extremely interesting, and they are not really rare. About seven inches long, and with strong, sharp beaks, they are represented by three kinds in this country, the red-backed, the great grey and the lesser grey. There may be others, but the writer has never seen them. They live on all manner of insects, together with mice and small birds, and they impale their food on the thorn of some bush, generally close to the nest, that is known as their larder. Like owls they can eject the indigestible part of the food they eat, and this capacity enables them to prey upon everything that comes along, no matter how tough its casing. The shrike will fight anything, regardless of size; even rooks and magpies fail to frighten him. He is fond of grasshoppers and adds them freely to his store house. The enemy of birds, whether they build on ground, on bush or on tree-top, he takes up an observation post and waits until something suitable comes within sight, and then flies, kills, spikes or eats, as hunger or prudence may suggest.

The lesser grey shrike is better than his cousins; he does not rob nests but lives chiefly on insects, while the red-backed is an enemy of every small bird within reach. He is a migrant, reaching England in May and leaving with the autumn. He will even attack dragon-flies on the wing, and is extremely fond of cockchafers. Experiments have been made to test the damage done by red-backed shrikes. One naturalist allowed a shrike to build in his orchard, with the result that all insect-eating birds forsook the place or were destroyed, and the orchard yielded no fruit.

When small birds are pursued by hawks, or grouse by eagles, they have very little chance because the heavier bird is swifter in flight. Their only way of escape is to crouch or else turn and twist, and so avoid the fatal stroke. But some birds will turn in yet another way. It is not an uncommon sight to see the small fry of birdland uniting to mob an enemy if that enemy be one of the smaller hawks or an owl, and very often when the owl is sitting in the semi-darkness of a hollow tree during the day time it is approached by companies of small birds that will drive it out and pursue for some distance. The cuckoo, whose flight resembles the hawk, is often followed in the like fashion, and finches and other harmless birds have been known to attack shrikes, but we may take it as a general rule that when a raptorial bird is hunting for a meal nobody dares molest him. At other times, particularly after a meal, the case is different. Both the hoodie crow and the mistle-thrush have been seen pursuing a golden eagle which, though it could kill either with the greatest ease, has preferred to fly away. Terns, gulls, plover, red-shanks, and the rest will frequently mob a marsh harrier and drive him from their haunts.

Many of the hawk family, when they strike a bird, half close their wings, perhaps to add weight to the stroke. The peregrine and the hobby do this. The kestrel, which takes most of its food off the ground, may often be watched hovering; the rapid wing beats pass almost unnoticed at the great height, and while he hangs in the air he is looking hard below with a vision that nothing escapes. The capacity of a bird to aim straight depends largely upon the expanse of tail, because it is the tail that serves to guide the stroke. The birds with a large spread can take the most deadly aim, and those that are not so well equipped are the ones that are more likely to miss.

The sparrowhawk has his own peculiar method of pursuit, the sideways flight, a circular rise in the air, and then the usual death stroke that comes with closed wings and is associated with perfect direction. When the claws have given the *coup de grace* the bird will often come to the ground to strip and devour. Quite small, the male being no more than 12 inches long, it will attack birds that are near to it in size. Among the short-winged hawks the females are the more powerful; in the sparrowhawk, eagle and falcon the female is much larger.

APART from the struggle that is concerned with life and death there are many birds that are constantly seeking to outwit one another, and there are others that seem to have a definite feud. The writer remembers how, many years ago in South Morocco, he was invited to wait in a certain part of the open country south of the province of R'Hamna to see what was described as an annual fight between ravens and storks. Circumstances beyond his control made it impossible for him to go, but he sought the facts and was told that every year the storks and ravens met in the spring, and in that part of the country, and attacked one another with great fury. There were many onlookers, who did not interfere. If the storks prevailed the ravens left, and it was held that the year would be a good one, but if the ravens drove the storks away, their victory was a sign of bad times. He was shown a photograph of countless storks ranged in line; they were said to be waiting for the coming of the ravens.

Indian sea eagle

Monkey-eating eagle

African martial hawk eagle

African hawk eagle

Black-breasted harrier eagle

W. S. Berridge

Harpy eagle

WAR IN THE AIR: SOME OF THE MIGHTY WINGED EAGLES THAT WAGE IT

Adopting the same tactics that airmen use in war, the eagles soar high up towards the clouds and cruise there until some signs of prey appear below. These great birds have wonderful powers of sight, whether they prey on hare or fish or monkeys in the tree-tops. There is a swift, silent, downward rush, a quick stroke of a powerful claw, and the victim is borne off to some convenient spot, torn to pieces, and devoured at leisure. These kings of the clouds are mighty warriors indeed.

W. S. Berridge

WINGED WARRIORS THAT HAVE PROVIDED MAN WITH CENTURIES OF SPORT

Hawks that chase and catch other birds on the wing are successful owing to their wonderful turn of speed, and to the way in which they have become supreme in flying skill. A good hawk will even fly down a woodcock, following every lightning swerve and swoop of the terrified quarry like the shadow of death itself. Hawking is still practised a little in England. The chief bird at which trained hawks were flown in the old days was the heron. Here are a kestrel (left) and a peregrine falcon (right).

Now and again this country is visited by the rare red kite, which will come to earth in pursuit of snakes, mice and poultry. The bird was formerly common in England, lived in great numbers in the New Forest and Epping Forest, and was seen about London streets where it played the part of scavenger. To-day it may be found very occasionally near wooded districts and particularly in mountainous Wales, and as it is very fond of mice, should be pardoned for occasional raids on half-fledged poultry. Another predatory bird to be seen almost any day in the Lake country, the hilly parts of Wales and the Highlands of Scotland, is the common buzzard, which lives on frogs, lizards, mice, rats, moles, and occasionally rabbits and young hares. I have seen it in recent years hanging almost motionless over certain hilly districts of this country; but for the fact that certain land-owners preserve the buzzard it would become extinct; the flight is very slow.

A bird that carries on warfare from the air, if not actually in it, is the kestrel which can be seen so often hovering over pastures and stubbles. It is not a pursuer of birds, at least not of flying birds, and it has a peculiarity of flight in that, although it closes its wings and drops when about to strike, it spreads them before the fall is quite through and so saves the shock and apparently directs the aim. This practice enables it to be as effective on the ground as other destroyers are in the air. It can catch insects on the wing and is a deadly foe of mice. Half fledged partridges and pheasants may fall victims, but this does not happen very often.

A real enemy of the countryside, though a very attractive one, is the comparatively rare marsh harrier, once known as the moor buzzard. As its name implies, it is a great frequenter of marshes and reed beds and is guided to many delightful singing birds by their song. It is also a robber of nests and will take eggs and young birds. There are a few to be seen on the Norfolk Broads still. Nearly allied to the marsh harrier is the hen harrier, only to be seen on rare occasions in very remote districts in the Highlands and Welsh mountains. It attacks the nests of all ground building birds and will pick up new born leverets, but makes some return by its fondness for mice. Nearly all the birds that have a bad reputation devour mice, and this should help to give them some claim to favour.

Turning to the insect world we have to recognize at once that destruction in the air is part of the law of life. Wasps apparently are the very cruellest of insects. One known as the Cerceris will attack certain beetles with its sting and paralyse them, but they do not die, nor are they intended to do so. They will live for quite a long time, until the young of the wasp have eaten them alive. Another wasp (the Sphex) will take a cricket much heavier than herself and drag him to her burrow, the victim being killed by three thrusts of the sting and always in the same places. The larvae of the wasps live on him. Sometimes an egg is laid on a dead body so that when the grub is born its food is waiting, the egg being always placed on a spot near the wound of the sting, generally on the thorax.

Bembex, another wasp, lays her egg on a fly that has been paralysed by the sting and when the young grub has finished with it brings more. Her pursuit of flies is as keen as that of a swallow or a house-martin and far more cruel. Caterpillars rather than flies are the food that some wasps choose for their larvae, probably because they make more tender eating. The ordinary wasp that we know too well, also pursues living insects, bites off the parts that she does not care for pulps the rest with the aid of her mandibles and feeds the pulp to her larvae.

Of the many ways in which insects are taken in the air, nothing is more interesting than the fashion chosen by the common bat which we see fluttering about in the twilight. If you watch a bat flying over a pond in early summer, you will see that it repeatedly seems to be about to fall, and to recover itself with an effort. What has really happened is that it has caught some flying insect between its wing and its body, has closed the wing suddenly so as to crush its prey, and has then recovered in time to maintain its flight. This is very necessary in the case of the bat, because it is not easy for one to get off the ground. I have watched the flight of bats over a pond at a time when what the country folk call "May bugs" are out, and their movement in flight has given the impression of an ordered display; one after another appears to tumble and recover just in time.

W. S. Berridge

GOLDEN AND WEDGE-TAILED EAGLES

The golden eagle which, even when young, has a suggestion of the warrior in its pose (bottom) is still to be seen floating high above the glens and crags of the Scottish Highlands. A chapter has been devoted to this fine bird (see pp. 1135–48). Above is a wedge-tailed eagle

A terror of our summer fields is the wolf or robber fly (*Asilus crabroniformis*) which may be found clinging to long grass on heaths and taking short, sudden flights. It has been seen on the Wareham Road in Dorsetshire. The mouth forms a projecting beak, the feet are large and the claws are thick and blunt The robber fly belongs to a very large family with at least 3,000 species, and is very voracious, seizing alive wasps, flies and tiger beetles. One has been known to kill eight large moths in twenty minutes and all are insatiable eaters, so that even the harmless, pleasant and beautiful dragon-fly that adds so much to the delight of late summer is liable at any moment to find his enemy rising from the grass.

Here in England we see little more than the beginnings of the great fights in the air because for many reasons—climate and game preserving may be cited as two—the number of birds and insects that suffer from attack of their own kind is comparatively small, but when we reach the tropics life is far more plentiful and we find that pursuit goes on endlessly throughout the day and the night.

It might be that the pursuers would end by exterminating the pursued had not nature come to their rescue. She has given all manner of hunted birds and insects a definite means of helping themselves; it is known as protective colouring.

American Museum

FOUR QUEER ANIMALS THAT TRAVELLED THE PRIMEVAL WORLD UNTROUBLED BY MAN

These photographs show (bottom left) a smilodon or sabre-toothed cat; (bottom right) a model triceratops; (top left) dinoceras and (top right) triceratops. Study of fossils enable such illustrations to be made, but it is to be remembered that the geologic record is tantalisingly incomplete. There are about four very good reasons why. In the first place the ancient animals could hardly arrange to die always in places where sand or mud which would one day be hardened by pressure into rock was available. Secondly, only those rocks that escaped distortion, crushing or erosion have left any record. Third, the finding of fossils at all is a matter of luck; and, fourth, their discovery by persons who know their meaning is luckier still.

Chapter CXLVI

Animals that Lived Before Man

By W. E. Swinton

Of the Natural History Museum, South Kensington

IT is obviously difficult to give a general yet brief description of the animal forerunners of man. To start with, what we know of them is based entirely on the series of fossils which sedimentary deposits yield, and the geological record is tantalisingly incomplete. Again, only creatures with shells, bony or horny skeletons, or relatively hard parts, are suitable for preservation; and soft parts, or, rather, their impressions, are rare.

Then, again, only very few animals died in places liable to the quiet deposition of sand and mud, and otherwise favourable to the ultimate fossilization of remains, or, having died, were transported to such favourable localities. Only a part of these rocks in turn escaped such folding, crushing and erosion as would entirely destroy the contained fossils. Again, it is only by chance that fossils are unearthed, and still more unlikely that they fall into the hands of one capable of understanding their significance and structure.

But, in spite of all this, thousands of fossil-species are known, and students, in reducing chaos to order, are helping to make palaeontology an exact science. Palaeontologists can trace the sequence of life throughout geological times, and have even been able to forecast almost correctly the nature of missing links. It is, perhaps, neither scientific nor wise to attempt to number in even millions of years the long period during which life has been present on earth. Even if we could do so the number would pass human comprehension, but we know sufficient to realize that, giving man even a generous portion of time, his age compared with the history of animal life is almost as nothing; some of the groups which we shall mention held sway for millions of years.

There are two common fallacies, however, of which we must dispose. Man did not come into being until millions of years after the extinction of the giant reptiles with which the cartoonist and the advertiser frequently associate him; nor are these giants of the past mere figments of the enthusiastic specialist's imagination. Part of the evidence for them exists in many colleges and museums of this country and is available for all who would read it.

The first living beings, those simple protoplasmic bodies which must have preceded the higher so-called Metazoic forms, are from their very nature and the age and complexity of the rocks in which they would be preserved, hardly to be expected as fossils. From time to time phosphatic particles are discovered in the rocks and claimed to be the remains of such organisms, but so far no satisfactory case has been established. The earliest forms of life were aquatic, and so it is that the earliest known fossils are those of water-living animals. But no gradual evolution from simple to complex creatures is to be seen in the early geological deposits; life bursts forth like a flower, complex, varied, and well established with the long, preliminary developmental period hidden from our eyes and left to our imagination. The oldest fossils that we know are from the first definite geological period, the Cambrian.

"HUMERUS" OF MAN AND DINOSAUR
In man the "fore-limb" has become the arm. The principal bone in this limb is called the humerus, and here we see the humerus of a man compared with that of one of the dinosaurs that for thousands of years before man's advent dominated the world.

The seas of this time

TWO OF MAN'S FORERUNNERS ON THE EARTH
Many of the boldest thinkers hesitate to number, even in millions of years, the time during which life has existed on the earth. But this is sure, that man is a very recent addition to its inhabitants. Years, too, are very inadequate units by which to measure the vast epochs of Time in which the animals that lived before him evolved. Here are trachodon and allosaurus.

have been formed from their remains.

Another interesting series of fossils whose remains are both numerous and widespread is the ammonites, which are known best from the Jurassic and Cretaceous periods. They are preserved as coil-like shells, diverse in form, which, when sectioned, reveal a number of chambers like the shell of a modern nautilus. Most probably the chambers were gas-filled, and the shell served as a float, while the cuttlefish lived in the last chamber.

Although we know very little actually of the soft parts of these particular fossils, the form of the shell, and the knowledge we have of modern cuttlefish enable us to picture them with a fair chance of accuracy. The cone-shaped, horny, internal skeletons of a kind of cuttle-fish are common under the name of belemnites. These are analogous to the "pen" of the squid, but are more solid. Impressions of the soft parts of the actual cuttle-fish have been found in clays.

Very many other kinds of fossils are known from the early days showing that in many ways the life was pretty much like that of our own time. Coral building animals made great reefs just as are found round tropical shores to-day. Particularly common in all the later periods are the remains of Mollusca, or shell-fish. This group, which includes the ammonites and belemnites, also includes the common shells of modern beaches, as well as an extraordinary fossil found quite recently in England. This last is known as Dinocochlea, and parts of two spirally coiled "shells," collected from a quarry near Alexandra Park, Hastings, are in the Geological Department of the British Museum.

One of these gives sufficient information for the reconstruction of the whole shell, which apparently was over seven feet high. This is a gigantic size for a mollusc, if, indeed, that is the correct interpretation of the specimen. It seems probable that it is no more than a concretion though its origin must remain a matter for speculation. Other creatures with shells similar to those of the mollusca are the brachiopods, or lamp-shells, so-called because the shell resembles a Roman lamp.

teemed with life, and the remains of shellfish, corals, trilobites, sponges and worms are to be found in its deposits. The most notable of these early animals were the trilobites, which are now extinct. Distantly related to the crabs, they had the back of their bodies protected by a hard covering or carapace, while on the underside were many jointed limbs. Although several other kinds of Crustacea are known from the early deposits, the Cambrian period is known as the Age of Trilobites.

Other notable invertebrates found fossil are the crinoids, or sea-lilies, which flourished in the seas of Silurian and later times. These were beautiful animals of plant-like appearance and belonging to the starfish group. They had a long flexible stalk attached to the sea-floor, and at the upper end a sort of starfish with many thin fingers. So numerous were they in some places that beds of limestone

The number of these invertebrate fossils is many times that of the vertebrates, but it is the latter that are the more interesting to the general public, and the term "prehistoric animals," as a rule, connotes vertebrates. The earliest backboned creatures that we know are fishes from North American rocks of Ordovician age. Many curious types followed them, some destined to have descendants living to-day and others to be lost in the evolutionary byways. In this latter connexion may be mentioned the strange armoured fishes or ostracoderms, which were at first speedy and unarmed, but later became slow-moving and lived at the sea bottom. Having lost their speed a new method of escape from their predatory contemporaries had to be found and the result was—armour. They became armed over the head and front of the body, leaving a small tail free for swimming. Some of their successors grew to a great size, as much as fifteen feet long, and had great cutting jaws, but it was all to no effect.

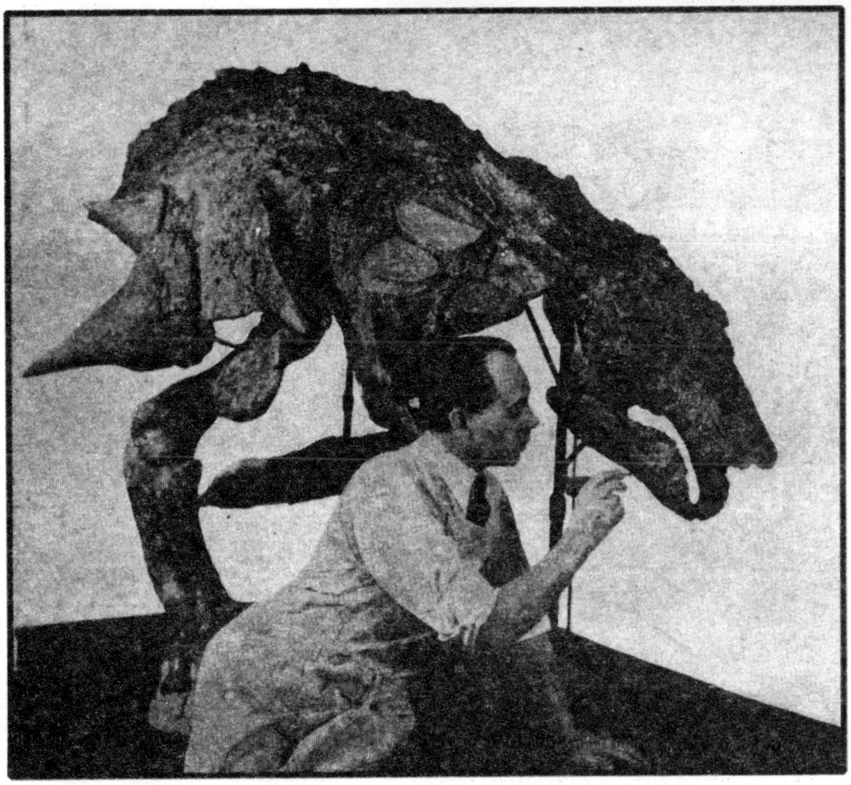

RECONSTRUCTIONS OF LONG LOST CREATURES

Here we see the reconstructed skeleton of palaeorincus (bottom) being mounted and (top) a drawing of chatosaurus. By means of a study of thousands of fossil specimens it is possible for experts to make such reconstructions with some tolerable certainty of general accuracy. Chaos has been reduced to order and palaeontology become a more or less exact science.

Armour has been tried in many groups of animals, but has seldom been successful and these fishes were no exceptions, their smarter, unarmed contemporaries ousting them from the field. Living at the same time, however, were other fishes which developed a method of escape from a fate which overtook many of their fellows. As the river pools of Old Red Sandstone (Devonian) time dried up, many fishes were killed, but some found a way of supplementing the oxygen deficiency of the water by gulping air. From these there arose gradually fish with lungs. The lung-fishes split into two groups; one produced eventually most of the common fish of to-day, while the other gave rise indirectly to the amphibia.

No living amphibian attains anything like the size or grotesque appearance of its Carboniferous ancestors. Part of the latter's life was, of course, spent in the water, but when they emerged to live adult life on land they must have preserved the soft moist skin we associate with the frog. At least no trace of any dorsal protection has been found in any of the fossils although, as a relic of their ancestry, the

DINOSAUR'S EGGS PRESERVED FOR AEONS

The dinosaurs laid eggs—the primitive way of birth. Below is a specimen egg and above a number of eggs just as they were found. These reptiles, some of them eighty feet long, had disappeared from the earth long before man appeared. Pictures representing them as chasing or being hunted by man are only examples of the "artist's licence."

creatures kept scales on the ventral surface of their bodies. They must have lived chiefly in ponds and rivers, using their sprawling limbs to escape from swimming enemies or to make short journeys over land. They had, of course, to return to the water to lay eggs. Among their successors of Permian times we find two different conditions have arisen.

From certain Texas fossils we can deduce that some forms (for example, Cacops) lived habitually on dry land and went back to the water only to lay eggs. Many amphibia were of great size, some 12 feet long, and with limbs which stuck out from the sides of the body and must have made walking extremely awkward. The reptiles in Permo-Triassic times were gradually rising in competition with the amphibia and had not their limitations. Accordingly, to escape this competition some amphibia delayed the completion of their larval gill-breathing period, like the modern axolotl, and eventually became entirely water-living. Metoposaurus was an animal which became secondarily aquatic in this way.

It is when we come to the reptiles that we find the prehistoric monsters par excellence. This group provides us with a variety of strange forms unrivalled among land animals of any age for variety of form and size. More than this, reptiles were for millions of years the dominant creatures, occupying in the

Mesozoic world the position that the mammals hold to-day. Some reptiles flew, or rather glided, in the air, others swam in the seas, or walked in the shallow waters of lakes and estuaries, or on dry land.

Among the earliest whose remains we know is dimetrodon, a curious creature resembling in appearance some of the larger amphibians. Its remains are found in the rocks of Texas and show that the animal had a large head with sharp-toothed jaws suitable for eating flesh. The body was low and broad, with the belly resting on the ground, and the limbs sprawled out from it like those of the large amphibians already mentioned. Most striking of all, however, was the series of spines running along the backbone. These were elongations of the vertebrae and sometimes had cross-pieces on them like spars on a mast. The whole of this bony frame-work was covered with a web, the purpose of which is quite unknown, though some palaeontologists consider it to have been a secondary sexual character, and the animals bearing it to have been males.

ANIMALS OF THE LOST WORLD FOUND IN THE ROCKS

When Sir Arthur Conan Doyle wrote his thrilling " Lost World " he pictured an isolated plateau on which things had remained unchanged since the time of the dinosaurs. Palaeontologists, however, have no wonderful plateau to help them, but only the lessons hidden in the rocks. Here are diatryma (bottom) and (top) tylosaurus and porthur.

In the seas of the Mesozoic period were two great reptilian groups whose remains are often found in quarries in England. These were the ichthyosaurs and plesiosaurs. The former were sea-going creatures with a long triangular head and slender jaws fitted with numerous, sharp, conical teeth. Bony sclerotic plates supported the eyeball and helped in focussing. Only a short neck separated the head from the porpoise-like body. Propulsion in the water was achieved by four paddles, formed by the modified limbs, but specimens in which the impression of the skin has been preserved show that a small triangular fin was present on the back and that the downwardly

there was a small fin probably on the tail. Swimming was done by means of four paddles. These creatures probably came out of the water to lay eggs or bask in the sun. When swimming they must have resembled large shell-less turtles and no doubt the "plesiosaurs" sighted and reported every now and then are large turtles. Ichthyosaurs and plesiosaurs had similar food, but while the former relied on speed in the pursuit of their prey, the latter relied on quickness in turning the head and on the sharp, snapping movements of the jaws. Both ichthyosaurs and plesiosaurs were secondarily aquatic, being derived from land living ancestors. Both forms also possess a parietal foramen on the skull for the third, or pineal, eye.

While these were maintaining their temporary monarchy

bent end of the tail (compare that of fish) also supported a fin.

Some species of ichthyosaurs grew to forty feet in length, but the average is much less than this. The stomach remains found fossilized show that the food consisted chiefly of fish, cuttle-fish and occasionally a small ichthyosaur. In this connection, it is interesting that several specimens are known whose body cavities contain almost complete skeletons of very small ichthyosaurs which must have been embryos. It would, of course, be advantageous to sea-going animals like the ichthyosaurs to have their young born alive, and thus be under no necessity to return to the shores to lay eggs.

The plesiosaurs were also water-living reptiles, but they had a shorter and smaller head and, in the earlier plesiosaurs at any rate, a much longer neck. The body was large and barrel-shaped and without the fins of the ichthyosaur, though

IRISH ELK AND A PREHISTORIC BISON

In the Irish bogs many remains have been found of *Cervus giganteus* the so-called Irish elk (bottom) which roamed Europe in Pleistocene times when Man was just beginning to emerge. These huge Irish deer had enormous antlers, palmated like those of the present-day moose. Above we see a kind of bison found in the Pleistocene alluvium of parts of North America.

of the seas, other reptiles were flying over them. The word "flying" is perhaps not quite correct for well-preserved remains of pterodactyls show that the arms were not capable of the flying movements characteristic of birds. Flying reptiles glided on the wind rather than flew. This inability to fly raises some pretty problems as to their habits. The hind legs were weak and almost, it would appear, incapable of supporting the cumbrous body, head, and arms. Probably the creatures launched themselves out from a cliff and glided over the water where some of them caught fish. If they landed on the water, almost inevitably they would break the tips of their wings, making further flight impossible. How they rose, if indeed they did, from a becalmed sea remains a mystery. In this group also much variety of size exists

A FOSSIL FROG AND A GIANT TURTLE

As the river pools of the Old Red Sandstone period dried up, many swimming things died. From the survivors came fish as we know them, and frogs. Many of the early swimmers were armoured like the giant turtle (top).

some of the pterodactyls were the size of sparrows, others measured 18 feet from wing tip to wing tip. This wing was a thin web of skin stretching from the shoulders to the greatly elongated fifth finger—which was its main support—and from it to the hind leg. The skull was a long narrow one and the head was balanced by the strongly marked crest at the back: some forms were toothed, and others toothless. The bones of these creatures are amazingly light and the skeleton of the 18-foot-wide pterodactyl mentioned (pteranodon) weighed under six pounds.

These aerial invaders came from the same stock that produced the remarkable group known as the dinosaurs. These were land animals which adopted various habits and bodily forms. For convenience we may divide them into three groups. The first group contains the largest animals ever known on earth; the giant brontosaurus, and the diplodocus, which grew over eighty feet long and was twelve feet high at the shoulders. These great animals, weighing thirty or forty tons, walked in the shallow waters of lakes and estuaries where the water eased their weight and where their long necks and rake-like teeth were suited for collecting an abundance of plant food.

Of these tyrannosaurus was a gigantic creature which ran on its hind legs, using the shortened fore-arms for seizing its prey. About forty feet in length.

E.N.A.

HORSE ANCESTOR AND CARNIVOROUS DINOSAUR

Horses developed through various ancestors, one of which we see here (bottom), from the little doglike animal called eohippus. The upper photograph shows the tyrannosaurus, a 40-foot dinosaur. It ran on its hind legs instead of on all fours like many of its relations, and so had an advantage over them which it exploited by eating them.

with a four-foot-long skull and standing about twenty feet high, it must have inspired the maximum terror the feeble dinosaurian brain could conceive. The remains of this reptile are found in North America, but a smaller form, megalosaurus, had a wider distribution, and is common enough in England.

Not all of the dinosaurs sought safety in speed or in retreat to shallow waters: certain herbivorous forms armed themselves with a covering of bony or horny spines and plates. These armoured dinosaurs can be divided into two main kinds: those which had the body unprotected, but had horns on the skull and a bony frill over the neck; and those with the main armour on the body. The first of these two classes includes triceratops, a remarkable rhinoceros-like dinosaur twenty feet long and with three-foot spines on the great skull which itself is six feet long.

The second class includes stegosaurus, furnished with bony plates on its body, and the remarkable scolosaurus, which looks rather like a great spiny tortoise. All these animals were herbivorous and very likely laid eggs, indeed the eggs of eoceratops are known from Mongolia.

Various families made their appearance and disappearance during the long Mesozoic Era, but the end of that time saw the last of the dinosaurs. By the end of the Cretaceous period the reptiles were no longer dominant, and the mammals were free to assume that position which they still maintain. From animals closely related to the dinosaurs, however, there arose the birds. These are rare as

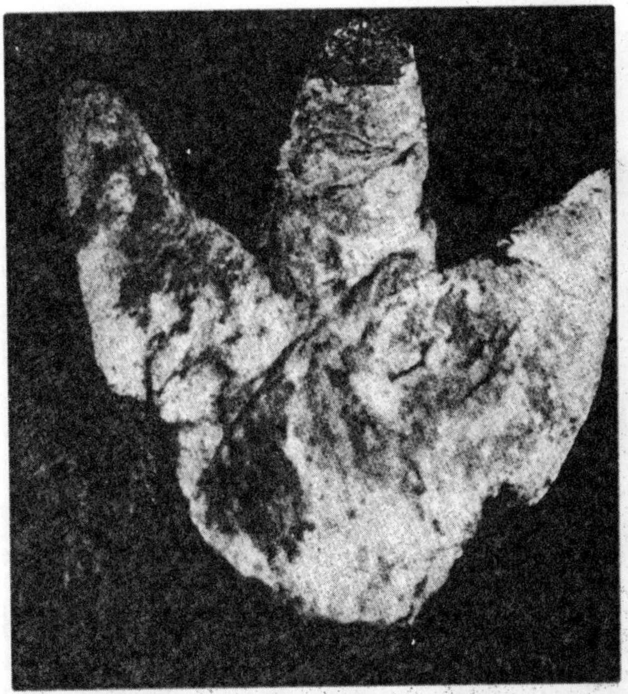

FOOTPRINTS FROM THE SANDS OF TIME PRESERVED FOR OUR INFORMATION

A skeleton of an animal that lived millions of years before man is impressive, but it takes an expert to make anything of it. But a footprint ten million years old, or so, is such living evidence of the amazing past that anyone must thrill at it. On the left is the print of a dinosaur's foot, and on the right the tracks of varanus in petrified mud. One warm afternoon, so many years ago that if we knew their exact number the figure would be beyond our real comprehension, that track was made in some unimaginable swamp.

fossils and the first, the most remarkable and most interesting one we know, is archaeopteryx, known only by two nearly complete skeletons (one in the Natural History Museum, London) and a feather. Fortunately the two specimens tell us a great deal about this primitive, reptilian-looking bird. But for the presence of feathers one would class it as a reptile, since it has teeth, and free clawed fingers.

During the time that the great reptiles and the primitive birds were living the mammals had been slowly evolving, but the remains of early forms are few. Some of these were marsupials whose descendants are the curious indigenous mammals of present-day Australia. The rocks laid down at the close of the Mesozoic or Secondary Era are known as the Tertiary, and contain abundant evidence of the sovereignty of the mammals culminating in Man himself. Five periods—the Eocene, Oligocene, Miocene, Pliocene and Pleistocene—are comprised within the geological term Tertiary, and since Man is now considered to have existed from Pliocene times, only the first three of these periods need concern us. In them, however, are found many remarkable forms bearing none the less characters familiar to us in modern mammals.

One can roughly divide the early mammals into two classes: those which increased in brain; and those which added brawn. The former led to the many mammals familiar to us, while the latter produced the large grotesque creatures which, to a small degree, paralleled the great reptiles and met a similar fate. Two or three of these large forms are worthy of note. The Eocene produced, in North America and Egypt respectively, the large herbivores dinoceras and arsinoitherium, creatures somewhat larger than a rhinoceros and with bodies and limbs of elephantine appearance. The constructive powers of Nature ran riot, however, on the skull and produced a number of horns, giving an appearance reminiscent of some of the armoured dinosaurs.

Another interesting group known from the Miocene and later deposits of America, Africa and Asia is the chalicotheres. These are distantly related to the horses and are best known from the remains of moropus. This creature appears to have been a mixture of ground sloth and horse, and had clawed feet, used, no doubt, to dig up plants and roots on which it fed, a horse-like head, and front legs longer than the rear ones. Living at the same time as the Miocene chalicotheres were numerous herbivorous animals: pigs, including some very large forms, rhinoceroses, antelopes, okapis, and three-toed horses. The last were descended from the tiny dog-like eohippus of the Eocene period.

Preying on these were numerous wolves, hyenas, bears and large sabre-toothed cats. This diverse fauna had a wide distribution in Europe and Asia, but towards Upper Pliocene time it passed southwards into Africa, and its place was taken by true elephants, true horses and various kinds of deer. Upper Pliocene times also saw the advent of Man whose influence, of necessity, affected the contemporary and subsequent faunas.

Martin Duncan

J. J. Ward

DEADLY BIRD-EATING SPIDERS OF TROPICAL SOUTH AMERICA

The horrible-looking bird-eating spiders of Brazil and other parts of tropical South America do not actually construct traps for their prey, but, in the sense that they set a trap for birds by lying in wait for them, they come within the scope of our subject in this chapter. These photographs show one of these big, poisonous spiders as an anxious bird might look down on it from an upper branch (bottom), and (top) one taken from the side. The method of capture is to leap upon a sitting bird.

Chapter CXLVII

Pigmy Trappers of the Animal World

By J. R. Ainsworth-Davis

Formerly Professor of Zoology in the University of Wales

According to the nature of their food, animals may be divided into carnivorous, herbivorous, and omnivorous forms, of which cat, sheep and pig respectively are familiar types. We are concerned here with small or very small creatures that feed entirely or mostly on other animals, and by means of a great variety of devices secure an adequate diet, without having to worry about balanced rations and those important but elusive compounds known as vitamins.

The word "trapper" must be interpreted very broadly, since comparatively few animals construct traps or snares for the undoing of their victims, but there are many whose bodies are shaped or coloured so as to attract these unfortunates or lull them into a sense of false security. Others again adopt effective hunting tactics that prove them to possess trapping instincts.

The outstanding example of pigmy trappers and hunters is afforded by spiders (Arachnida), sometimes mistaken for insects, but easily distinguishable from these by the possession of eight instead of six legs, and the absence of feelers (antennae) upon the head. A spider has a curious pair of jaws (chelicerae) each with a sharp claw-like end joint, working on a hinge as the blade of a penknife does. Near but not at the tip of this claw is the opening of a poison gland, an arrangement similar to that found in the hollow needle of a hypodermic syringe, and which works much in the same way. After the victim's skin has been pierced a paralysing fluid is squeezed into the wound. The spider cannot chew up the prey, but sucks its juices.

The habits of these interesting creatures have been described so fully in Chapter XXXVII (The Skill of the Spider) that it will suffice here to give some supplementary information.

One human invention for catching animals, the net, has been anticipated by the web-making spiders, and this is seen to perfection in the elaborate and beautiful snare constructed by our common garden spider, which far surpasses any man-made contrivance for similar purposes. Upon the six little spinnerets of this form are to be found some 600 very minute cylindrical tubes (spools) and 18 slightly larger conical ones (spigots), and from every one of these a silk thread of extreme tenuity can be emitted. But it would be a mistake to suppose that a great number of these are woven together to make a single line of the web. Even the strong foundation lines consist of quite a few spigot threads reinforcing one another. Six spigots are concerned with making the sticky spiral and eight of them spin silk for the egg cocoons.

The question is sometimes asked: "Why doesn't a spider get caught in her own web?" (Note the "her"—Mr. Spider is an idle loafer.) Such a misfortune is prevented by the exercise of extreme care, besides which the legs of the spinner are covered with an oily exudation that prevents adherence to the sticky spiral so fatal to prey.

There has been much speculation about the evolution of spiders' webs through stages more and more complete until the complex constructions made by some forms came into existence. We know that a wandering or hunting spider, which makes no web, pays out a "drag line" on leaving its lair, perhaps as a means of finding its way back. The remains of a number of such drag lines radiating from the animal's lurking place might very well act as a simple snare, and this was possibly the first stage in web evolution. Next might come untidy little casual webs such as are made by certain pretty little spiders between holly leaves. Sheet webs, like those of house spiders, are a further advance, and the geometrical web of the garden spider (see Chapter XXXVII) approaches perfection.

W. S. Berridge

A HUMBUG TRAPPER

Called the praying mantis because its attitude, when waiting to seize some incautious insect, suggests someone at prayer, the mantis deceives prey by its stillness and is no hermit, but an ogre.

There are, however, interesting variations of this. A North American orb-weaver spins its web horizontally, afterwards giving it a domed shape by attaching stay lines from above. Other spiders of the kind deposit bands of reserve silk on their snares, to furnish material for wrapping up victims into food parcels. Still more striking are the webs of some Indian orb-weavers, to which are added zigzag lines, sometimes all over, sometimes in the form of a St. Andrew's cross, or there may be additions taking the form of broad bands of silk mixed with vegetable debris. These devices are supposed to make the

F. W. Bond

H. Bastin

GARDEN SPIDER'S STICKY NET

Trapping by means of a net, the garden spider of England spins its viscid threads with beautiful and scientific precision. An oily substance secreted by the feet prevents the trapper being trapped in his own deadly but beautiful net.

spider herself difficult to be seen by prospective prey, and a comparison may be made with the "dazzle painting" which helped many ships to escape hostile submarines during the Great War.

This by no means exhausts the possibilities. The webs so far considered are "passive" snares awaiting passers-by, but those of some other forms are used actively by their makers, somewhat after the fashion of the casting net with which a "retiarius" was equipped when pitted against a swordsman (secutor) in a Roman gladiatorial contest. Such a case is that of the triangle spider (*Hyptiotes*), which makes a small triangular web attached by its base. From the apex of this web a strong line runs to the spider, lurking under a leaf, and she pulls it taut with her front legs, the slack being coiled up. Should an insect touch the web, the spider lets go the line, and a sudden jerk is given to the web, so that the victim gets thoroughly entangled.

Still more remarkable are the methods employed by a Natal spider (*Menneus camelus*), which has a taste for moths. In a bush by the side of a stream she constructs a small web consisting of a rectangle made of irregular threads, attached to the lower side of which is a "trap" of the same shape provided with about 20 transverse sticky threads, and no bigger than a postage stamp. The spider stands waiting for prey with her four front legs planted on the corners of the trap. If a moth comes within range she pulls out the elastic trap to five or six times its

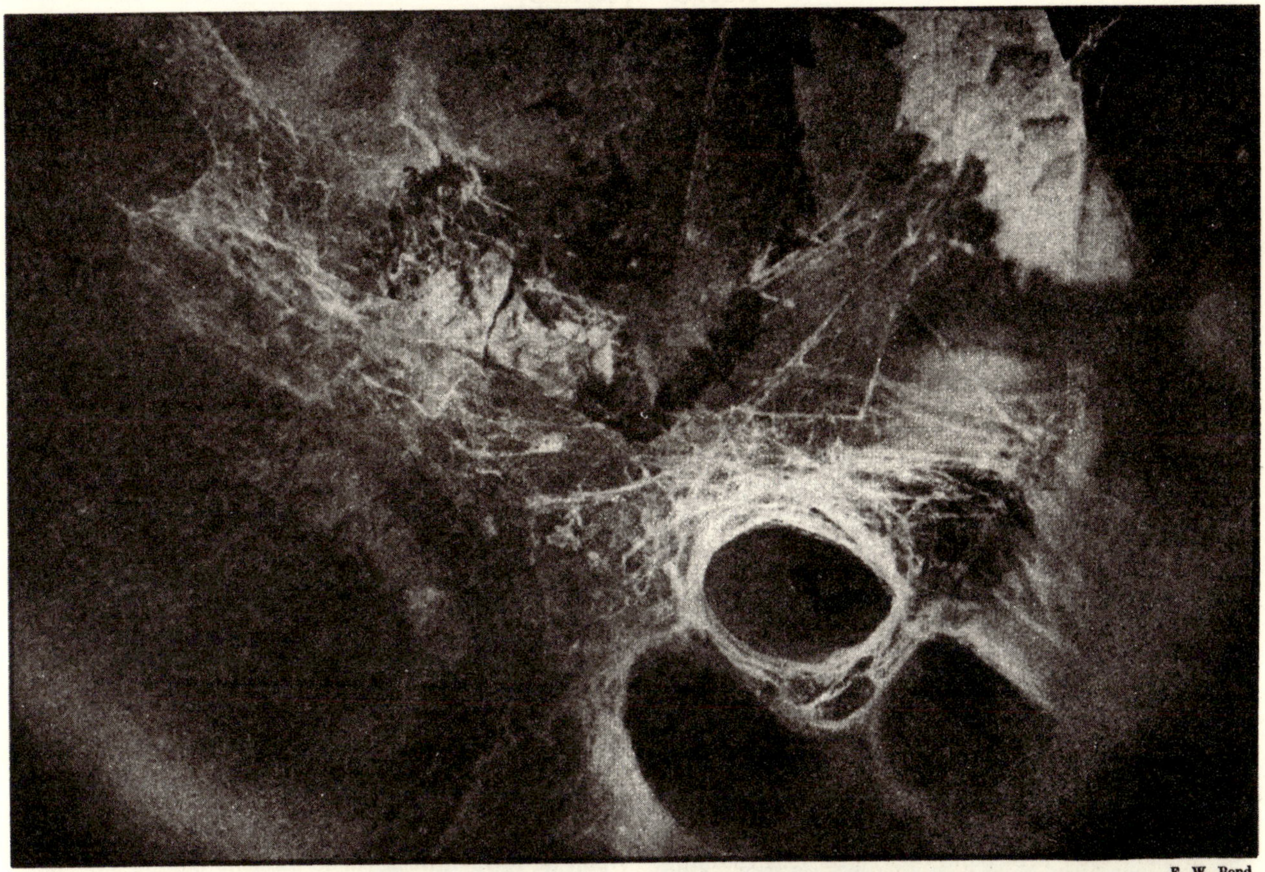

F. W. Bond

J. T. Roberts

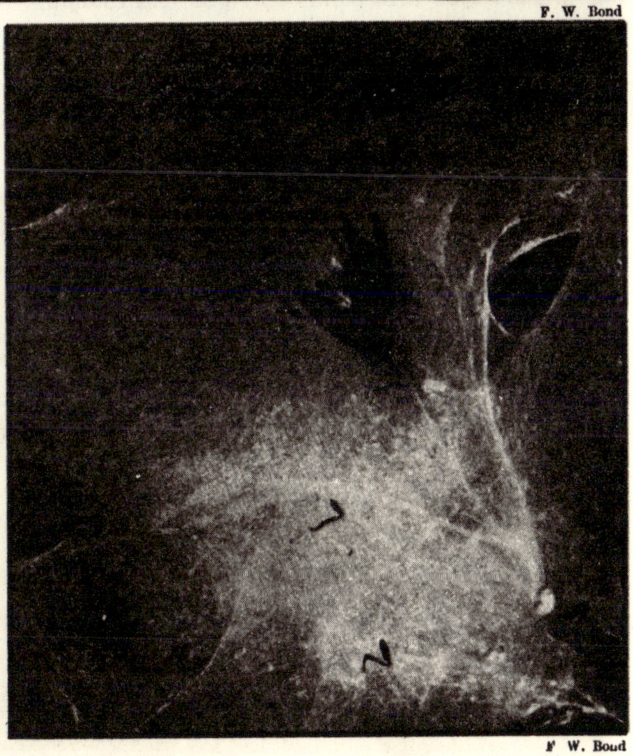

F. W. Bond

NET TRAPS OF HOUSE SPIDER, LABYRINTH AND TUNNEL-BUILDING SPIDERS

Cobwebs, so troublesome to those who endeavour to keep rooms clean because they are always spun in inaccessible places and betray any shortcomings in broom-work, are the work of the house spider. In the lower left-hand photograph we see one of these industrious creatures stalking a fly. The labyrinth spider (bottom right) constructs a most complicated snare such as we see here. Notice that several flies have become entangled in it. Above we have the web of a tunnel-building spider.

J. J. Ward

THE CLEVER GREENHOUSE SPIDER TRAPS AND SECURES ITS PREY

People sometimes refer to spiders as insects. This is quite wrong, for the characteristics of the insect are its possession of six legs, and antennae or feelers. The spiders, on the other hand, have eight legs and no feelers. The proper name for members of their family is Arachnids. Here we have three stages in the hunting of a greenhouse spider. It approaches its quarry (left), tangles threads round it (centre) and pulls them tight (right). All is now ready for the meal.

original size, at the same time throwing herself forward upon the quarry.

South America.. ostriches are often captured by means of the "bolas," consisting of a cord with a weight at each end. Thrown skilfully so as to give a rotary movement, this gets entangled with the legs of the bird and brings it down. Here, again, man has been anticipated by a Natal spider (*Cladomelea akermani*) which does not make a web though a relative of our garden species. She spins a single thread four-fifths of an inch long, with a sticky knob at the end rather larger than a pin's head. It is held by one of the third legs and whirled rapidly round in a horizontal plane for about 15 minutes. Should there be no luck the globule is swallowed by way of light refreshment a brief rest is taken, and another bolas made. Dr. Akerman, the discoverer of this form, says that this curious performance may go on for several hours.

An Australian cousin of the preceding species (*Dicrostichus magnificus*) attains success without such tiring efforts. In this case the bolas is held in readiness by one of the first pair of legs, stretched out expectantly. It is swiftly thrown at any fly venturing within reach, and should the cast prove successful the victim is pulled to the spider's mouth, and its juices sucked.

Trapdoor spiders sometimes make snares, a good example being afforded by a form living in the Greek island of Tinos. After sunset the trapdoor is opened and a vertical web six inches long and half an inch high is spun, designed to catch low-flying

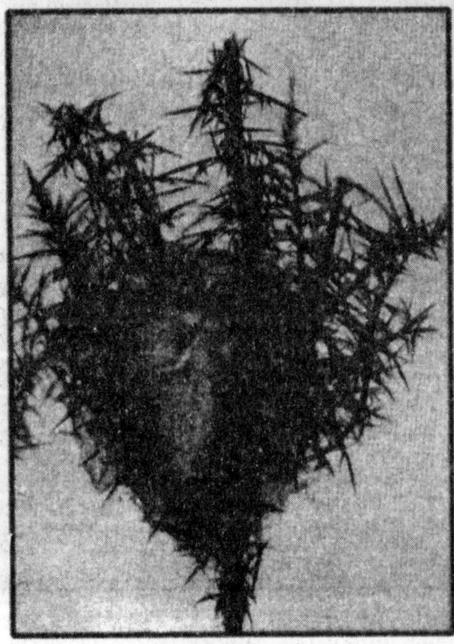

W. S. Berridge

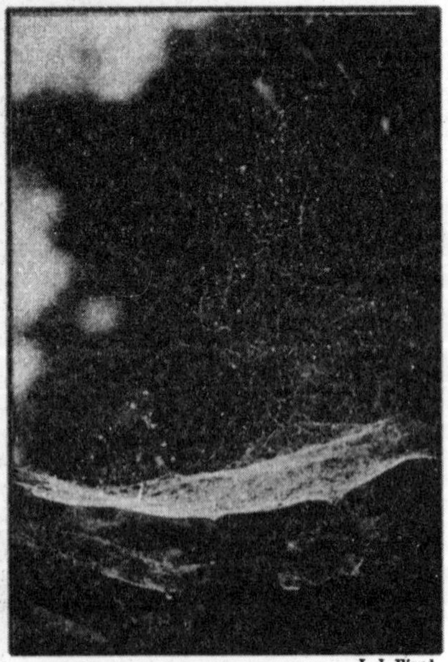

J. J. Ward

THE REMARKABLE NESTS OF LABYRINTH, TRAP-DOOR AND SHEET-WEAVING SPIDERS

Spiders use their amazing spinning powers for other purposes besides that of making webs. Their nurseries, where the eggs hatch and the young spend their early hours, are fashioned out of this same silk, and so is the mother spider's home. Sometimes this home is also a trap at the same time It is in the case of the trap-door spider (centre), which lurks beneath the hinged lid of the trap till something comes within reach and then darts out. Here, too, are nests of the labyrinth (left) and sheet-weaver (right) spiders insects. The web is removed before dawn, when the spider retires to its burrow and shuts the trap-door.

In the chapter on The Skill of the Spider, reference is made to some of the little crab spiders which render themselves inconspicuous by changing colour to match the surroundings., One of these creatures (*Phrynarachne decipiens*) living in Java makes itself resemble a common object. It spins a patch of white silk on the upper side of a leaf, and then lies down on this and tucks in its legs, presenting a close resemblance to a bird dropping, and thus imposing on the credulity of its prey.

Readers interested in spiders are referred to Warburton's "Spiders," and Savory's "Biology of Spiders," from which much of the information given here has been taken.

The blood-sucking ticks, distant relatives of the spiders, are well-known pests, particularly abundant in the hotter parts of the world, and disseminating a number of serious or fatal diseases among mammals. They patiently lie in wait among herbage, and drop on victims passing their lurking places.

The great class of six-legged backboneless animals which includes insects is a veritable treasure house to those who write on natural history topics.

Hugh Main

BEETLE TRAPPER AND AN INSECT PITFALL

In the lower photograph a preying beetle is dragging a captured cicada into the carefully concealed burrow where it lies in wait. Above is the pit made by an ant-lion. This is a specimen of the pitfall type of trap which has been used by primitive man for centuries in securing dangerous animals. Once it has fallen in there is no escape for the luckless victim.

Nor is this surprising, for these ubiquitous creatures, the earliest conquerors of the air, include more kinds or species than all other land animals put together, for more than a quarter of a million have been described and named, and ten times that number probably exist, according to the late Professor David Sharp, a great authority.

Insects propagate with astonishing rapidity, so that if it were possible to take a "census" of the insect world the figures would be too vast to grasp clearly. Placed in one pan of a super-titanic pair of scales this insect population would most likely outweigh the rest of the land population, were this piled up in the other pan.

Apart from spiders, the only creatures that spin webs for

the entanglement of prey are the fresh-water larvae of certain American caddis moths. These are not really moths, but make up a special group of their own (Trichoptera = "hairy wings"). There are plenty of them in this country, and the larvae are familiar to anglers as "caddis worms," which live in protective cases made by sticking various materials together with silk. There are no spinnerets, but parts of the salivary glands are converted into silk-producing organs.

In a Brazilian caddis worm (*Rhyacophylax*) the case is rather more than a quarter of an inch long, and is fixed to the upper side of a stone facing up stream. The cases of a number of individuals are placed side by side in successive rows, as many as thirty of them in a row. The "trap" is a very elegant affair, consisting of a funnel-shaped "verandah" projecting from the mouth of the tube, and lined by a delicate silken net with square meshes. Any small creatures drifting into the verandah are caught by the net and gobbled up by the caddis worm.

A NORTH American caddis worm (*Hydropsyche*), not associated with others, makes a somewhat similar but larger snare, also facing up stream. Here the tube expands into a small "verandah," the edge of which is continued into a strong funnel-shaped web, square-meshed as before, with its rim supported by bits of water plants.

Among the net-winged insects (*Neuroptera*), which include dragon-flies and may-flies, there is one notable European trapper, the ant-lion (*Myrmeleo formicarius*). When adult it is not unlike a dragon-fly, and not particularly remarkable, but the young form or larva, which lives in sandy places, has been studied for over 200 years, and its habits have attracted much attention, being responsible for the popular name of the species.

Our "lion" is far from beautiful, with its powerful head provided with enormous curved jaws, a thorax without wings but bearing six strong legs, and an oval elongated abdomen. It walks backwards, but this is no sign of a modest disposition. The problem of securing food is solved by digging a conical pitfall at the bottom of which the lion lies in wait. This insect navvy does not begin by excavating at what will be the centre of the trap, but commences operations by tracing a circular groove to correspond with the edge of the proposed pit and then works round and round on an ever narrower circuit.

BURYING its abdomen in the sand, the loose material is piled up on its broad head and thrown to some distance with a jerk as it gradually moves round. When the task is completed it buries itself at the bottom of the trap, save for the front part of the head. Should an unfortunate ant, or other insect, step over the edge of the pitfall it will gradually slide downwards, such descent being accelerated by the ant-lion, which throws sand on the hoped-for prey. When finally gripped by the powerful jaws escape is impossible, for by means of an ingenious suction pump arrangement the juices can be extracted from the victim without any necessity for letting go. The shrivelled remains of the meal are thrown out to some distance, which is not only in the interest of sanitation, but prevents eligible wayfarers from being scared away.

Some of the carnivorous ants possess the "pack instinct," and unite together in formidable "drives," of which the success is very largely due to the marvellous instincts and relatively great intelligence of ants, a question of brain power. The work of the community is divided between several kinds or "castes" of individual, including "workers" or undeveloped females. They possess powerful biting jaws and a more or less formidable sting in the tail, consisting of two sharp saw-edged stylets, protected by a sheath and connected with a poison gland secreting formic acid.

The blind driver ants (*Anomma arcens*) of West Africa, nocturnal in their habits, move from place to place in vast armies of workers, devouring everything of animal nature that comes in their way. Their habits were long ago described by Savage, who says that they check "the more rapid increase of noxious insects and smaller reptiles; consume much dead animal matter, which is constantly occurring, decaying, becoming offensive, and thus vitiating the atmosphere, and, which is by no means the least important in the Torrid Zone, often compelling the inhabitants to keep their dwellings, towns, and their vicinity in a state of comparative cleanliness. The dread of them is upon every living being. Their entrance into a house is soon known by the simultaneous and universal movement of rats, mice, lizards, Blapsidae, Blattidae, and of the numerous vermin that infest our dwellings." It is alleged that, in former times, one native method of executing criminals was to tie them up in the path of an advancing army of these ants, a gruesome practice which should have proved an effective deterrent to serious offences.

BATES, in his "Naturalist on the Amazons," gives a graphic account of the habits of somewhat similar South American foraging ants (species of *Eciton*), where the workers are of two kinds, "large heads" and "small heads," the former possessing particularly powerful jaws. Bates speaks as follows of the commonest Brazilian species, in which eyes are present: "These Ecitons are seen in the pathways of the forest at all places on the banks of the Amazon, travelling in dense columns of countless thousands. When the pedestrian falls in with a train of these ants, the first signal given him is a twittering and restless movement of small flocks of plain-coloured birds (ant-thrushes) in the jungle. If this be disregarded until he advances a few steps farther, he is sure to fall into trouble, and find himself suddenly attacked by numbers of the ferocious little creatures. . . . Wherever they move, the whole animal world is set in commotion, and every creature tries to get out of their way. . . . The main column, from four to six deep, moves forward in a given direction, clearing the ground of all animal matter, dead or alive, and throwing off here and there a thinner column to forage for a short while on the flanks of the main army, and re-enter it again after their task is accomplished." Some species are blind, and these use grains of earth in the construction of covered roads, along which they march to suitable hunting grounds.

Many aggressive insects are made inconspicuous to their prey by their resemblance to surrounding objects, or by colours which match the surroundings. Good examples are to be found in the group (*Orthoptera*) of which cockroaches and grasshoppers are familiar examples. Among these the highly voracious soothsayers or praying insects (*Mantidae*) merit attention. The green or brown praying mantis (*Mantis religiosa*) harmonizes with its surroundings and stands patiently waiting for insect victims with its forelegs stretched out as if in prayer. They are really effective seizing organs. Dr. Sharp says: "This appearance of innocence and quietness . . . is of the most deceptive character, for the creature's activity consists of a series of wholesale massacres carried on day after day, the number of victims it sacrifices being enormous."

Many of the tropical mantids are curiously shaped and coloured so as to resemble the surrounding foliage and flowers, and a pink Siamese species when settled with up-turned tail on a group of similarly coloured flowers can hardly be distinguished from them.

SEVERAL carnivorous bugs living in fresh water are of great interest, and indefatigable as pigmy trappers. The pond or wayside pool, usually regarded as a symbol of complete placidity, is in reality a scene of constant carnage. Here dwells, among other active and bloodthirsty creatures, miniature tigers after their fashion, the water scorpion (*Nepa cinerea*), a flat brown bug with a slender spike projecting from its tail, this being a breathing tube made up of two grooved pieces, which can be pushed out of the water to take in air. The front legs are used for seizing prey, not for walking, and enable the "scorpion" to get a firm hold on a tadpole or small fish. The piercing mouth-parts are then thrust into the victim and its juices sucked out. The eggs of this creature are laid within the tissues of water plants, and each possesses a tuft of delicate threads that project externally and serve as breathing organs, absorbing the oxygen dissolved in the surrounding water.

The long water-bug (*Ranatra linearis*) is a slender cousin of the water scorpion, which it resembles in structure and habits. Staveley says: "The creature looks cruel and hungry, but where it stows all the prey for which it is so greedy is a problem."

Another voracious pond insect is the great water-beetle (*Dytiscus marginalis*), which not only preys upon various invertebrates, but also on newts, tadpoles, and small fishes. The unattractive wingless larva is even more ferocious, and possesses a formidable pair of sharp jaws, each traversed by a canal along which the blood of the victim is conveyed. Still larger is the great black water-beetle (*Hydrophilus piceus*), which, when a larva, is fierce and carnivorous, but in adult life, repenting of its turbulent youth, becomes a harmless vegetarian.

As another example of the pigmy trappers we may take the bloodsucking leeches, greatly specialized aquatic worms formerly much used in medicine for blood-letting, and lending their name to practitioners of the healing art. The mouth is in the middle of a sucker, and provided with three horny saw-edged jaws able to make a three-rayed incision. A peculiar secretion, injected into the wound, prevents the blood of the victim from coagulating, thus enabling the leech to suck out a satisfactory meal without difficulty. Land leeches, which swarm among damp vegetation in tropical countries, such as India, Ceylon, the East Indies, and parts of South America, are particularly bloodthirsty, and are said to have sometimes surprised and slain sleeping human beings. A case is on record where an entire battalion of English troops had to beat a hasty retreat from a leech-infested wood. These unpleasant pests have the true trapper instinct, lying in wait for their prey, either on the ground or among vegetation.

AMONG the curious marine siphon worms (*Gephyrea*) is one, the green bonellia (*Bonellia viridis*), with remarkable habits. The male is a degenerate parasite living within the body of his robust mate, who has a fat green body about two inches long and shelters in a rock crevice. Protruding from the front end of this body is a proboscis, forked at the end, which can be stretched out to the incredible length of five feet in search of prey, when it looks like a slender green thread. Suitable victims are first seized and then passed down a groove on the under side of the proboscis to the mouth.

As a final example of living traps we may take the sea-anemones, to be found attached to the walls of rock pools at the seaside. When contracted an anemone looks like a rounded lump of coloured jelly: in one case like a little heap of fine gravel, for little bits of stone stick to its surface. When expanded it resembles a flower (hence the name "anemone"), but the apparent blossom is really an animated stomach with a greedy mouth surrounded by circlets of tentacles, varying in colour with the species.

THE tentacles are thickly studded with microscopic nettling organs or "thread cells." Each of these is a minute bag full of poisonous fluid and with a long hollow thread coiled up inside it. Should a shrimp or little fish touch a tiny projection ("trigger hair") from the cell the thread is squeezed out, the skin of the victim is pierced by sharp barbs that first protrude, and the rest of the poisoned thread is then forced into the wound, with paralyzing effect. These offensive weapons are grouped into "batteries," so many of them can work together. They can only be used once, and are constantly being replaced by new ones.

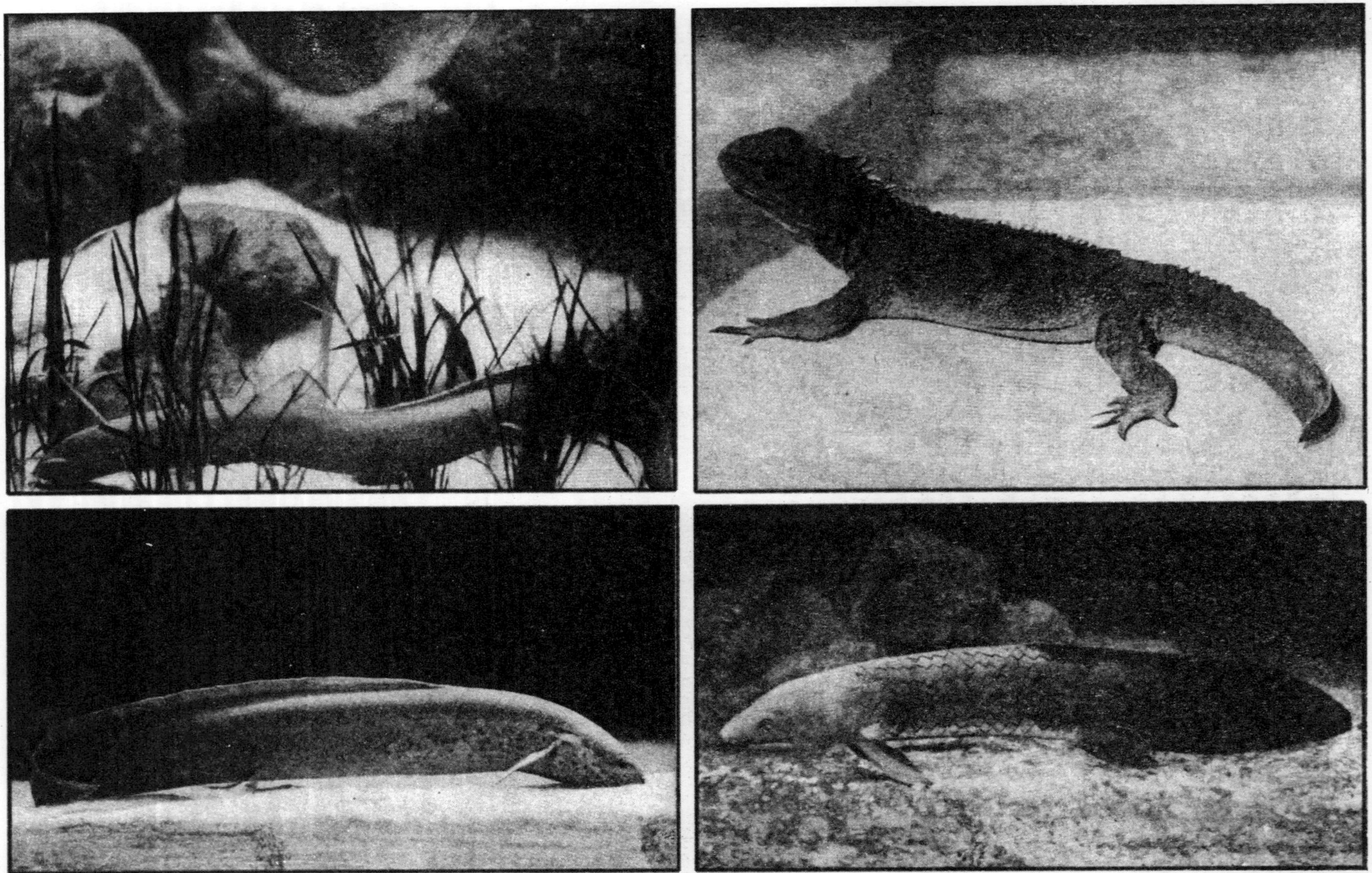

W. S. Berridge

STRANGE ANIMALS OF TO-DAY WHOSE NEAR RELATIVES WERE FOSSILISED THOUSANDS OF YEARS AGO

Life, so the rocks tell us, started in the water and from thence colonised the land. The earliest creatures to try the experiment were the Amphibians—newt-like forms. But some of the fishes that lived in the Devonian era seem to resemble those Amphibians in some respects. Perhaps some of these fishes were also trying to breathe air. At any rate there are fish living to-day in the Amazon, and in some of the rivers of Australia and Africa which much resemble these fossil fish and breathe air as well as water. Our photographs show (bottom left and right and top left) African, Australian and American lung fish and (top right) the tuatera (see also pp. 1218 and 1723) whose only relations are the giant dinosaurs, fossilised thousands of years ago.

Chapter CXLVIII

The Oldest Creatures and the Newest

By Dr. W. T. Calman, F.R.S.

Keeper of Department of Zoology, The British Museum, South Kensington

WHEN the doctrine of evolution became generally accepted it gave a new interest to those types of life which seem to preserve for us the characteristics of a bygone age. It seemed likely that by studying them we might learn something of the structure, appearance, and habits of the far-off ancestors from which living things of the present day have descended.

Among animals there are a number of old-fashioned and primitive forms which have attracted much attention on this account. It soon became evident, however, that no living animal can have preserved quite unchanged the structure of an ancestral type. Evolution has not stood still for any of them, and the more closely they are studied the more evident does it become that those features which stamp them as old-fashioned are usually combined with and overlaid by others that are the products of recent development. On the other hand, animals which we regard as highly evolved frequently show in some parts of their anatomy structures that have apparently changed but little from the conditions found in their remote forefathers. If the evolutionary position of man, for example, were to be judged from the skeleton of the hands and feet, he would be assigned to a very low position among mammals.

By far the most primitive of living mammals are, without doubt, the duckbill, or platypus, and the spiny anteaters, or echidnas, of the Australian region. Unlike all other mammals, they do not bear living young, but lay eggs. They are marked as mammals by their hairy covering (mixed with spines in the echnidnas) and by the fact that the young are nourished with milk, but in many features of their skeleton and other organs they are more like reptiles. They are much less " warm-blooded " than other mammals ; not only is the temperature of the blood lower, but it shows a tendency to rise and fall with the external temperature in the same way as that of a lizard or a frog. The young platypus has temporary teeth which are lost in the adult, and these teeth have much the same form as those of some of the earliest known fossil mammals.

IN many respects, however, these egg-laying mammals are far from resembling the ancestral types. They are all toothless when adult, and have developed very special methods of feeding, the platypus grubbing in the mud with its flattened, skin-covered muzzle like a duck's beak, and the echidnas catching ants with their long, sticky tongues. In these and other respects they have developed along lines of their own, and are far removed from the primitive forms whose remains are found in rocks of the Triassic period and of which it is sometimes hard to say whether they should be classed as reptile-like mammals or mammal-like reptiles.

The reptiles that live to-day are only the survivors of what was formerly a much larger and more varied assemblage of animals. Many of the reptiles that, in the Mesozoic era, dominated the living world, belonged to groups that have left no descendants, and the very earliest reptiles which, at the end of the Palaeozoic era, branched off from an amphibian stock, have no representatives at the present day. There is, however, one living reptile which is the sole survivor of a very ancient group. This is the New Zealand tuatera, a lizard-like creature, about two feet long, which formerly inhabited the mainland of New Zealand, but now survives only on some small islands off the coast. In spite of its resemblance to a lizard, it differs fundamentally not only from the lizards but from all other living reptiles in the arrangement of the bones of the skull, in the teeth, and in many other points of its anatomy. Among other things it is remarkable for having a well-developed eye-like organ on the top of its head. In some other reptiles a vestige of this eye can be detected, but in none is it nearly so well developed as in the tuatera.

IN rocks of the Triassic period in various parts of the world there are found remains of reptiles so closely resembling the tuatera that they are classified in the same Order. Even in the preceding Permian period, at the close of the Palaeozoic era, some members of this Order existed, and they can be traced as late as the Chalk, after which their history is a blank till we come to the still living tuatera. In the Triassic period they are found together with, and seem to have been related to, the earliest dinosaurs, the group of reptiles which became dominant in the periods immediately succeeding. In this way the tuatera forms a link with the gigantic land reptiles of the Mesozoic era. It does not appear, however, to have become greatly specialised in any direction, but remains, in all probability, much like its far-off ancestors whose relics are found in the rocks.

One of the most important steps in the evolution of the vertebrate animals was that taken when some of them left the water and learned to breathe air and live on dry land. The first land animals were members of the class Amphibia, to which newts, salamanders, frogs and toads belong. All these pass the early stages of their life in the water, and when a tadpole changes into a frog it recapitulates in a general way this momentous epoch in the history of backboned animals. The exact mode of the change, however, is very obscure, and existing amphibians give us only an imperfect idea of the great salamander-like creatures that first breathed air in the swamps of the Carboniferous forests. On the other hand, some of the fishes that lived about the same time or in the earlier Devonian period seem to resemble the earliest amphibians in the arrangement of the bones forming the roof of the skull and to give hints of the way in which their paddle-shaped fins became converted into five-toed limbs suitable for creeping on land.

We must suppose, though the fossils can tell us nothing on this point, that these fishes were beginning to supplement their water-breathing gills by gulping air into their swim-bladders, and this transition is preserved for us in the lung-fishes of Queensland, West Africa, and the Amazons. Of these, the Australian lung-fish (*Ceratodus*) is perhaps the most interesting, for its characteristic teeth are found in fossil form in Mesozoic rocks all over the world and its history can thus be traced back to the Triassic period, at the very beginning of the Mesozoic era. Although they come of so ancient a race, however, the lung-fishes had already diverged very far from the stock that gave rise to the amphibians.

The farther back we go in the history of the animal kingdom the more obscure do the records become. Some of the earliest fish-like forms which are found in Silurian rocks seem to have had no jaws or teeth and no paired fins, and in other ways to have resembled the lampreys and hagfishes of the present day. Earlier than this the first vertebrates had no skeleton or other hard parts capable of being preserved as fossils. We can only guess what they may have been like by the hints that we get from such lowly creatures as the lancelet, a little fish-like animal found burrowing in sand in the sea on our own coasts and more abundantly in the Mediterranean and other warm seas. In many ways the lancelet is like a preliminary sketch of a vertebrate, though it is specialised for its own peculiar way of life and only the broad outlines of its structure are primitive.

When we leave the backboned animals and turn to consider the various classes that are grouped together as "invertebrates" the story of their evolution becomes still harder to decipher. The great class of Arthropoda ("jointed feet"), including insects, spiders, crabs and their innumerable kindred, is the only one besides the Vertebrata which has successfully and on a large scale invaded the dry land. That the insects, for instance, came from water-inhabiting forms is certain, but what these forms were and how the transition was effected we can only vaguely guess. Insects of several different Orders existed in the Carboniferous period, but earlier remains are scanty and give no hints of the transition from aquatic ancestors. Millipedes are found in rocks of the Devonian period, but their remains are equally unhelpful from this point of view.

Among living arthropods, however, there is one form (or rather a group of species) which presents very primitive characters and has been regarded as a surviving link between the worms and the air-breathing arthropods. This is the form known as peripatus, the different species of which are found in tropical forests in various parts of the world. They are soft worm-like creatures not clearly divided into segments, but with numerous pairs of stumpy feet and a pair of feelers on the front of the head. They breathe, like insects, by means of fine air-tubes ("tracheae") which open on the surface of the body and carry air directly to the internal organs. The kidney tubes, of which a series is present on each side of the body, are remarkably like those of the segmented worms and in other parts of their anatomy they are very unlike other arthropods. There are difficulties, however, in fitting peripatus into any scheme of descent which will connect it with insects, although the details are too technical to be discussed here. All that we can say is that although peripatus is, in most respects, a very primitive type, it cannot be directly linked up with any known or imagined ancestral stock.

With regard to the origin of the other great group of air-breathing arthropods—that of the Arachnida, or scorpions, spiders, and their kindred—we are a little better informed. An undoubted scorpion has been found fossil in rocks of the Silurian period, and there is reason to believe that, unlike the existing scorpions which live on land and breathe air, it lived in water, possibly in the sea, and breathed by means of gills. Whether it did so or not, a great group of aquatic, air-breathing arthropods, known as the Eurypterida, which flourished throughout the Palaeozoic era, is undoubtedly related to the scorpions, and must have come from the same stock.

Another branch of the same group, beginning at least as early as the Silurian epoch, leads up to the living king-crabs. In spite of their name, these are much more nearly scorpions than crabs, though their general appearance does not suggest this relationship. The American name "horse-foot crabs" fairly well indicates their shape, the back being covered by a broad horseshoe-shaped shield, with a long tail-spike behind. Kipling's entertaining tale of "The Crab that Played with the Sea" does not give an altogether trustworthy account of the evolution of the Arthropoda, but it may serve to remind us that the king-crabs live in the seas of Malaysia as well as on the eastern coasts of the United States. Fossils that resemble very closely the living king-crabs are found as early as the Triassic rocks and their unmistakable relatives can be traced back to the Silurian and perhaps to the Cambrian epochs.

Among living Mollusca none is of greater interest from the point of view that concerns us here than the pearly nautilus, the beautiful spiral shell of which is well known. It belongs to the group Cephalopoda, which includes the cuttlefishes and squids, but it is unlike all the other living members of that group, not only in having the body enclosed in a shell which is divided by internal partitions into a series of chambers, but in having four, instead of two, gill-plumes and in many other points of anatomy.

The Oldest Creatures and the Newest

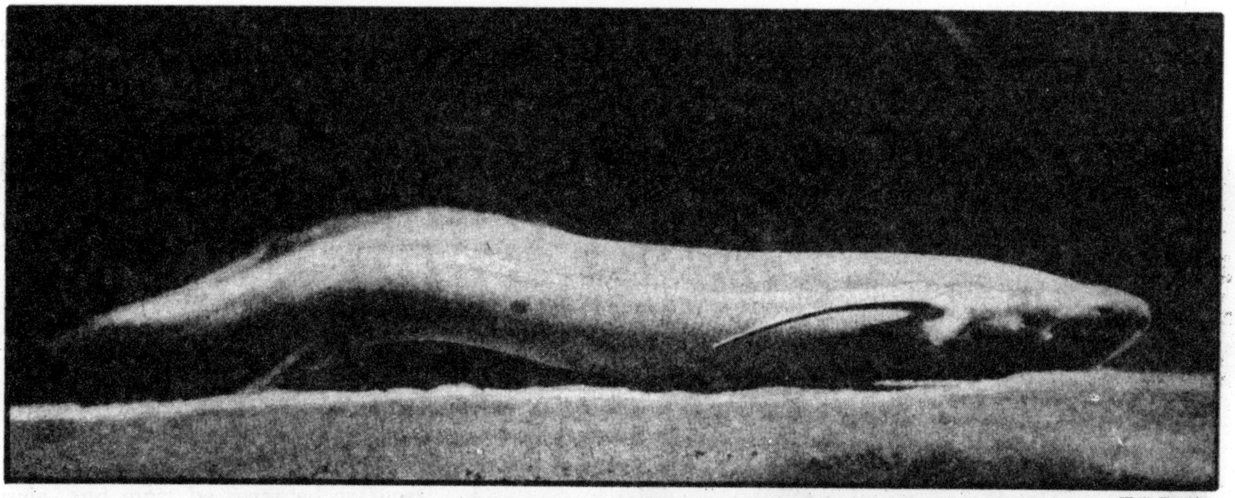

W. S. Berridge

LUNG-FISH THAT THROWS A SIDELIGHT ON ANIMAL EVOLUTION

Geologists pry into the secrets graven in the rocks. Zoologists study living animals from the forms of their eyes to the structure of their feet. But they are not rivals. The one science stimulates and supplements the other. Above we have a lung-fish, the peculiarities of whose manner of living are dealt with in p. 491. Here we have to notice another point of importance. This fish illustrates for us a transition from water-life to land-life which took place probably several millions of years ago.

The nautilus is the sole survivor of what was once a very large and varied group. Shells differing only in trifling details from that of the living species are found as far back as the Trias, at the very beginning of the Mesozoic era, and farther back still, throughout the Palaeozoic era, their relatives can be traced downwards to the Cambrian, almost at the beginning of the history of life as far as the rocks have preserved it. It was formerly supposed that the nautilus was closely related to the ammonites, of which the fossil shells are so abundant in the Liassic rocks in many parts of England from Whitby to Lyme Regis. It is now believed, however, that although the ammonites have spiral chambered shells like the nautilus, they belong to a different branch of the Cephalopoda and their ancestral types can be traced side by side with those of the Nautilus group as far back as the history of the Cephalopods can be followed.

THE lamp-shells or brachiopods are a group of marine animals which, in spite of their resemblance to bivalve molluscs such as cockles and mussels, have nothing to do with the molluscs, but form an independent group of the animal kingdom. Those living in the seas of to-day are only a dwindling remnant of the multitudes that existed in former ages, so that the rocks in many places are crowded with their shells. Several of the living species differ only in small details from the fossils of very remote epochs. In particular, lingula is represented in some of the oldest known fossil-bearing rocks of the Cambrian epoch by shells that are hardly to be distinguished from those of the existing species. It is possible that, in the anatomy of the soft parts, concerning which the fossil shells can tell us little, these very ancient lingulas may have differed slightly from those of the present day. Probably lingula is as good an example as one can find of an animal for which evolution seems to have stood still.

We have mentioned only a few of the more striking examples of persistent types of animal life. There are many others, and they serve to show that evolution has proceeded at very different rates. While other branches of the animal kingdom were moving with the times and developing an ever-increasing complexity of structure and behaviour, they have clung to their old-fashioned ways and have managed to survive somehow in a world that is vastly different from what their forefathers knew. Why they have survived is a puzzling question, and to try to answer it is to realize how little we yet understand the process of evolution. It is sometimes said that these "living fossils" have survived without change because they live in places where the conditions of life have been unchanging and where the struggle for existence has been less keen. There may be some truth in this, but it is not the whole truth.

The New Zealand tuatera lives in burrows in the earth which it is said to share amicably with a petrel that nests and lays its eggs in the same burrows. But when the first of the tuatera stock come to our knowledge in the Triassic epoch no birds had, so far as we know, appeared on the earth. Whatever enemies the modern lingula has to contend with, they are not the same enemies that persecuted the lingulas in Cambrian seas, where there were no crabs or lobsters, no predatory molluscs of modern types, and no fishes at all. Had these long-lived races discovered some perfection of adaptation on which no improvement was possible, just as the mason's mallet has not changed its shape from the days of the Pharaohs? Or is adaptation to environment not so all-important as we are accustomed to think, and must we fall back on a somewhat vague suggestion of "stability of racial constitution"? The more we consider such questions the less do we feel inclined to be dogmatic about the long and mysterious process of evolution that has led from the oldest creatures to the newest.

HEREDITY IN THE SERVICE OF THE MEAT TRADE: BULL AND COW CATTALOS

While domestic cattle do well in the sort of territory in which they have always been reared, it has been found that great parts of Canada do not seem to suit them. On the other hand, the indigenous bison or "buffalo," as it is often erroneously called, thrives in these same parts. It was therefore decided to produce, by means of the power science provides, a race of hybrid cattle-buffalos and call them cattalos. The idea was to attain mass production of palatable meat from animals not needing too much attention

Chapter CXLIX

The Wonder of Heredity

By Ruth C. Bisbee

Lecturer in Zoology, University of Liverpool

The fact that like begets like must have been recognized ever since man could reason at all. Dogs produce dogs, horses produce horses, rabbits produce rabbits. There are no exceptions, and this is the great fundamental fact of heredity.

Not only in general type, however, but also in small details, such as colour of hair or colour of eyes, parent and offspring are often remarkably alike. They may, on the other hand, be extremely unlike in regard to these very same characters. There is inheritance, but it seems to be erratic, uncertain. To a casual observer it seems to be a matter of pure chance whether, on any given occasion, a particular character will or will not be inherited; and until about the middle of last century such inheritance was regarded as a matter of chance. No underlying law had yet been discovered.

But about 1860 a monk was working away quietly in a monastery garden in Austria, crossing different varieties of the ordinary garden pea and making observations which were to reveal to the world a law of heredity as definite as the laws of chemistry and physics. This monk was Gregor Mendel, abbot of a monastery in Brünn. Before his time many workers had experimented with crosses between different varieties of plants in order to study the formation and constitution of hybrids, but they had always given their attention to the sum total of the characters, and no new discoveries had been made. Mendel, however, confined his attention to one pair of alternate characters at a time, and by so doing discovered an orderliness in their inheritance which had not hitherto been suspected.

He worked chiefly with the ordinary garden pea. In this plant there are many clearly marked characters by which one individual differs from another. Certain races are very tall, being as much as six feet high; others are dwarfs of only about a foot and a half. In some the ripe seed is green; in others it is yellow. Sometimes the coat of the seed is smooth; sometimes it is wrinkled. And it was to these simple, clearly defined characters that Mendel devoted his attention.

For one set of experiments he chose tall and dwarf plants. The talls had been found to breed true to tallness through many generations, and the dwarfs to breed true to dwarfness. He crossed these two varieties and obtained hybrids all of which were tall. He then crossed these amongst themselves, and obtained talls and dwarfs in the proportion of three to one. The dwarfs were tested and found to breed true for the dwarf character through many generations. The talls were also tested, and one-third of them were found to breed true to tallness, whereas the other two-thirds behaved like their hybrid parents and gave three talls to one dwarf amongst their offspring. These results can be seen more clearly in the diagram given below.

He worked also with green and yellow seeds, and with smooth and wrinkled seeds, and obtained exactly similar results.

In all these experiments there is exactly the same kind of result; that is, the hybrids show only one character of the pair under observation—tallness, yellowness, smoothness. The other character seems to have been lost. Yet in all, when the hybrids are crossed amongst themselves, this "lost" character reappears, showing that it has not been lost but only masked by the other. In all, too, the proportions in the F_2 generation are the same: one which breeds true for one character; two hybrids, one which breeds true for the other character.

Pure bred tall parent **T** x **D** Pure bred dwarf parent

Hybrid **T** x **T** Hybrid . . . F_1 i.e. First filial generation

T Pure — **T** Hybrid — **T** Hybrid — **D** Pure . . . F_2 i.e. Second filial generation

Pure bred yellow parent **Y** x **G** Pure bred green parent

Hybrid **Y** x **Y** Hybrid . . . F_1 generation

Y Pure — **Y** Hybrid — **Y** Hybrid — **G** Pure . . . F_2 generation

Pure bred smooth parent **S** x **W** Pure bred wrinkled parent

Hybrid **S** x **S** Hybrid . . . F_1 generation

S Pure — **S** Hybrid — **S** Hybrid — **W** Pure . . . F_2 generation

MENDEL'S GREAT INHERITANCE THEORY

By quietly experimenting with the growth of peas the Abbot Mendel, seventy years ago, discovered an order in inheritance as shown in these three simple groups. The first concerns tall and dwarf plants, the second yellow and green seeds and the third smooth and wrinkled seeds

Mendel called the character which appears in the hybrid the dominant, and the character which is hidden he called the recessive. Thus tallness, yellowness and smoothness are dominants, whilst dwarfness, greenness and wrinkledness are recessives. In order to account for the reappearance of the pure strains in the F_2 generation, Mendel suggested that a germ cell or gamete carries one character or the other of a pair, but never both. This was his great conception of the purity of the gamete. He claimed that, although both the members of a pair of alternate characters are present

DOGS THAT SHOW HUMAN INTERFERENCE WITH THEIR HEREDITY
The very fact that dogs are usually referred to by the specific name of their " breed " shows the important part that human influence has played in the heredity of these animals. Their amenability to training caused primitive man to use them as his allies against other animals, and special characteristics were soon found to result from breeding like with like. Now knowledge has reached such a pitch that a new breed can be rapidly evolved to order, true to the desired shape, size and colour.

together in the hybrid, they separate again completely when that hybrid forms its germ cells, half of the germ cells receiving one character and half receiving the alternate character. This separation of alternate characters is spoken of as segregation. Segregation and the resulting purity of the gamete are the two fundamental postulates in Mendel's theory of inheritance.

If this theory is correct, it is evident how Mendel's results were brought about. For example, in the cross tall x dwarf peas, the tall parent, being from a pure strain, would carry only tallness. Thus every germ cell would have the determiner for tallness. In the pure dwarf every germ cell would carry the determiner for dwarfness. When these two strains were crossed, a tall-carrying germ cell and a dwarf-carrying germ cell would come together at fertilisation, and the resulting hybrid would carry the determiners for both characters. When its germ cells were formed, however, half of them would receive the determiner for tallness and half the determiner for dwarfness ; no cell would receive both. Thus the germ cells of the hybrid would be as pure as those of the original pure-bred parents, only each hybrid would have both kinds, tall-carriers and dwarf-carriers.

Now when two such hybrids were crossed together there would be *four* possibilities in regard to the meeting of germ cells : (1) a tall-carrying female cell might meet a tall-carrying male cell, giving a pure tall individual ; or (2) a tall-carrying female cell might meet a dwarf-carrying male cell, giving a hybrid ; or (3) a dwarf-carrying female cell might meet a tall-carrying male cell, again giving a hybrid ; or (4) a dwarf-carrying female cell might meet a dwarf-carrying male cell, giving a pure dwarf individual. Thus, if it were a matter of pure chance which germ cell should meet which, the result of the mating of two hybrids would be : one pure tall, two hybrids, one pure dwarf. And this is exactly the result Mendel did obtain. As tallness is dominant to dwarfness, the pure talls and the hybrids all look alike ; only their subsequent breeding results reveal their true constitution.

HEREDITY EVOLVED THE FINE FEATHERS OF THE WILD DUCK

If we examine the evidence relating to that far-off time when the reptiles and birds were only just beginning to take their separate ways through the distance of evolution, we find that feathers and scales alike evolved from skin. At the other end of time stands this wild duck, a perfect bird-form, highly specialised for flight. Its feathers, furthermore, distinguish it from other birds and, indeed, during the course of Life's development, the feather has become amazingly variegated.

Naturally, if the number of fertilisations is small, it is unlikely that this exact proportion will be produced. In, say, four fertilisations it may well happen that a dwarf-carrier meets a dwarf-carrier three or even four times out of the four. But in four hundred fertilisations a dwarf-carrier would certainly not meet a dwarf-carrier three hundred times out of the four hundred by pure chance. In four hundred cases the 1 : 2 : 1 proportion would be fairly exact.

Mendel published his results in 1865 in "The Proceedings of the Natural History Society of Brünn." The scientific world, however, was not at that moment concerned with the problem of inheritance, and consequently Mendel's epoch-making discovery was passed over practically unnoticed, and it was not until 1900 that his paper received any attention. Men of science were by that time thinking of heredity, and Mendel's work was hailed as a revelation.

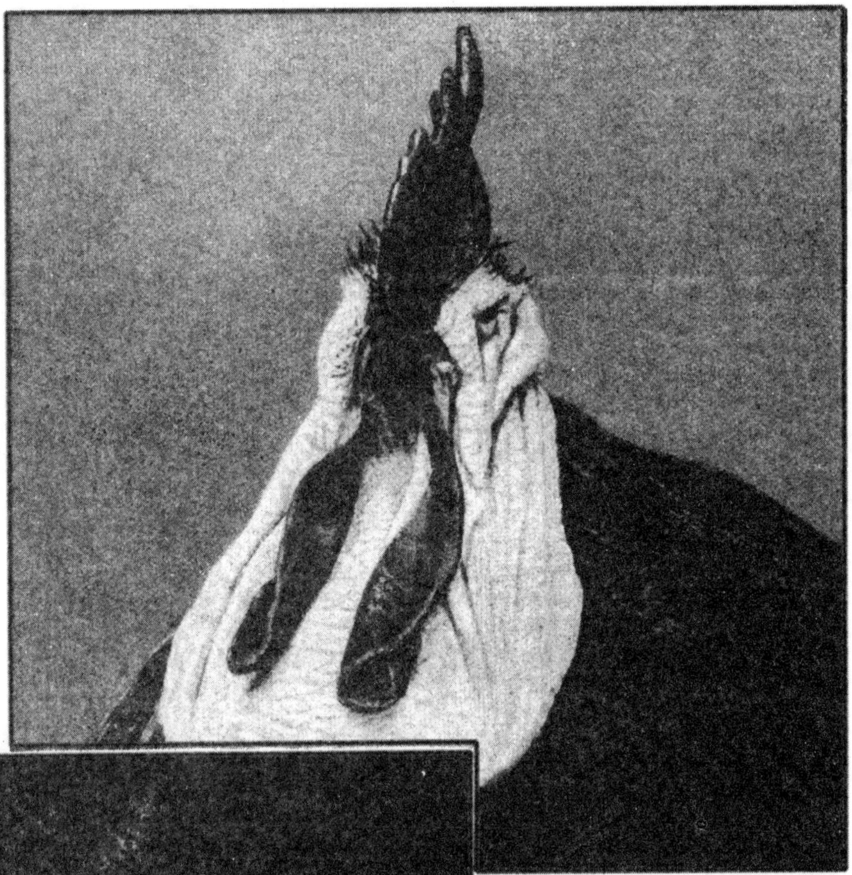

E.N.A.

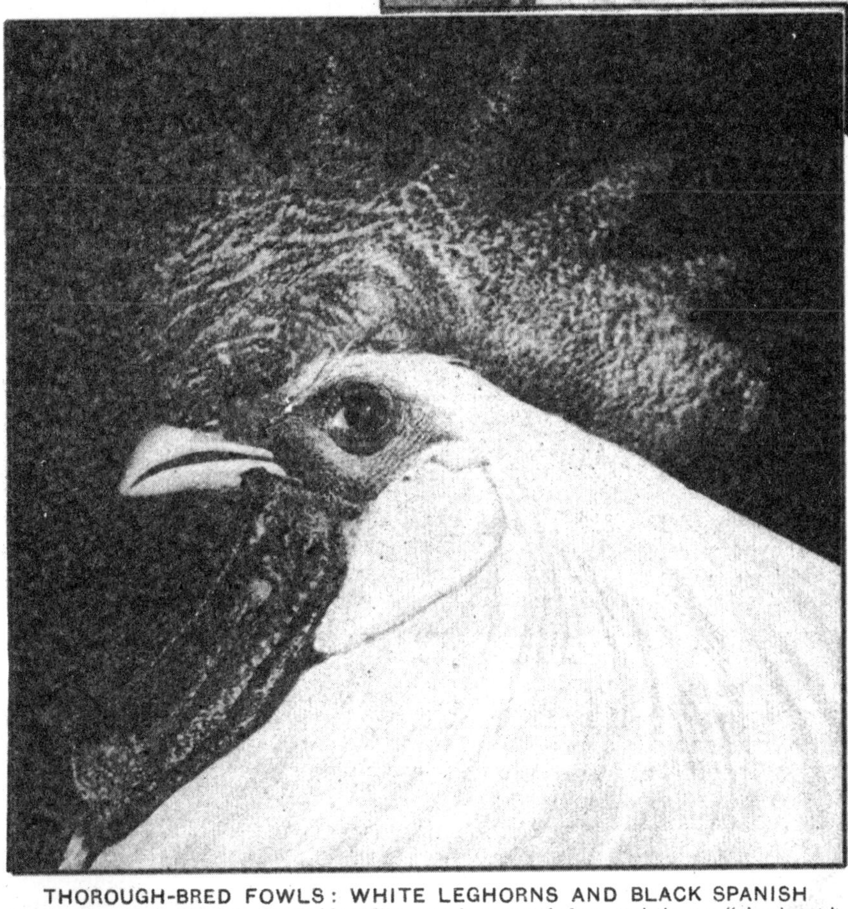

THOROUGH-BRED FOWLS: WHITE LEGHORNS AND BLACK SPANISH
It is now known that, by the laws of heredity, certain parental characteristics are "dominant" to others. In humans, for instance, brown eyes are dominant to blue, i.e. if one parent has brown eyes and the other blue, the child will be brown-eyed. From fowls much has been learned about heredity. Here, white is not dominant to black, a hybrid being "blue."

Since then many workers have carried out breeding experiments along Mendel's lines with both plants and animals, and in a great many cases have obtained results very similar to his. There are some characters which may not be inherited at all. There are others which are inherited but do not seem to follow any known law. Amongst those characters at present investigated, however, the vast majority seem to show perfectly typical Mendelian inheritance. In guinea-pigs, for example, there is great variety of characters. In some the hair is long; in some it is short. In some it lies flat and smooth, whilst in others it forms rosettes. In some it is white; in others black. In others it is agouti, or "ticked."

And most of these characters are inherited according to Mendel's law. Short hair is dominant to long hair; a rosette coat is dominant to a smooth coat; the ticked or agouti colour is dominant to black; a coloured coat of any colour is dominant to a white coat. In rabbits the case is very similar. Short hair is dominant to long hair; agouti is dominant to black; any coloured coat is dominant to a white coat. In cats, also, the ticked or tabby colour is dominant to black, but the white coat colour is dominant to any other colour. And all these pairs of characters behave in inheritance according to Mendel's law. In all cases the hybrid shows only the dominant character; in all cases the hybrids, when mated amongst themselves, give roughly one pure dominant, two hybrids, one pure recessive.

We now know that the dominance of one character over another is not a necessary feature of Mendelian inheritance. There are some cases where the hybrid, instead of showing the dominant character, shows a mixture of the dominant and recessive, or something intermediate between the two. Thus pure-bred white Andalusian fowls crossed with pure-bred blacks give "blue" hybrids; neither black nor white is dominant. But when these hybrid blues are crossed amongst themselves the typical Mendelian proportion appears in the next generation, viz.: one black, two blues, one white. The blacks crossed with blacks breed true to black; the whites crossed with whites breed true to white; the blues breed exactly as did their blue parents, giving approximately one black, two blues, one white.

Sometimes, even when the inheritance of a character is known to follow Mendel's law, most unexpected results appear from certain matings. In rabbits, for instance, the wild agouti colour is known to be dominant to black, so that black cannot carry agouti. Black is also known to be dominant to white. In most crosses between blacks and whites the offspring are all black, as would be expected; but sometimes some or all of them are agouti. This seems to be a departure from Mendel's law. The agouti character, however, appears to be the result of the interaction of three different kinds of determiners or factors, two which together produce black and one which causes the ticking of the hairs and so changes black to agouti. Now, if the factors for black are present without the ticking factor, the animal is black; if, however, the ticking factor is also present, the animal is agouti.

Now these factors behave quite separately in inheritance; they may be together, or any one may be present without the other. The ticking may thus be present in an albino animal, but, naturally, in the absence of colour, it has no visible effect. But if a black rabbit is mated with a white one which carries the factor for ticking, then the black factors and the ticking factor may come together at fertilisation, and so produce an agouti instead of the expected black. An even more surprising result is obtained when two pure-bred albinos give coloured progeny. This sometimes happens with rabbits and guinea-pigs, and with rats and mice. Yet albinism is a pure Mendelian recessive to all colour. An albino is white because there is no colour present in its constitution.

How, then, can two albinos give coloured offspring? Occasionally, both in plants and animals, "sports" arise—individuals with new characters. These new characters often seem to be the result of the loss of one or more factors from the germ cell of the parent. Thus black has almost certainly arisen from the wild grey or agouti by the loss of the ticking factor. And black itself seems to be the result of the interaction between a factor which gives rise to a colour base and one which gives rise to a colour developer. A strain of albinos may arise from a strain of blacks, therefore, by the sudden loss of the colour developer; and these albinos will still carry the factor for the colour base. Bred amongst themselves, however, they will remain perfectly true breeding for albinism, for the whole strain will lack the colour developer. Similarly, another strain of albinos may arise from black by the loss of the colour base; these will retain the colour developer. They will breed true generation after generation if bred amongst themselves, for none of them possesses the colour base. If, now, members of these two different true breeding albino strains are mated together, they will give black offspring, for at fertilisation the factor for the colour base and the factor for colour developer will be brought together, and colour will consequently develop in the resulting individual.

Such cases of unexpected results from the mating of pure bred parents are fairly common and, at first sight, seem to contradict Mendel's law. They are usually spoken of as throw-backs or reversions to ancestral type. They are cases of reversion, but on careful analysis they are usually found to support, rather than to contradict, Mendel's law. They are the results of the recombination of certain factors which have been separated from each other in two different strains, but which were all present together in some common ancestor. The crossing of these two strains has brought all the factors together again and has so produced the ancestral character. By complicated experiments it is possible to trace out the history of the different factors involved and to show that, together or apart, they are steadily following Mendel's law through generation after generation.

The facts of Mendelian inheritance are, then, firmly established; and nothing in our present knowledge is opposed to Mendel's original explanation of these facts as being due to the segregation of characters in the hybrid and the resulting purity of the germ cells. When Mendel put forward this explanation he had no idea how this segregation of characters was brought about; he only saw, from the facts of inheritance, that it must take place. Since his time, however, our knowledge of the structure of plants and animals has greatly advanced, and now we do know a mechanism by which separation of alternate characters could be brought about.

The tissues of nearly all plants and animals are built up of small units of living matter called cells. They are invisible to the naked eye, but are clearly visible under a microscope. Within each cell there is a specialised part, called the nucleus, which is surrounded by a thin membrane and which is chemically different from the rest of the cell. When a tissue is cut into fine sections and stained with certain dyes it is found that small granules inside the nucleus stain more deeply than the rest of the cell. This deeply staining material is called chromatin. Now all cells arise from the division of pre-existing cells and during such division the deeply staining material within the nucleus behaves in a peculiar way. It first becomes concentrated into a definite number of small bodies called chromosomes. These differ in shape and size, but there are usually two of each kind. When a cell divides into two, each chromosome also divides, half going to each new daughter cell. Thus the number is kept constant throughout successive divisions.

When the germ cells are maturing, however, they undergo one division which is different from all other in that every chromosome remains whole, but one member of each pair goes to each daughter cell. Thus a germ cell has only one member of each pair of chromosomes. If the chromosomes carry the determiners of Mendelian characters, this separating of the members of each pair of chromosomes during the formation of the germ cell will bring about the very segregation of characters which Mendel postulated.

Neville Kingston

HYBRIDS: "TIGON" AND ASS-ZEBRA

At the Zoological Gardens in London there has been produced a most interesting hybrid between a tiger and a lion. It has been dubbed the "tigon" (bottom). It is decidedly not a noble-looking beast, is very long in the leg, where the stripes are most prominent, and of a general sandy hue. Such a "cross" could never have occurred in Nature. Above is an ass-zebra.

The Wonder of Heredity

Whatever may be the explanation of Mendelian inheritance, however, the facts remain the same and the importance of the discovery of Mendel's law can scarcely be over-estimated.

It has thrown a flood of light on our conception of evolution. Many writers have claimed that evolution must have taken place to some extent by the perpetuating of new characters which have arisen in nature as "sports." There was always the objection,

C. Reid

however, that such characters would quickly be lost by cross-breeding. But we now know that characters that follow Mendel's law are not so lost. They may be hidden in one generation, but they appear again in succeeding generations unaltered and true-breeding. They are, therefore, well able to establish new strains and so to make their contribution to the process of evolution.

Mendel's discovery has also completely revolutionised stock-breeding. In the past breeders worked by a slow process of selection. Sometimes they succeeded; often they failed. Now, however, when a desirable character is found, in plant or animal, a very few crossing experiments suffice to show whether or not it is inherited according to Mendel's law. If it is so inherited, a pure-breeding strain can be established in minimum time, at a minimum cost, and with almost absolute certainty. Also, with our present knowledge, characters can be separated or brought together in almost any desired combination by making the necessary crosses. Naturally, all this is of the utmost importance commercially.

In regard to the human race, too, there are many new problems to face in the light of Mendel's discovery. Certain human characters are known to follow Mendel's law. Blue eye colour is recessive to brown; certain types of feeblemindedness are recessive to the normal condition; night blindness, colour blindness and deaf mutism all seem to follow Mendel's law. Now eye colour is perhaps of little importance to the race, but feeblemindedness is a grave social and economic menace. When the mode of inheritance of a character is known, however, it only remains for the conscience of the people to decide whether it shall be weeded out or allowed to remain. In human beings, as in animals and plants, the importance of the right kind of parentage cannot be over-estimated.

HEREDITY USED TO PRODUCE GOOD FOOD AND CLOTH

Domestic sheep are always called "silly." Wild sheep, on the other hand, are anything but silly, and yet both come ultimately from the same stock. The difference is caused by heredity. Wild sheep are bred from the strongest, most agile and most intelligent parents, because all the silly ones were eaten by enemies. Here we have some prize domestic specimens.

Chapter CL

High Jumpers and Long Jumpers

By Edward Step, F.L.S.

Author of "By Seashore, Wood and Moorland"

When we read the reports of Olympic games, and similar athletic gatherings, we learn with pleasure that whilst Brown has added to his sporting fame by establishing a new record for the high jump, Smith also has covered himself with glory by outdistancing all predecessors in the length of his leap. We are greatly interested in these achievements, not necessarily because we are ourselves athletes—a very small percentage of the race can make such a claim—but perhaps from a subconscious feeling that it is good that a few of us are keeping our physical powers at the maximum in an age when mechanical transport is tending to the muscular degeneration of the race.

Although in most of the classes of animal life we find that certain species have developed considerable leaping powers, both vertical and horizontal, it is not probable that man in his uncivilized state had much occasion for the high jump, though the long jump must have been useful often for the crossing of streams and chasms in the days before he had invented the bridge.

To many of the wild creatures below him, however, the power to leap in the pursuit of prey or as a means for escaping from their natural enemies must have been most valuable; and so we find the springing character retained in certain groups of animals, ranging downwards from the mammals to molluscs, insects and crustaceans. With modern man and his hunting horse the accomplishment is mainly a matter of sport, requiring practice for its development and continuance; but with the wild animals the power is inherited, and their habits keep the muscles concerned in full efficiency.

It is among the mammals, of course, that the most imposing exponents of jumping are to be found, owing to their superior size attracting our attention; but for at least a hundred and fifty years it has been the practice in numerous natural history books to exalt the leaping powers of the flea at the expense of relatively feeble man. It was said that the nimble insect can leap to the height of a foot, which is a hundred times its own length, and that if a man of six feet could make a similar vertical spring it would carry him well over St. Paul's. (Mitzmain, a recent investigator, says the flea's vertical leap is only seven and three-quarter inches, though horizontally it can accomplish thirteen inches.) But the comparison is misleading and worthless, because it ignores the respective weights the two performers have to lift.

A BUCKING STEER

With all four powerful legs springing together and the great spine working in conjunction with them in a series of "bucks," the steer bounces like a ball in its efforts to dislodge the cowboy rider.

The kangaroos provide us with the most striking examples of jumping beasts, owing to their habit of going about on two legs in an almost erect attitude, the two largest species standing about five feet high, and using their huge, stiff tails as the third leg of a supporting tripod. The fore-limbs are small and take no part in locomotion, being used only when the animal is grazing.

To get over a country covered with patches of scrub alternating with tall grass, kangaroos do not attempt to walk or run, but proceed by a long succession of jumps which have been recorded variously as fifteen to twenty and even thirty feet. They are enabled to make these mighty bounds by the great development of the muscles of the hinder thighs and the loins. These long jumps, however, are not quite so great as is claimed for the performance of the well-trained hunter horse, which is estimated to be between thirty-three and thirty-seven feet when a ditch or fence has to be taken in the course of the run. But, in justice to the kangaroo, it should be pointed out that the hunter is not able to repeat his feat at short intervals, as do the kangaroo and jerboa; his weight is too great for such exertion.

A similar type of structure is common to several other of the marsupial beasts of Australia, including the kangaroo's near relations, the wallabies and the smaller kangaroo rat, which has very long hind feet and advances by repeated great bounds. This last-named must not be confounded with the kangaroo rat of North America, which is a true gnawing animal or rodent, and allied to the Old World jerboa.

The bandicoots, also marsupials, but with less disproportion between the fore and hind legs, get over the ground rapidly with a movement that is half run and half jump. The jumping pouched mouse, another marsupial of smaller

FINE RUNNING JUMPS MADE BY DOGS

Now that thousands of pounds are lost and won every year at greyhound racing over hurdles, the jumping powers of dogs are brought forcefully before the public While some breeds like that of the greyhound specialise in the running jump, others are better at a standing "take-off." Here are two dogs showing off their powers over a hurdle and a fence respectively.

size, has the power of continuous leaping, though it cannot use it as do the kangaroos for surmounting bush; but it is considered that its saltatory motions are baffling to the birds of prey that are its chief enemies.

Turning to the rodents or gnawing animals, which include the true mice, squirrels and rabbits, we have a well-known example of the high and long jumper in the jerboa, whose short fore limbs are in strong contrast with the excessively long and bony, bird-like hind legs, whose feet have only three long toes. In entire length the jerboa measures about a foot, but about seven and a half inches of this length is contributed by the slender, tufted tail, which is useful as a balancing organ in the jerboa's hopping walk and its long jumps; every leap takes him about nine feet farther from his pursuer. Like many other of the rodents, the jerboa is also a burrowing animal.

E.N.A.

FOUR-LEGGED AND TWO-LEGGED JUMPING

Although the kangaroo uses only one pair of legs for its jumping, yet this animal is renowned as one of the finest performers in the animal world. Except when browsing the leap is its ordinary mode of progression and some specimens are credited with "long jumps" of thirty feet. The dog seen above is clearing a number of forms with a combined long and high jump.

The Cape jumping hare or "springhaas" resembles the jerboa on a larger scale, for its entire length is nearly three feet, of which one-half is a stouter, more hairy tail than that of the jerboa. Also a burrower, it makes very long leaps when above ground. The North American jumping mouse, though its long hind legs do not appear to exceed the front ones greatly, is a very capable leaper, covering from three to five feet at a bound. The kangaroo rat, of the same country, has long hind limbs which it uses on occasion for similar exercises. The hare, that often makes high jumps when coursed, has been known to take successfully the long jump across ditches four yards wide.

Among the insect-eaters there is the African jumping shrew (also known as the elephant shrew, by virtue of its long proboscis), which has long hind legs enabling it to leap after its active prey, and to get quickly out of the way of pursuers. A larger member of this family, the colugo of the East Indies, is enabled to take long horizontal leaps by a mechanism that is quite different. From the neck to the tail-tip on either side, and connected with all the feet, there is a broad expansion of skin which, when the limbs are extended, forms a parachute.

The animal lives in the tree-tops; and when it wishes to change its feeding quarters, instead of descending one tree and climbing another, it leaps the intervening space direct, though the distance may be as much as two hundred feet. The initial impulse is provided by the muscles of the chest and loins, and the creature then planes across to its objective. The unrelated flying squirrels of the same region, and the flying phalangers of Australia,

DARING JUMPS FROM GREAT HEIGHTS BY DOG AND MOUNTED HORSE

Though some animals dive for the fun of the thing, especially those with a strong disposition to play, like the otter, yet diving must be in most cases a distasteful business only performed under stress of danger. Even a hippopotamus will precipitate itself from a high bank in such a moment. Such a manoeuvre, from the spectacular point of view, of course, puts the dive-loving sea-lion in the shade, but animals can be trained to perform diving feats as we see here, though to persuade such a nervous creature as a horse to do so is an achievement.

have similar arrangements. The "flying" of their names is deceptive, for they cannot rise into the air, though they can extend their almost horizontal leap or make a sloping descent from a height. In this respect they greatly resemble ordinary squirrels, which have no skin-flaps to assist them.

The goats, sheep and antelopes are a very agile and sure-footed race, and many of them possess considerable jumping powers, using them in places where it would be very dangerous for most bulky animals to do more than put one cautious foot slightly in advance of the others. These, instead of trusting to the muscles of one pair of limbs, bring the four feet close together and unite the muscular powers of all the limbs in one effort.

The chamois, for example, is undeterred by the chasms and precipices of the mountains he affects; he leaps across wide gulfs and, if necessary, lands upon a very small area, his feet being planted firmly together. The little African klipspringer, or rock jumper, can do much the same, and will leap with ease to ledges or peaks that are two or three times his own height above him.

The great cats, lion, tiger and leopard—though built on a plan very different from that of some of the leaping animals mentioned—are good exponents of the long, rapid jump. The legs, made to appear rather short owing to their relatively great girth, scarcely indicate their capabilities in this direction; but the long, supple spine and the muscular development of the shoulders, loins and limbs enable them after a patient "stalk" to hurl themselves suddenly upon their prey, with an accurate estimate of the distance to be covered.

The huge and heavy marine mammal, the cachalot, or sperm whale, one of the largest of all beasts, is able by a few strokes of its tail-flukes to leap com-

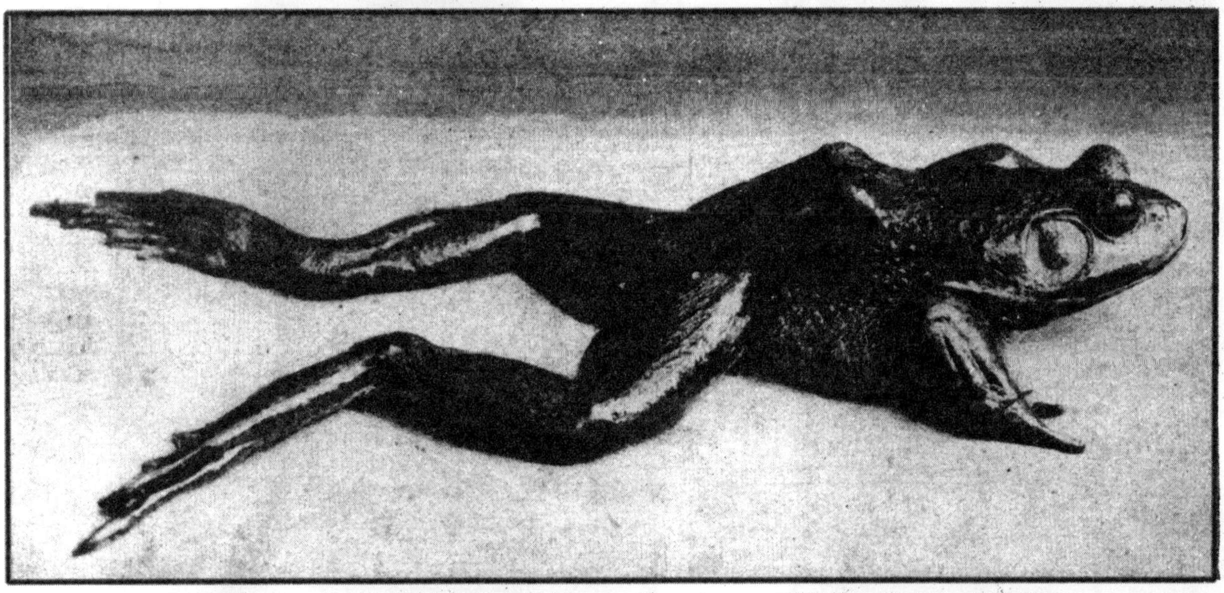

POWERFUL HIND LEGS MAKE THE FROGS VERY DIFFICULT TO CAPTURE

The small child who, attracted by the pretty markings of the frog, tries to catch one, or the angler who, in following the excellent advice of the great Walton, essays the same feat to provide himself with bait, are immediately treated to a fine object lesson in the leaping powers of the animal. The common frog of the English meadows can jump eighteen inches or so off the ground, while the much larger bull frog of the United States (top) is said to clear five feet when put to it.

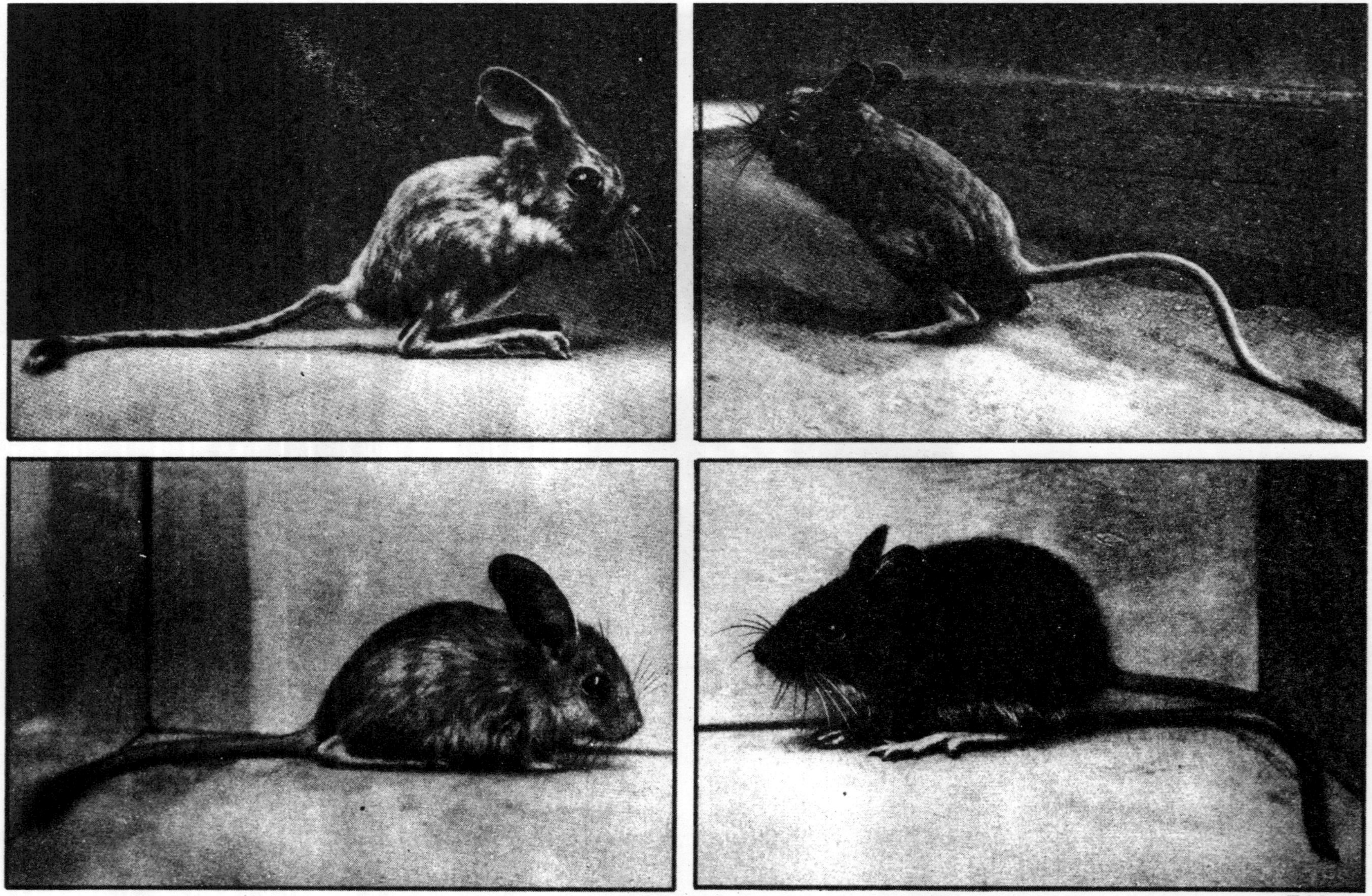

W. S. Berridge

LONG JUMPERS AMONG THE RODENTS OF TWO CONTINENTS: AFRICAN JERBOAS AND CANADIAN MOUSE

Although the jerboas, which inhabit various parts of Africa, are as a rule no more than a foot long and over half that length is made up of tail, yet many of these active little beasts can jump nine feet if pressed by some hungry pursuer. They have long, bony and rather bird-like legs and move in a series of hops. Our photographs show (bottom left) a four-toed jerboa; (top left) a desert jerboa rat and (top right) a large three-toed Egyptian jerboa. The right-hand lower illustration is of a Canadian jumping mouse. This little rodent can make a long jump of from three to five feet, a fine performance for so small an animal and one on which its life often depends.

pletely out of the water and to repeat the performance several times, although its weight is more than a hundred tons! The more graceful gambols of the dolphins and porpoises are effected by similar means.

Coming to the lower classes of the backboned animals, we find some power of horizontal leaping in the lizards; and this is shown in their structure by the superior length of the hind limbs and their thicker, more muscular, thighs. On the ground this leaping is combined with running, and they are enabled by such very swift movements to elude pursuers by the rapid taking of cover under stones or amid dense vegetation. Frequently, however, it may be observed as a pure leap; as, for example, when the common little viviparous lizard of our heaths, having climbed the stems of the heath shrubs, leaps across the intervening plants to reach another desirable top-shoot, gripping it firmly with its long fingers and toes.

W. S. Berridge

SPRINGHAAS OR CAPE JUMPING HARE

Resembling a jerboa on a large scale the springhaas, or Cape jumping hare, measures nearly three feet from nose to tip of tail, of which the tail takes up about eighteen inches. Though called a hare, this animal burrows like a rabbit and, when frightened, makes for its underground home at great speed by means of long, rapid jumps.

In the heavier, more bulky, toads and frogs we have better opportunities for comparing jumping methods and the mechanism by which they are accomplished. The toad is the more heavily built, with thick, powerful limbs, but their use is mainly for the scraping of shallow pits in which he can lie with his back level with the ground. The hind legs, though longer than the combined length of head and body, are more adapted for walking than for leaping; but in the evening, when he is active, we may see him getting over the ground quickly by a continuous series of short, heavy jumps.

The more gracefully-built frog with his longer legs can take leaps that are both high and long. Our own common species ordinarily lifts its body a foot and a half to two feet off the ground; but the bullfrog of America is said to take a high jump of five feet, and to land at a distance between six and ten feet from his starting-point.

There has always been, and to some extent there still is, a good deal of controversy as to whether the movements of the flying herring above the surface of the sea are to be considered as real flying effected by muscular movements of the long, wing-like fins, or a leap continued for a distance by the fins acting as planes supporting the fish. Much good evidence has been given in support of each view; but whether the fins are worked as wings or not—probably they are—it is certain that the initial movement from the sea is accomplished by a great leap, impelled by the tail-fin. It is estimated that by these means the flying-herring may be carried through the air to a distance of five hundred feet! Very similar is the case of the flying gurnard.

Salmon and sea trout, in their determination to reach the shallow upper waters of rivers for the purpose of depositing their eggs in the clean gravel, have to make great vertical leaps up falls and over weirs. This is accomplished mainly by the powerful muscles of the tail and the alternate bending and straightening of the body. Sir Herbert Maxwell, who has a very intimate acquaintance with salmon, says that six feet is the limit of the fish's leap, a waterfall of seven feet being too high for it to surmount; others, however, assert that ten feet is not too high to discourage it. Pictures with further particulars of these leaps are given in pages 496 and 497 of this work.

Leo Walmsey

SEA JUMPERS SHOWING OFF THEIR POWERS

The dolphin, whose leaps out of water have always been described as sportive, really comes up to the surface to breathe, for it is a mammal (bottom). The huge herring known as the tarpon (top) comes into rivers after the mullet. Tarpon fishing off the Florida coast is famous sport as the fish, often scaling 2 cwt., leaps ten feet out of the sea to shake off the hook (top).

Not unlike the sustained leap of the flying fishes is that of the flying squid, though there are here no movable fins to assist it. This marine mollusc has at the end of its back a united pair of triangular flaps which look like a huge arrowhead. When pursued by big fish, the squid ejects water forcibly through its funnel forwards, which has the effect of sending it, rear-end foremost, out of the water ; and the flaps support it for some distance through the air.

A few other molluscs have leaping powers of a sort, differing from those mentioned. Some of the larger species of cockle, though the large, muscular foot is used chiefly for pulling the bulky shells down into mud or sand, can employ it on occasion as a spring by whose sudden extension the animal in its shell jumps a short distance. The lighter scallops, with their thinner, flatter shells, have another method for shifting their quarters. The two valves of the shell are closed by means of a very powerful muscle which connects them, but its powers are opposed by an elastic ligament at the hinge that strives to keep them open. When the usually open valves are closed with a snap, the scallop is sent flitting through the water to a distance of several feet, when the action may be repeated again and again without the mollusc coming to rest. One of the very delicate thin-shelled land snails, known as the pellucid glass snail, has a protective trick of giving a jerk of its tail to its support, which has the effect of making the snail jump shortly sidewise into the surrounding moss, where it escapes notice.

It is among the insects that we find the most numerous examples of jumpers and leapers, and of these the most striking and best-known are the grasshoppers, locusts and crickets. Here the hindmost of the three pairs of legs are lengthened greatly, and

SAILFISH AND TARPON LEAP FOR LIFE WHEN HOOKED

Off Miami, Florida, the fishing is good. The sailfish (bottom), for instance, is a tough customer. Its sail-like dorsal fin gives it its name. The tarpon (top) owes its popularity as a game fish to its leaping habits when hooked. It has happened that a fisherman who has gone alone has had his canoe sunk by a tarpon crashing down on it.

their thighs are much thickened to accommodate the mass of muscles by which they are worked. Held to its support by the hooks and pads of the jointed foot, the flexed leg is straightened suddenly, with the result that the heavy body is thrown into the air. If necessary, this effort can be seconded by a stroke or two of the wings, which lengthens the leap considerably and brings the insect to a distant grass-stem, upon which it alights with certainty.

Numerous members of the great bug family share this leaping power, and familiar examples are to be found in the frog-hoppers, which in the nymph stage hide themselves by producing the so-called "cuckoo-spit" of our garden plants. There is not here so marked a difference in the size of the hind legs compared with the others, but the leap is high enough and quick enough to take the hopper beyond the reach of the bird's bill.

Some of the beetles also have jumping powers, which are indicated usually by the thighs of the hinder legs being enlarged, as in the grasshoppers. A small example is familiar in the misnamed turnip-flea, so destructive to the young foliage of the vegetable whose name it bears. Several related species are equally obnoxious to cultivators of any of the cabbage tribe, and exhibit the same methods for eluding capture. An original form of leaping is that in vogue among the skipjacks or click-beetles, These neat, polished beetles have a strange penchant for falling on their backs after flight, in which position most beetles have a difficulty in righting themselves and become an easy prey for insectivorous birds. But the skipjacks have a spring arrangement in the fore-body by which this portion and the head are jerked violently against the ground, sending the beetle into the air and enabling it to right itself.

Chas. Barrett

MARSUPIAL ANIMALS THAT ARE CONFINED TO A SMALL PORTION OF THE WORLD

It is only a narrow channel of the ocean some 25 miles wide that rules a definite line of demarcation between two entirely different faunas, and this division, called Wallace's Line, runs between the islands of Bali and Lombok. It is continued between Borneo and Celebes. To the east of the line the animals are of the Australian type that was cut off from fresh invasions of other types so long ago that they have kept distinct. Here are three marsupials, an Australian opossum, a tree kangaroo (bottom right) and a wallaby (top).

Chapter CLI

The Geography of the Animal World

By Dr. Marion Newbigin

Author of "Animal Geography"

It is one of the simplest facts of observation that all animals, to a greater or less extent, are fitted for the surroundings in which they live naturally. Thus, deer are fitted for life in wooded country, and there are many deer in the forests of Europe, of temperate and tropical Asia, and of North America. Can we assume then that in any part of the world where forests or park-like country exist there we shall find deer? Africa south of the Sahara has vast tracts of wooded land, yet throughout its length and breadth there are no deer. Australia has great belts of bush but has not a single deer. Nor is this an isolated case. We think of the tiger as the typical jungle beast, and know that it does haunt the jungles of India. When we form a mental picture of the jungles of Africa the temptation is great to people them also with tigers, and not a few imaginative writers succumb to the temptation. But there are not now, and there never were, tigers in Africa.

The dense equatorial forest of the Amazon basin shows in many ways a close analogy to that of the Congo basin; but the difference between their faunas is profound. No elephant, no rhinoceros, no gorilla lives in the Amazon area, but it contains animals like sloths, howling monkeys, little furry marmosets, and others which are equally unknown to tropical Africa. Clearly, then, while it is true that animals are suited to their habitats, it is not necessarily true that a particular habitat will be occupied by the animals which seem best fitted to the conditions prevailing there.

The same conclusion can be reached by following another line of argument. Wild cattle and wild horses, in their respective habits, their bony structure, their digestive organs, and so on, are admirably fitted for life in wide, open, grassy plains, which yield the food they need, and permit them to move from place to place as they exhaust the grass of a particular area. In their different ways, indeed, they may be said to represent the perfect adaptation to life in the world's grasslands. Such grasslands cover wide areas in South America, no less than in Asia and Africa. But South America has no native cattle or horses, though when introduced by man both throve in a fashion that shows that their absence was not due to unsuitability of climate or relief, or to insufficient food. We have to find some other reason.

But the problems of animal geography would not be half so interesting and so complex if we only had to deal with facts like these. The faunas of tropical and sub-tropical South America, it is true, are very different from those of Africa After all, however, the two countries are remote from each other, and why should we expect their animals to be identical, even if in parts the climate and relief are closely similar? The great plains of South America had no cattle, no sheep, no horses, no donkeys, no goats, till man brought them there, have never carried the vast herds of antelopes which graze the plains of Africa. But they were not empty, for they fed great numbers of rodents (animals related to beavers, rats, mice, rabbits, etc.), such as the viscachas of the Argentine pampas, which were admirably fitted, along their own lines, to take advantage of the natural conditions.

Are we, then, to conclude that regions remote from each other will always have very different faunas, and adjacent regions similar ones? South America will again afford us examples showing that the generalisation is too hasty. We have spoken of the apparent poverty of its fauna, particularly so far as the larger hoofed animals are concerned. But there are exceptions.

In the forests of Brazil, Paraguay, and Northern Argentina there lives a tapir, originally described by Linnaeus as a terrestrial hippopotamus. But a hippopotamus is a kind of pig with four toes on each foot, while a tapir resembles a rhinoceros in having only three toes on the hind foot, as well as in other ways. Another kind of tapir lives high up on the Andes of Columbia and Ecuador, and two other species in Central America, one extending northwards into Mexico. South and Central America have thus four kinds of tapirs.

No tapirs occur in Africa or India; but it is a very remarkable fact that the forests of the Malay peninsula, with those of the adjacent islands of Sumatra and Borneo, do contain a tapir. It is larger than any of the American forms, and is curiously coloured; but in all essentials of structure it is closely similar to the New World forms. The living tapirs thus illustrate what is called discontinuous distribution. They fall into two groups, separated by a distance equal to about half the circumference of the globe, and within this intervening region no tapir or tapir-like animal now exists. Further, while there are four kinds of tapirs in Central and South America, and the tapir stock there has a wide extension in latitude north and south of the equator, and a notable range in altitude from the low-lying plains to a height of from seven to eight thousand feet above sea-level, in the Malay region there is but a single species with a remarkably restricted range.

Almost as striking an example of discontinuity of distribution is furnished by the camel family. True camels no longer exist in the wild state, but it is believed that the larger, one-humped form was originally a native of Arabia, while the two-humped Bactrian camel came from the deserts of Central Asia. There are no camels or camel-like animals in

REINDEER AND HIPPO OF RESTRICTED RANGE

Reindeer may be said to have a restricted range in that naturally they are confined to Eurasia, though extending for thousands of miles there. But lately man has artificially increased their range to a new continent by introducing them into North America, where they thrive. The upper photograph shows the hippopotamus confined also by Nature to one land-mass—Africa

North America, but in the western and narrowed southern part of South America llamas occur, of which there are two wild species and two domesticated races. Strictly speaking, llama is the name of one of the latter, but we may conveniently use it as a general name for all. Llamas are animals closely related to the camel, but differ in the smaller size and the absence of any hump on the back. The range of the wild forms is wide, alike in latitude and altitude, for llamas are intolerant of great heat, so that in equatorial regions they live high up on the Andes, while in the cool south they descend to sea-level. In the mountains they take the place in nature occupied elsewhere by sheep, with which they are sometimes confused. It is a very remarkable fact that while both North and South America have a mountain backbone in the west, in North America we find sheep as the characteristic hoofed animals of

JAGUAR, A BIG CAT FOUND ONLY IN THE NEW WORLD

The jaguar is the biggest representative of the cat tribe in the New World. It is fond of thickly forested territory in which its elaborately spotted ccat makes it virtually invisible as it lies along a branch waiting for some suitable quarry to pass below. The Amazon forests are its particular home, but it also ranges south to the Argentina, attracted perhaps by the plentiful supply of cattle and sheep on the pampas.

THE ELEPHANT IS FOUND IN WIDELY SEPARATED PARTS OF THE WORLD

Burma, Siam and India are inhabited by one sort of elephant and Equatorial Africa by another, seen here. Between these two territories a wide gap is fixed in which there are now no elephants. But at one time there seems to have been another race of these beasts in North Africa and the remains of a dwarf species have been located in one of the Mediterranean islands where they had been cut off by the influx of the sea. There are still, too, pigmy elephants in parts of Central Africa.

JAGUAR OF RESTRICTED RANGE AND THE WIDESPREAD LEOPARD

The cat tribe has successfully established itself all round the globe. The only considerable land masses from which it is entirely absent are Australia and Madagascar. Below is the jaguar, found only in South America, and above, the leopard, which has spread almost all over Africa and through a large part of Asia. Once it seems to have maintained itself in Europe

this mountain belt, as they are also of the high mountains of Asia, but in South America there are no sheep, but instead llamas, whose nearest allies live in the deserts of the Old World.

These examples show us that we cannot explain differences in the faunas of two areas merely as a result of their separation in space, for tapirs occur in South America and in the Malay region, which are widely separated. Nor can we say that continuity of land surface necessarily involves similarity of faunas, for though North and South America are linked together by land, and resemble each other in the presence of a western mountain belt, their faunas are markedly different.

When, instead of looking at the faunas of particular areas we consider world distribution, other peculiar facts emerge. Some animals, like some plants, seem able to make almost any part of the surface serve their needs, and are thus very widespread

Others are limited to particular, often small, areas, as though they required conditions so delicately adjusted that they occurred in these places and nowhere else. Examples of such highly localised forms are most frequent in islands, especially islands remote from land masses. Thus, certain of the Hawaiian islands contain a number of different kinds of tree-snails belonging to a family represented on no other part of the earth's surface.

These snails, which have beautifully coloured shells, are nocturnal, rarely leave the trees on which they live and feed, and are found only in damp woods so that the clearing of the land for cultivation leads to their disappearance. It is stated that some kinds are limited to small groves of trees, not being found elsewhere. If true, this is an extreme example of limited distribution. What is at least certain is that even within the archipelago the snails are distributed in a curiously erratic fashion. They are not present in all the islands, and no single species is common to two islands—that is, each island in which they occur has its own group of forms. Further, it is on the small rather than the large islands that most kinds occur, the big island of Hawaii having fewer land shells than some of the smaller ones.

RACCOON AND PORCUPINE

While the raccoon (bottom) is confined to North America—the Algonquin Indians gave it the name—the porcupine (top) is found both in the Old World and the New. The forests of Brazil and Borneo each produce fine specimens.

Another remarkable case is that of sphenodon, or the New Zealand lizard. It is the only living representative of an order of reptiles which in geological time was represented by a number of widely distributed forms. It is thus a true living fossil. At the present time sphenodon occurs only on certain islets in the Bay of Plenty, where it is protected by law; but it seems formerly to have lived in the main islands of New Zealand. Its highly limited distribution in the Dominion is thus due in part to human action.

What makes the case particularly interesting, however, is that its fossil allies once lived in Europe,

SQUIRREL AND AMERICAN BEAR

The squirrel is an energetic little beast (bottom) and has planted itself firmly in America and Eurasia. The imported American grey squirrel is ousting the English red variety from its native land. Bears extend all over the northern hemisphere.

in Great Britain as well as in France and Germany, and that at the present time it is the only representative on the face of the earth of a vanished stock. There is something which appeals to the imagination in the idea that the ancestors of this primitive little creature crept southwards and ever southwards in search of a land where safety could be found. That safety the lizards found for a time in New Zealand, till they were followed there first by the Maoris, and later by the white man, when they lost ground rapidly.

As contrasted with such cases of highly limited distribution, we have others of successful and dominant stocks, apparently able to triumph over nearly all obstacles to universal spread. The tree-snails of the Hawaiian Islands, lost in the midst of the Pacific, have been able, as it would seem, to vary almost indefinitely in the absence of the checks which act in lands forming thoroughfares of migration. But their hold on their own territory is slight, just because the different forms are adapted to life in very circumscribed areas, and any change in that area brings the probability of extinction. The sphenodon of New Zealand, on the other hand, seems to belong to a dying stock, one which has lost the power of variation. But the barn or screech owl of Britain and most of Europe, occurs over the greater part of the globe, even in Australia, though that island continent has for the most part a fauna of its own, entirely different from that of any other part of the world. The screech owl runs into local races in different parts of its vast range, and changes its habits also to fit itself to local conditions, but there is no evidence that the different races are "fixed"—that is, incapable of free interbreeding. It thus affords an example of a species practically cosmopolitan in its range.

AMONG mammals the leopard is an example of a form with a very wide range. It extends through the whole of Africa, a large part of Asia, avoiding, however, the plateau of Tibet and not reaching Siberia, and seems formerly to have extended into Europe.

Even more interesting, in a sense, is the distribution of another of the great cats, the puma of the New World. This ranges from British Columbia and New England in the north, to Patagonia in the

YOUNG OSTRICHES HATCHING OUT, AND IN THE PARENTAL NEST

When the story-tellers of olden time wished to invent some fabulous bird of enormous size they usually pictured it as being of more or less eagle-like form with huge wings and comparatively short legs. But, in reality, the world's biggest birds have large legs but wings so ill-developed as to be useless for flight. The ostrich, seen here, of Africa, the emu of Australasia and the rhea of South America are the only living examples of the bird's attempt at producing a really large-size model.

W. S. Berridge.

STRANGE LEAF INSECTS FROM TROPICAL ASIA

In many parts of the East the leaf insects are found, and they have colonised some of the islands in the Indian Ocean. The wing-cases and legs are flattened like leaves, and their colour varies from fresh green to faded brown. The substance causing this coloration seems to be akin to chlorophyll, which produces the green colour of plants.

south—that is, over some 100 degrees of latitude, and can apparently adapt itself to almost any kind of climate or physical conditions—hot tropical swamps, open grasslands, forests, high mountains up to the snow-line, river valleys, or rocky country. Its range right down the west coast of the two Americas is in striking contrast to that of the Rocky Mountain sheep, which extends no farther south than Mexico.

Leopard and puma are examples of the true cats which, because of their keen senses, their intelligence, and the beautiful adaptations to the predatory life which they show, may be said in some ways to be physically the most perfect of the mammals. It is thus interesting to note that, except for the island of Madagascar, the Australian region, and the smaller islands of the great oceans, no part of the world is devoid of some kind of cat, large or small.

The exceptions are interesting and bring us to the great problem of migration. Most zoologists are of opinion that every animal stock originated in one particular part of the earth's surface, and one only. From the region of origin its members tended to spread outwards in all directions until some impassable barrier was reached.

So far as land animals are concerned the most important of such barriers is the sea. A water surface is of course not a complete obstacle to flying animals such as birds, bats, and many insects. But even these, when terrestrial in habit, are not likely to cross voluntarily great expanses of ocean. Most land mammals, again, can swim, but despite this fact, even comparatively narrow straits set a limit to their spread. Thus the tiger, though it is a good swimmer, has never crossed the forty-mile Palk Strait which cuts Ceylon off from India. It is true that in the case

LOCUSTS, A WINGED PESTILENCE WITH A DANGEROUSLY WIDE SCOPE

North Africa probably suffers more from locusts than any other part of the world, but the wings of these pests, aided sometimes by the wind, enlarge their effective range of operation to a truly terrible extent. South Africa is also scourged with them and their attacks are common in South-east Europe, in Eastern and Central Asia and in North-west India. The ocean is, of course, the chief barrier to them and the wind, which so often helps them, sometimes brings them to destruction.

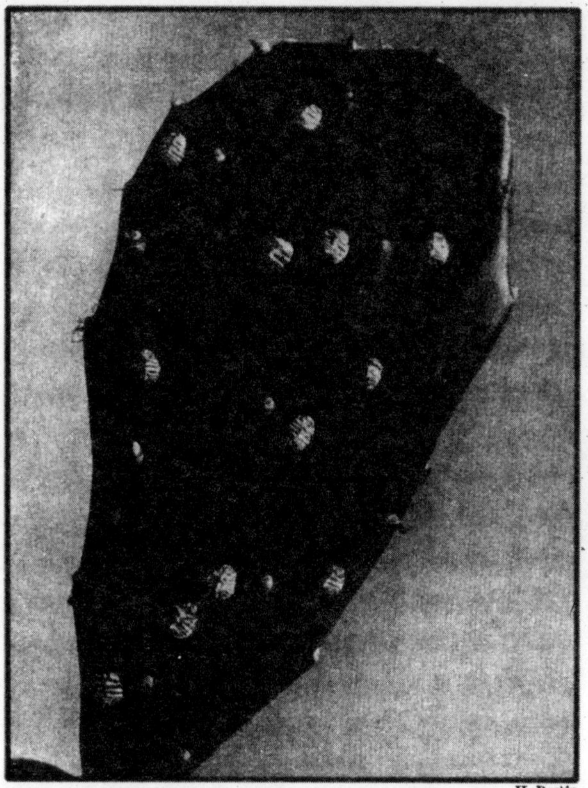

H. Bastin

MEXICAN COCHINEAL INSECTS

Found on cactus plants in Mexico, the cochineal insects supply the dye of that name. It is obtained by collecting the insects wholesale and crushing the bodies of the little creatures. They are incidentally relations of the ladybird.

of small mammals, such as rats and mice, some reptiles, and various kinds of invertebrates, especially mollusca, there are great possibilities in the way of passive dissemination. Floods often sweep masses of trees and other vegetation out to sea, and on such natural rafts small creatures may be carried great distances by marine currents. Aquatic birds have been shown to carry in mud on their feet eggs or resting forms of various kinds of simple animals. Since such birds often perform vast migrations they may act as important agents of distribution. Tropical storms also may carry migrating birds or insects far out of their courses, and so help to populate remote islands.

NEVERTHELESS, we may say broadly that the sea is the greatest obstacle to the spread of land animals, and if we could assume that land and sea had always had their present relations, our problem would be relatively simple. But we know that changes in the past have been very great, and the farther we travel back in geological time the more difficult does it become to reconstruct the vanished lands and seas. We cannot, for example, be certain whether the Hawaiian islands represent a fragment of an old continent, or whether the ancestors of their peculiar tree-snails reached them across the ocean. But since mammals are of relatively recent origin, and the possibility of passive transference overseas is small in the case of the larger land forms, it is generally possible to offer some explanation of their present range, if not of that of simpler types of animals.

Let us take a few outstanding examples. The great land-mass of Eurasia is separated from North America by Bering Strait, some 36 miles wide at its narrowest point, and generally shallow. There is a remarkably close resemblance between the mammals of temperate Eurasia and North America, and this suggests that the separation between the two is of quite late origin. On the other hand, as we have already seen, there is a striking contrast between the mammals of North and South America, although they are linked together by land. It is probable that this connexion is recent, and that South America was for long an island, and has been linked to North America for too short a time for a complete intermingling of the faunas. During the period of isolation it must have formed an asylum for primitive creatures like sloths and tapirs.

Madagascar is separated from Africa by the wide Mozambique Channel, though the Comoro islands and certain submarine banks suggest former links between the two. Madagascar has no true cats as Africa has, but contains a civet-like creature related to the civets of Africa and India, which are less highly organized than the cats. Nor has it any monkeys, but it contains more than half the known species of lemurs, which, though monkey-like, are more primitive creatures that are found elsewhere only in Africa and south-east Asia. It is fairly certain that Madagascar was linked to Africa after civets and lemurs had appeared on the earth, but that the link was broken before true cats and monkeys appeared.

Even more striking is the case of the Malay archipelago. As Alfred Russel Wallace first showed, a line (Wallace's line) drawn along the straits which separates the island of Bali from that of Lombok, and continued along Macassar Strait, which lies between the islands of Borneo and Celebes, separates two distinct faunas. To the east of the line the islands are included in the Australian region, characterised by the abundance of marsupials or pouched mammals and the absence of higher forms. To the west the islands, beginning with Bali and Borneo, have the same rich fauna as that of Sumatra and the Malay peninsula, and marsupials are absent. In this case the narrow strait—it is but 25 miles wide but very deep—which cuts off Bali from Lombok must be an old feature of the earth's surface, and has formed an effective barrier to the migrations of the higher mammals.

Man's influence on distribution at the present time is enormous, but man is only a newcomer on the earth. With the virtual conquest of space, human influence has been both deliberately willed and involuntary. Man has carried the larger domesticated animals to the utmost ends of the earth, and in so doing has displaced many of the larger wild mammals. But multitudes of the smaller animals have attached themselves to him as undesired messmates, and so assured a spread otherwise unattainable.

Chapter CLII

Frightfulness in Low Life

By Frank Finn

Author of "Wild Animals of Yesterday and To-day"

There is an old proverb which says "He who fights and runs away will live to fight another day," but in the struggle for existence in the world of the lower animals he who can bluff his opponent and get off without fighting at all is even better off, for fighting may mean damage and a handicap in the struggle aforesaid.

Thus we find many forms of "frightfulness" resorted to in the effort to avoid fighting, and some of these are familiar to everyone, such as the arched back, raised tail and bristling fur of the cat when confronted by a dog, a piece of bluff which is so successful that very few dogs will attack a cat unless it loses its nerve and turns to run.

Another form of bluff is exhibiting the weapons, as when the dog itself snarls and shows its teeth; and some of the monkeys, baboons specially, yawn with the same object. The porcupine and the skunk, offensive in the rear, display backwards, the porcupine expanding a fan of quills, and the skunk, erecting its tail as a sign of the scent-pouch threatening below. The mongoose, when about to attack a snake, bristles up its coarse fur, and this serves a double purpose, for the snake, if it does happen to get home a blow at its active adversary, is very apt to strike short of its mark. The same applies to the spreading of the feathers and wings which is found in so many birds, a class of animals which have a particular advantage in their plumage, which enables them to make themselves look a great deal bigger than they really are, and thus terrorise their opponents.

This is familiar in the case of the brood hen defending her young, and in a cock when offering to fight an enemy of his own kind or of any other. The turkey can make an even more impressive display by way of bluff, for when he is excited his feathers alter altogether; not only does he blush to a brilliant red, but the false nose over his beak elongates and hangs down, making him quite unrecognizable, to say nothing of the bristled plumage.

Even the peacock uses his wonderfully beautiful display for bluff at times, and probably in his Indian home often frightens carnivorous enemies like the tiger and leopard; it must be a great surprise to such a creature, stealing up to a big bird which promises a meal, to see it suddenly change into a bush of shivering staring eyes. A man the writer once met in a park where peacocks were kept said he was once riding past a peacock when the bird suddenly went into display, and he had the greatest difficulty in preventing his mount from bolting forthwith, as may easily be supposed. The cat tribe are just as nervous as horses, and no doubt successful practice of this ruse accounts for the story told by Indians that the peacock will often fly at a large feline enemy—a tiger or leopard—rather than from it, and often lose his life in this way; Pavo, no doubt, tries his trick of bluffing once too often, and succumbs to an enemy who knows a little too much for him.

The most persistent bluffer is the swan, which is chronically in display all through the nesting-season, with the bridling neck and mantling wings which are so much admired. The pose, however, is rather puzzling, and often misunderstood by artists; it consists in raising the elbow-joints of the wings, and thus expanding the secondary quills, and allowing the primary quills, usually concealed, to be seen below them; the pinion-joints which carry these, however, are still kept tucked in under the flank-feathers, the swan, like other wild fowl and indeed many other birds, habitually keeping his hands in his pockets, so to speak. When very angry, however, he takes them out, and is then liable to strike with them—just like a man showing his fists, in fact.

The Upland goose also makes this fistic display when much excited, but in this case the pinion-joint is lowered, while the rest of the wing remains closed, and, the bird keeping on land, where it usually stays, it looks as if the joint had dropped owing to an injury. The Orinoco goose, another land-loving water fowl, also likes showing its fists, which are armed with coral-red knuckle-dusters, but in this case the wings are not disarranged otherwise than by taking the pinion-joints out of the flank-feathers.

Owls are great at frightfulness, bristling, spreading their wings widely, and adding point to their menaces by hissing and snapping their beaks, though when it comes to actual fighting it is their talons that will do the damage.

In all cases mentioned the bluff can be sustained by vigorous and painful action, but many weak creatures will display when they can do nothing to hurt a foe. A good case of this is furnished by the Indian painted snipe, a harmless bird with gray quills beautifully spotted with buff. When disturbed it erects one speckled wing, that farthest from the enemy, but on being pressed faces him like an owl with both widely expanded, meanwhile giving off a hiss so vigorous that it sounds exactly like a piece of red-hot iron plunged suddenly into water. As none of the spots are visible in the bird's ordinary pose with closed wings, the change of appearance is very considerable, and no doubt is effective against many of the enemies of so helpless a bird; in fact, one has been known to survive when considerable execution had been done on other ground birds by a rat which had made its way into an aviary.

A bird may even use concealed variegated quills

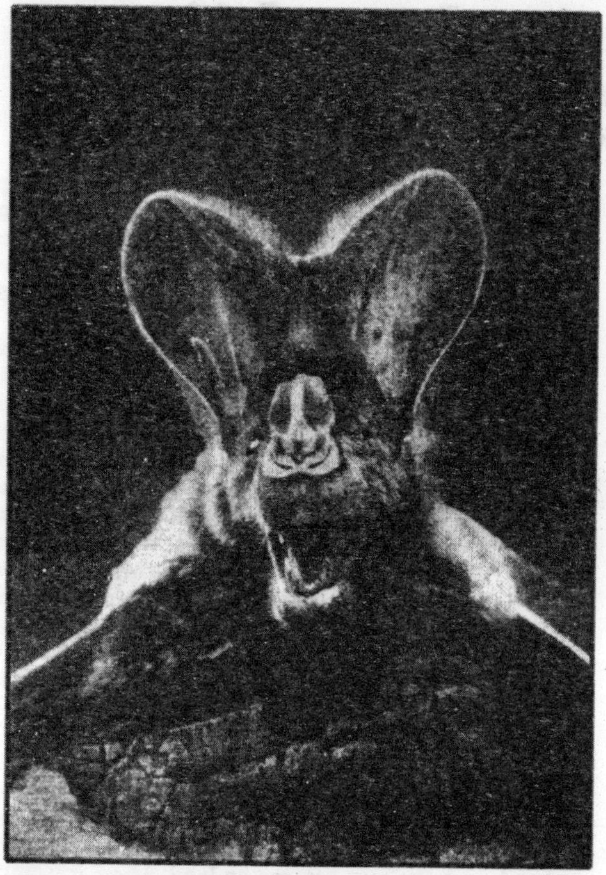

E.N.A.

DREAD FEATURES OF A BAT

There is no need for any assumed "frightfulness" on the bat's part, for it is ordinarily horrific enough in appearance to justify all the grim stories gathered round it. For frightful features the average English flittermouse would beat Dracula hollow.

in its wings for bluff alone, as is the case with the kagu of New Caledonia, a creature which with its lavender plumage, ruby eyes, and dreamy look, might have stepped straight out of "Alice in Wonderland." It is about as big as a fowl, with a long, strong beak and handsomely barred wings which it uses for terrifying display, but not for flight. But they are of no avail now that dogs run loose all over its island home, and it may be that the three now in the Zoo are the last we shall ever see alive; it would surely be worth while to transfer a pair or two to some safer island, while there is time, for this poor bird is not only the sole member of its family, but a friendly creature, easily tamed, a good pest-destroyer, and a weather prophet.

Before the birds, with their plumage "properties" so well adapted for staging an imposition, came into being, their ancestors the reptiles were probably making faces at each other, for plenty of them are doing so still.

The most notable is the Australian frilled lizard, which a few years ago gained great notoriety by showing that it could get up on its hind legs and travel as a biped like so many of the old dinosaurs. But many other lizards with fairly long legs are now known to be able to do this, and the great speciality of the frilled lizard is its power of "putting on frills." A full Elizabethan ruff of scaly skin surrounds its neck, and is expanded in grand style when the creature is excited, at which time it also opens its mouth, which is of a bright orange-yellow inside, and has canine teeth noticeably developed, so that the display made is quite a terrifying one for a creature a yard long.

A smaller lizard, the lyre-headed lizard of Ceylon, which has only a pair of severe bony eyebrows as militant decoration, also tries to impose upon enemies by opening its mouth, which in this case is bright scarlet inside. In the much commoner western garden lizard, known as the bloodsucker, the outside of the head turns red on excitement, though the colour here is not so bright.

The chameleon changes, but all over, on excitement in certain cases, for the writer has seen an East-African flap-necked chameleon become sooty black all over when a smaller specimen took the liberty of crawling over its head.

Among the snakes, the cobras, both African and Indian, have long been notorious for the way in which they rise up and expand their necks into the well-known "hood," thus, no doubt, often saving themselves needless expenditure of poison. The great eastern king-cobra or hamadryad also expands a hood, but in this case it is much smaller than that of the inferior reptiles; the size of this serpent, the biggest poisonous snake known, may well render imposition less necessary for intimidation.

But what is very curious is to find harmless snakes also with the power of expanding the neck, and that in a region where there are no cobras, so that mimicry is out of the question. The hog-nosed snake of North America is well known for this habit, and, as it hisses vigorously at the same time, is commonly believed to be venomous and dubbed puff-adder, though this name properly belongs to a large and vicious viper of Africa. The saw-scaled viper of North Africa and India produces a hissing by mechanical means, rubbing its coils together and so grating its scales, which are furnished with lines of minute saw-like teeth, against each other.

The well-known rattling of the rattlesnakes may be a means of exciting terror, but little is definitely known of this. But we get a case of tail-terrorism in an East Indian snake—and a harmless one at that—which is perhaps the most curious of all, for this creature displays by hiding its head in its own coils and then pretending it has one at the other end, the tail being raised and curved over, while the red under side may convey the impression of a gaping mouth.

The frog and toad tribe very rarely bite, that habit being confined to the horned frogs of South America, but many of them puff themselves out when annoyed, which at any rate makes them look bigger; the old fable of the frog which tried to make itself as big as an ox has so much of foundation in fact. And a

quite small European creature, the fire-bellied frog or toad, has a quite unique form of display, turning its arms and legs upwards and outwards to show as much as possible of its red-blotched underside; the red is a true warning colour, for this creature has a very nauseous skin-secretion which effectively puts it out of court as an article of food for carnivorous enemies.

Fish can do their share of putting on warning appearances, as we see in the case of our own perch, with its black tiger-stripes advertising the prickly back fin which makes it an awkward morsel. These are assumed and lost very quickly, and it is said that the perch assumes its stripes when it finds itself near a pike, and loses them when approaching a small fish it intends to prey upon, so that in this case it looks, with its red fins, rather like a harmless roach—a unique case of double-bluffing.

Otho Webb

JEW LIZARD AND OWL, PRACTISED IN FRIGHTFULNESS

Brown in general colour, the frilled or jew lizard of Australia and Tasmania (bottom) has a black throat which it inflates when alarmed and then looks so frightful that it would be a bold creature that would attack. Above is an owl. Owls are famous for their displays when frightened. They fluff out their feathers and snap their beaks, the incarnation of dangerous rage

The little fighting-fish of Siam spreads its fins, assumes brilliant colours, and expands the black membrane of its gills when approaching an enemy; and its relative the paradise fish of China, now so well known to keepers of the choicer fancy fish, does something similar. It is very amusing to see one specimen literally turn blue in the face with anger when approaching another, which, if he feels he is not equal to a fight, turns pale in response. Crabs and lobsters extend and open their claws when threatened, but they can, at any rate, like so many of the other creatures we have noticed, do something to make good their threats.

What is more remarkable is to find fearsome threats expressed by some caterpillars, the very embodiment of helplessness. Such a one is our elephant hawk moth caterpillar, which has eye-like spots on its back and can draw in its head and fore part so that the whole front end looks like what ought to be the head of some larger and more formidable creature, the eyelike marks serving for eyes, and the real caterpillar head for the end of the muzzle. This attitude has actually been seen to frighten small birds and that a tame jay devoured the humbug at once is not astonishing, for a really small beast would have had no better chance with such an intelligent bird.

stern the two last emergency legs form a forked tail from which are protruded two pink whips, so that the whole effect is that of an uncanny little monstrosity.

Although all the insects here mentioned are British, none are so familiar as a very accomplished bluffer, the devil's coach-horse beetle, which turns up its hindquarters as if it could sting. At the same time it is ready to put in some real offensiveness with its strong jaws, and experiments with these should be carefully made, as this beetle is a foul feeder, and a bite from it may have unpleasant consequences.

J. J. Ward

CATERPILLARS THAT EFFECTIVELY MENACE THEIR FOES

Certain caterpillars put up a most effective bluff, like the larva of the lobster moth (bottom). On its hind end the "emergency legs," are developed into what looks like a forked tail. This is bent forward over the back, while the front end is raised turning it into a monster. The larvae of the puss moth (top left), and of *Eacles imperialis* (top right), have similar tricks.

The lobster moth caterpillar succeeds in looking like something that does not exist, but is uncanny-looking enough to make enemies of ordinary caterpillars careful how they meddle with it. The minute true legs found on the fore part of caterpillars generally are in this case developed into full-sized insect limbs, while the hind part of the creature is thick, and has the "emergency-legs" found on the hind quarters of caterpillars—but not in perfect insects—developed into a forked tail which represents antennae; so when this thick part is bent forwards over the back and the fore part with its long legs raised, the result is a sort of composite monster which might be capable of anything. Professor Poulton found that a marmoset, a very insectivorous creature, though it at once seized and ate an unfortunate "lobster" which was offered it in a box, was very careful how it meddled with the next, which had been given a fair chance of getting into the show position. In a state of nature it would no doubt have turned to something easier. He also found a lizard very cautious in tackling the hornet clear-wing moth, which looks like a wasp, and writhes its abdomen as if about to sting when taken in the hand.

The puss moth caterpillar has long been renowned for its display, which in this case has something to back it. When irritated, it rears up and draws in its head, the part of the body next to this bearing two black spots above for eyes, and a red bordering, which altogether produce "a caricature of a face," while from below this the creature squirts out a highly acid fluid capable of producing a painful smart in the entomological eye. At the

We see, therefore, that the principle of bluff is very widely spread in the animal kingdom; indeed, it extends from such small fry as we have been last noticing to the mighty elephant. He needs not to show his teeth, which are projecting a few feet from his mouth already, but he makes himself a little bigger by expanding his great ears when infuriated; and his rival of the sea, the elephant seal, intensifies the horror of his open mouth by expanding his nose into a small caricature of a trunk.

The question naturally arises as to how the creatures learned these tricks, which, it will be noticed, always involve some change in appearance, and generally one which gives them greater apparent size. Size alone is some protection; wild cats will kill lambs, but they do not attack full-grown sheep, nor do lions and tigers, as a rule, trouble grown-up elephants and rhinoceroses, for, quite apart from their weapons, these do not offer a fair killing grip to feline jaws, however wide.

Although one can hardly avoid speaking of intimidating displays as if they were intentional, it must be borne in mind that this is not the case, at any rate, as a rule. An old experienced animal, if of any intelligent species, may learn that its display has a terrorising effect, and use it accordingly; but this is out of the question in the case of such essentially instinctive creatures as most insects, and all we can conclude is that the pose or other appearance adopted is one that is natural

Otho Webb

J. J. Ward

BEETLE AND SPIDER BLUFFERS

It is thought that the extraordinary devices of insects and especially of the more defenceless species, are purely instinctive and cannot be called "intentional" in the human sense. Here are a cocktail beetle (bottom) and a spider.

to the species under certain circumstances, and is unconscious. The skunk, for instance, will threaten by stamping and raising its tail after its scent-pouch has long ago been removed.

We often find that the same pose, or nearly the same, expresses either anger or affection according to circumstances. Thus, the courting display of birds is often very like their threatening attitude, and the tom-cat shows off to the female in very much the same pose as that in which he defies a dog, except that the fur is not bristled, and that the side view is presented, while the caterwauling is a love-song as well as a challenge. We see this in ourselves, for a flushed face may indicate either anger or affection, just as it does in the turkey, and a smile and a sneer both involve a curling of the lips and exposure of the teeth. Moreover, each species has definite methods of expression; the dog stiffens the tail when angry and the cat switches it; the swan draws back its head when threatening, the goose stretches it out and thrusts it upwards with open beak in a convincing display of anger. Both swans and geese hiss like reptiles.

So ingrained are these gestures in a species that little kittens will hump, bristle, and spit like old cats, and peachicks no bigger than pigeons expand their little tails. So the display was evidently early at hand for natural selection to work upon as occasion arose, and has in many cases been made more effective by the addition of such details as we have been considering, for young animals often show us the condition of the species in an earlier stage of its evolution. We know that habits can be fixed by selection, from the curious gestures and actions which are hereditary in some breeds of tame pigeons, and unlike anything seen in the wild rock-dove to which the tamed varieties owe their origin.

It may be added in conclusion, however, that bluff is a poor asset in the struggle for existence, and that the most successful animals are those which have more solid qualities, such as strength of constitution, activity, prolificacy, and before all, intelligence. We see a good example of this in the starling, the most progressive creature of our time, which rarely fights, and confines intimidation to the use of avian bad language, but owes its success to a good digestion and marvellously well-balanced activity joined to a discretion at times almost human.

E. N. A

ITINERANT TROUPES OF GOATS AND SNAKES ON SHOW IN INDIA

The lure of the performing animal is international. Man has found the mastery of animals a long and difficult task and perhaps it is some semi-consciousness of this that makes him so delight to watch beasts of various kinds in total subjection to their master's will. In India troupes of mountebanks are always travelling the country and many of them run small bands of performing animals or at least go in for a little snake-charming. Performing goats (bottom) are sometimes seen and " poisonous " snakes, with the fangs removed, are often on show.

Chapter CLIII

Should Animals Perform in Shows?

By Frances Pitt

Author of "Animal Mind"

There is no more vexed question than that of the desirability of having performances by trained animals on the stage and in the circus, or even that of training animals to do difficult tricks.

When we use the words "trained animals," it must be remembered that they cover a wide field, from such performers as wonderfully trained chimpanzees, troupes of lions and tigers, the clever stage poodle, the circus horse, performing sea-lions, elephants and so on, down to household pets that beg or "die for the king." Of course, the gap between a troupe of lions and tigers going through a set performance in the glare of the footlights, and a homely fox-terrier sitting up to beg for a tit-bit is wide indeed, yet the terrier is as much a trained animal as the most magnificent of the lions that delights and thrills a large audience by his obedience to his trainer's command, and the readiness with which he jumps through a loop or does something similar.

Now, to the thoughtful person, the first question raised by these sorts of exhibitions is: Do the animals perform willingly, or not? If we were certain that in all cases the animal performers enjoyed their exercises and were willing co-operators with their exhibitors, there would be no more to be said, nor any doubt whatever as to whether animal performances should be allowed; but that is just the question: Do they enjoy themselves, or do they act under fear and compulsion? When we remember that lions, tigers, sea-lions and elephants are tamed wild animals, and how very different their home life and natural environment is from the life and surroundings they have to endure in connexion with stage and circus work, to say nothing of the performances they are called upon to go through for the amusement of the audience, we may well doubt their enjoyment of their tasks!

But to get, or rather try to get, some insight into their side of the matter and their point of view, let us turn to the dog and cat, and see how our household friends respond to training, and their attitude towards "parlour tricks." Most of us, sometime or other, have taught a dog to beg, and will know the procedure; how at first the pupil seemed to have no idea what was required of him, and had to be made to sit up, though submitting willingly enough to be posed in the required position when he found it pleased his master, and that compliance was followed by a pat, praise, and a tit-bit. After several enforced lessons the dog began to associate the sitting-up attitude with food, and required less prompting, finally sitting up of his own accord at the sight of the raised hand holding food, accompanied by the word "beg." He had learnt to beg, and having learnt was ready to beg on any and every occasion, quickly grasping that the command "beg" meant "sit up," that begging would gain reward, and even that by begging of his own accord he might induce people to give him food.

Punishment, even by a harsh word, has been no factor in his education, and watching the dog you cannot doubt that he enjoys the attention which his performance attracts. His master's encouraging voice, the approving words of other people, move him to much tail wagging and signs of canine gratification. It is the same with more complicated tricks, which need longer and much more patient training, one can hardly doubt, unless the performer's mien is wholly deceptive, that having once grasped what is required, he enjoys doing the tricks, finding pleasure in his master's attention, patting hand, and the reward of good behaviour.

Of course, hearth-rug tricks are a different thing from stage shows, in which each performer must do his appointed act to the second, and in which any deviation, unwillingness or sulkiness must be met with immediate punishment. That punishment in itself is either wrong or cruel I do not admit. "Spare the rod and spoil the child" is but too true. Every creature, young or old, needs correction at times, whether it be a kitten smacked by the old cat, a lion-cub punished by its dam, or one of ourselves when we "get beans" from our fellows; but whether animals should be made to suffer in any degree because they do not perform mere stage tricks properly, whose purpose is amusement, is a question I will raise again when considering the shows given by lions and tigers.

Before going on to these latter, I want to give a few words to their small relative, our household cat, and consider what aptitude she shows for acquiring tricks. Cats can be taught to jump through the hands, to sit up and beg, and so on, but they do not show anything like the willing co-operation of the dog. A dog will do a trick to gain his master's attention; puss only does so if something tangible is likely to result! The actual doing of the trick does not appear to give the cat any pleasure, but she has found out that a certain sequence of actions will be followed by reward, so she obtains that reward as quickly as she can. The doing of the trick is merely a bore, and, being "the cat that walks by itself," she does not really care about her mistress' appreciation!

Now, lions and tigers are cats, and of cattish disposition; their enjoyments under natural conditions are the excitement of hunting and stalking prey, and the lazy ease that follows a good meal. Their social life is limited to that of the family, and they have not got the dog's inherited predisposition to try and please the pack leader, now the human master. The dog wants to stand well with his man, the lion or tiger does not care twopence for his trainer.

SEA LIONS, ONE OF THE MOST POPULAR "TURNS" ON THE ANIMAL STAGE

Quick, intelligent and beautiful to watch, the sea lions are always popular with the public whether the animals are merely being fed at a zoo or whether they are actually performing on the stage Sea lions have been trained to ride motor bicycles, to play in brass bands (with devastating results), and to play "catch" with burning torches—a miracle of training, this. Their ability to balance and bounce rubber balls on their noses, too, is fascinating, and they seem very happy to do it.

Familiarity may have made him tolerant, even friendly, with his keeper—but affectionate adoration ! Well, that is not in a cat's hereditary mental make-up !

WHAT is in the hereditary mental outfit of the great cats is a tendency to class mankind among their prey, hence a keeper and trainer has to instil respect into his pupils. As I said before, punishment is not necessarily cruel; children, dogs and horses must learn to obey, and there are cases where severe punishment may be kinder than lenience, as when a dog shows a tendency to chase sheep—better for him a good thrashing, than later an early death on account of sheep worrying ! But this is not the sort of thing to which we are referring ; it was the trainer's absolute necessity to instil respect into his dangerous pupils. His life depends on it, and the many accidents that have occurred from time to time among troupes of performing tigers, lions and bears, show what a slender thread this respect is. These trainers of dangerous wild beasts are indeed men of iron nerve ; and if they, with their lives in their hands, have to use the whip now and again, can we blame them ?

But are spectacles that involve this risk to the man desirable ? Is it not the thrill of danger at which the public exclaims ? And last, but not least, what about the animals ? We have referred to the cat-like mentality and disposition of the tiger and lion, and if their mien and behaviour did not convince us of it, would therefore conclude that the performance of uncomprehended antics before a crowd of people, in the over-heated atmosphere of a show, under the glare of the electric light, must be worse than distasteful, worse than boring—it must be a nightmare ! A nightmare that repetition has made them used to, but, nevertheless, one that is only gone through because they have got to do it. Then consider their quarters when off the stage or out of the ring, the necessarily small cages of the travelling circus, and the equally necessarily cramped quarters behind the scenes in a stationary show. Compare all this with the existence that would be led by these animals under natural conditions, roaming the veldt or jungle, either solitary or in small family parties, and able to enjoy peace and seclusion whenever they liked. Now they have to live in small cages, in incessant noise and disturbance, and are forced each afternoon and evening to go through, what to them are a series of senseless actions.

My opinion is that performances by dangerous wild animals are highly undesirable, involving a more or less miserable existence for the members of the troupe, and only appealing to the public by reason of the element of danger involved.

But the case is altered when you consider semi-domesticated animals like elephants, and domestic ones such as the horse and dog. The latter, as long as it is not asked to do something quite impossible or foreign to its nature, certainly seems to enjoy itself ; and the horse is under nearly all circumstances a willing slave, ready, if it can return to its stall when all is over, to pick up any series of actions sufficiently patiently inculcated by its trainer. No creature is quicker to form habits, its learning is of the

E.N.A.

PERFORMING BEARS, DANGEROUS PUPILS FOR SHOW WORK

Big animals, like bears, which have never been, and never will be, really domesticated, are ugly customers to handle and apt to be what is called treacherous; though whether an animal captured and forced to go through, to it, a meaningless series of antics, can be rightly called treacherous when its resentment gets the better of its fear of reprisals is a moot point. Here we have a bear which has been taught to ride a bicycle, an Angora bear and (top) some performing bears in India.

A DOG TABLEAU ARRANGED FOR AN AUDIENCE'S AMUSEMENT

Dogs, by the very fact of being born in a state of domestication, are virtually half-trained already. It is a sufficient incentive to them that their masters wish them to do certain things for them to learn willingly. On the other hand, large wild animals such as lions and tigers start as man's enemies instinctively and cannot see any reason in what they are made to do and are bored at best. Dogs obviously enjoy the performance, and so much so that their pleasure is infectious

parrot-like description, and as a circus performer it is incomparable, not because it is intelligent and understands why a thing should be done, but because when it has formed the habit of going through a particular sequence of actions, it can, once started upon them, be depended on to carry them out mechanically, without alteration or variation. There is none of that intelligent adaptation of means to ends that you will find in, say, a chimpanzee, and which leads the latter, though one of the most brilliant of animal stage performers, also to be unreliable.

WRITING of willing cooperators, no creatures can equal young anthropoid apes for sheer enjoyment of stage work. Like small children they obviously love dressing up and showing off, and what is more they enjoy the noise and excitement. They are most amusing to watch, their pleasure in what they are doing, their affectionate devotion to their human friends, and their whole behaviour being delightful. One does not feel that any hardship is being inflicted here. But in truth there is more real suffering and hardship involved in the exhibition of one specimen of a great ape, than in a performance by a dozen lions and tigers. I would, if I could, prohibit the latter, as for the former, I should forbid the export of anthropoid apes from their native countries. No chimpanzees, orang-utans or gorillas (only the first is usually seen on the stage) ought to be brought from their native homes.

Think of the suffering involved in their capture, the awful journey to the coast, packed in narrow crates, and then the voyage to Europe or America. However hard their captors try to save them suffering the suffering is unavoidable, and it is mental as well as physical. Highly intelligent and affectionate, most social in disposition, the solitary confinement alone is often fatal. Only those who deal in wild animals could tell us the number lost between the place of capture and delivery in London or New York, but the prices demanded and obtained for those that arrive alive show how fatal the journey is, not only when travelling but afterwards, for many of those that arrive alive do so with the seeds of disease in their frames, so that they succumb more or less speedily.

I have been speaking throughout of young ones. Adults are so extraordinarily difficult to capture

W. S. Berridge

CHIMPANZEES AT TEA AND A DOG TEAM FOOTBALL MATCH

An enterprising scheme has been carried out at the London Zoo whereby some chimpanzees took tea every fine afternoon with the Fellows in their private enclosure. This feature was a great success and the apes gave a performance the more interesting because it was largely spontaneous Chimpanzees are difficult to " show " owing to their susceptibility to a change of climate and to tuberculosis. The upper photograph shows a team of dogs playing football.

that their importation is rare. An exception was the family of chimpanzees exhibited for a short while at the Zoological Gardens in London; but they, poor things, soon obtained release, dying from contagious disease as do the majority of anthropoid apes. In any case adults are of no interest to us, as they are invariably too soured and surly, to say nothing of being too dangerously strong, to use in shows. No, it is young ones, chimpanzee children, if we may so term them, that we meet with on the stage, affectionate, jolly youngsters, delighting in play and make-belief, but, alas! doomed to a short, if merry life.

The exceptions that survive long are few indeed, the strenuous life, repeated performances, and continued exposure to the heated, disease-infested air of theatre or circus has its effect. The susceptible ape contracts tuberculosis, or, more quickly fatal, pneumonia, and one of the chimpanzees is gone from the little troupe. It is probably replaced, and the public fails to realize a tragedy, but the tragedy is there, nevertheless!

Yes, if I had my way I would limit animal performances on the stage and in the ring to domestic and semi-domestic animals, and exclude all dangerous wild beasts, strictly prohibiting the use of lions and tigers, and last but not least anthropoid apes.

Our cousinship with the latter should endow us with special sympathy for them, and not lead us to victimise them to provide half an hour's amusement.

CIRCUS ELEPHANTS AND DOGS

There is one thing about watching an elephant put through its paces in the ring—one can rest assured that "kindness does it"; no one dare ill-treat an elephant. Above we have a typical scene from the ringside. Below are dogs in fancy dress

Chapter CLIV

Battles of Big Fish and Other Ocean Beasts

By E. G. Boulenger

Director of the Zoological Society's Aquarium

Most thinking persons are probably pacifists at heart and look for the day when general disarmament shall be an accomplished fact and not a mere Utopian fantasy. Nature, however, is never likely to join the movement, and the poet was very near the mark when he described Nature as "red in tooth and claw." Every copse and hedgerow is as full of carnage as the densest jungle and nowhere is violence dispensed with a more lavish hand than in the watery world, whether it be an ocean or a rain-filled cart rut. Absorbing as all encounters must be to the scientists it is only the more striking and sensational which obtrude themselves upon the notice of the average man. To-day the ocean can furnish conflicts as terrible and awesome as any provided by the jungle or possibly the dinosaur-infested swamps of prehistoric times.

The whales excepted, fish are represented by more giants than any other group of the animal kingdom. The whale shark, for instance, may measure 75 feet, and tip the scale at 4 or 5 tons. The sawfish, a close cousin of the shark, is not far behind. Whilst rays and skate of over 15 feet across the "wings" and over a thousand pounds in weight are abundant in many tropical and sub-tropical seas.

Some fossil sharks are known to possess mouths bearing hundreds of teeth, each of which is four inches long and provided with serrated edges, and we can only conjecture what terrific conflicts may have ensued between such heavily-armed monsters. The special weapons worn by many fish are often developed for purposes other than those of mere defence. We find that in most cases the tender passion is the primary inspiration and indeed not infrequently weapons are only developed during the courting season. The male of the common salmon, for instance, develops in the breeding season a cartilaginous hook-like projection of the lower jaw which curves upwards and inwards and fits into a slot or cavity between the two maxillary bones forming the upper mandible, and the teeth become fangs of over half an inch in length. The adult male thornback ray develops sharp spike teeth in marked contrast to the pavement-like dentition of the female. What a skate conflict is like we cannot say, but the pugnacity of the male salmon and trout is well known, and so furious are their battles on the spawning beds that deaths are frequent.

In 1868 the keeper of certain waters on the banks of the Tyne found over 300 dead cock salmon all of which bore unmistakable marks of having been killed in action. Mere size, of course, is no guarantee of pugnacity, for the two fiercest fighters are also the smallest. The famous fighting fish of Siam seldom reaches a length of two inches, and is provided with no very special weapons. Yet when two males meet there ensues a duel from which one or sometimes both combatants merge far too damaged ever to fight again. Our own little common three-spined stickleback is likewise very pugnacious. In the spring the "robin" sticklebacks join battle with their sharp dorsal spines and the dagger fight which ensues often results in one of the belligerents being disembowelled. Both the stickleback and the fighting fish of Siam employ the jaws, seizing each other by the fins and holding on with bulldog tenacity.

But to return to the giants of the ocean world. The sawfish with its large beak set with sharp teeth-like structures on either side is one of the most dangerous inhabitants of the seas. Some of these monsters carry saws of more than six feet in length, such weapons bearing thirty or more teeth. The saw is possibly used for ploughing up the sand and dislodging such fish, etc., as lie buried in it, but more frequently it is deliberately employed to tear open other fish and even whales—the sawfish then feasting upon the lacerated flesh and protruding entrails. It is worthy of remark that young sawfish are born alive, the brood numbering about thirty. Each infant whilst yet in the parental interior has the saw protected by a tough, parchment-like sheath, a very necessary protection against damage to the mother's body-wall. Sawfish are fierce and blood-thirsty, sometimes ascending tidal rivers and there attacking bathers and waterside fishermen.

One of the most formidable of the true sharks is the "thresher," a rover of the warmer seas which occasionally visits home waters. Specimens of twenty feet are common, such monsters having tails eleven feet long, and the caudal appendage is said to be used as a whip which rounds up shoals of fish. More often, however, it is used as a club. The thresher's eyes are set almost on the top of its head, and by bending backwards and upwards it can well direct the scythe-like sweeps of its huge tail. It will knock a large fish senseless at a single blow, and even strike at a bait hook before taking it in its mouth, hence most threshers caught on rod and line are foul-hooked in the tail.

The swordfish, with its prolonged dagger-pointed upper jaw, may also be quoted as a giant fish of high fighting quality. Some species grow to sixteen feet, and have swords well over a yard long. The large dorsal fin is said to act as a sail whilst the immense sickle-shaped tail can propel the fish high into the air. As the swordfish feeds principally upon small pelagic fish, such as mackerel and half-grown bonito, it is difficult to account for its enthusiasm for attacking whales. It is also much given to charging blindly at ships, sometimes piercing the walls of small rowing boats. When a large ship arouses the fish's ire the

W. S. Berridge

FIGHTING FISH OF THE SALT SEAS: TARPON, ALBACORE, BLUE SHARK AND BONITO

Water is an element far more productive of pugnacity than earth, whether we consider the microscopic struggles going on in a rain-filled cart rut or the impressive battles of the deep sea. The tarpon (bottom left) is celebrated as a fighter with anglers. They engage the fish with sporting weapons—rod and line, just because it is such a good fighter. The albacore (bottom right) is allied to the mackerel and sometimes attains a length of six feet. It will follow a sailing ship for days on the watch for food. Above are (left) a great blue shark which is said to attain a length of twenty-five feet in some cases, and (right) a bonito that is related to the albacore.

sword is not infrequently snapped off short after penetrating four or five inches.

The fighting qualities of many fish whilst sufficiently menacing to impress the most blasé are easily eclipsed by the pugnacity of certain large aquatic mammals. With many times the brain capacity of the most intelligent fish these creatures can direct their vast bulks with terrible effect. Not even the great marine lizards of the past can rival some modern whales in sheer killing power. A justly famous example is that of the killer whale or grampus that well deserves its scientific title of *Orca gladiator*. It is a cosmopolitan monster ranging from the Arctic to the Antarctic and seen in the Atlantic. It attacks not only seals and porpoises but even the large and inoffensive whale-bone whales. These the killers attack in mass formation, half a dozen or more clinging to the monster and so harassing it that the victim at last opens its mouth. The killer thereupon seizes the opportunity to force an entry and tear out the tongue. Often the whale, in its agony will rise clear of the water—an incident which has been witnessed and portrayed by more than one sea painter. In a single killer washed up on the coast of Jutland was found the remains of thirteen porpoises and fourteen seals.

PENGUINS are a favourite item in this ogre's menu when patrolling the Antarctic. Surprised in the open sea, the penguins make off at top speed, and having gained sufficient momentum leap from the water and cast themselves high and dry upon an ice floe. The killer is baulked, but not always beaten, for it dives beneath the floe, and arching its back, endeavours deliberately to bump the birds back into the water. The whale's vivid dazzle pattern renders the beast hard to see some distance under water, although swimming at or near the surface, its huge back fin sometimes a yard high, is sufficient warning to all the creatures in its vivinity. The immense teeth carried by many whales take strange forms, and at one time led largely to their pursuit for ivory.

The sea unicorn or nar-whale has the two incisors developed into immense spiral twisted tusks six or eight feet in length, only one of the tusks, however—usually the left—reaching full development. In another big whale the canine teeth stretch upwards on either side until they form an archway over the whale's snout, when they become ineffective as weapons, and one would imagine a hindrance when taking nourishment. There are few more pugnacious beasts than the famous cachalot whale of the Antarctic, a monster reaching sixty feet in length, whose lower jaw alone is armed with some fifty huge conical tusks. With these the whale does great damage, not only to giant cuttlefish, as described later, but also to its own species. Sperm whales travel in schools of from thirty to fifty individuals, consisting of cows, young bulls, and one immense adult bull who convoys the community about the chosen feeding grounds. Fights amongst the young males are of almost hourly occurrence, the whales clinging to each other's tails and flippers and frequently leaping high out of the water. Sooner or later the old bull meets his match and is forced to hand over the leadership to a younger and more active aspirant. No creature has figured more largely in modern-time fiction than the sperm or cachalot whale. The head, comprising fully a third of the entire length, is buttressed in the forward portion with a huge area of connective tissue amongst which is found the valued oily substance known as spermaceti. This vast bulk of oil and fat doubtless adds great buoyancy to the animal and may further serve as a battering ram in its numerous encounters.

Size, no matter how well blended our judgment or clear our appreciation of "relativity," arrests the eye and stimulates the imagination. Thus, while an enormous crowd would stand and stare at a killer whale attacking a seal very few pause to watch an encounter between a starfish and an oyster, and yet the killer versus seal battle amounts to a mere dog fight compared with that between some of the smaller inhabitants of the seas, who bring the most ingenious machinery into play. A starfish when opening an oyster employs over ten thousand suckers and these, wrapped securely round the bivalve pull against the two big muscles which serve to close the shell. If the pull of the starfish exceeds that of the oyster the starfish wins. The pull of the mollusc is, however, considerable, and an oyster four inches in diameter has been known to close his shell upon the toe of a gull and the gull's superior brain and power of flight were insufficient to ensure victory.

Poisonous stinging cells as employed by the jellyfishes and sea anemones can likewise be deadly weapons of both offence and defence. The Portuguese man-of-war, for instance, is far more dreaded than the shark by the pearl divers, and even our own beadlet anemone can account for a full-grown prawn after paralysing it with its tentacles.

MORE amazing still is the defence put up by the common sea cucumber or cotton spinner, a creature abundant on our southern coasts. When disturbed this apparently helpless mass of animal matter slowly exudes from the tail end masses of a heavy viscid substance. The aggressor soon comes into contact with this, and at first attempts to throw off the encumbrance. Every effort to escape, however, really serves to draw the mass further afield. Eventually it resolves itself into countless silken threads which harden after some minutes' contact with the water but still retain extraordinary elasticity. The more the enemy struggles the completer his enmeshment in an ever-growing labyrinth of cords that refuse to break. A six-inch "cucumber" can thus bind a fourteen-inch lobster from head to tail in twenty minutes. This so-called cotton spinning is not always used purely as a defensive measure, as the cucumber occasionally uses its spinning powers for the purpose of obtaining a dinner.

Among the teeming ranks of the crustacea—the lobsters, crabs, and so on—pitched battles and duels to the death are an every-day occurrence. The majority of the crustaceans have one claw enormously

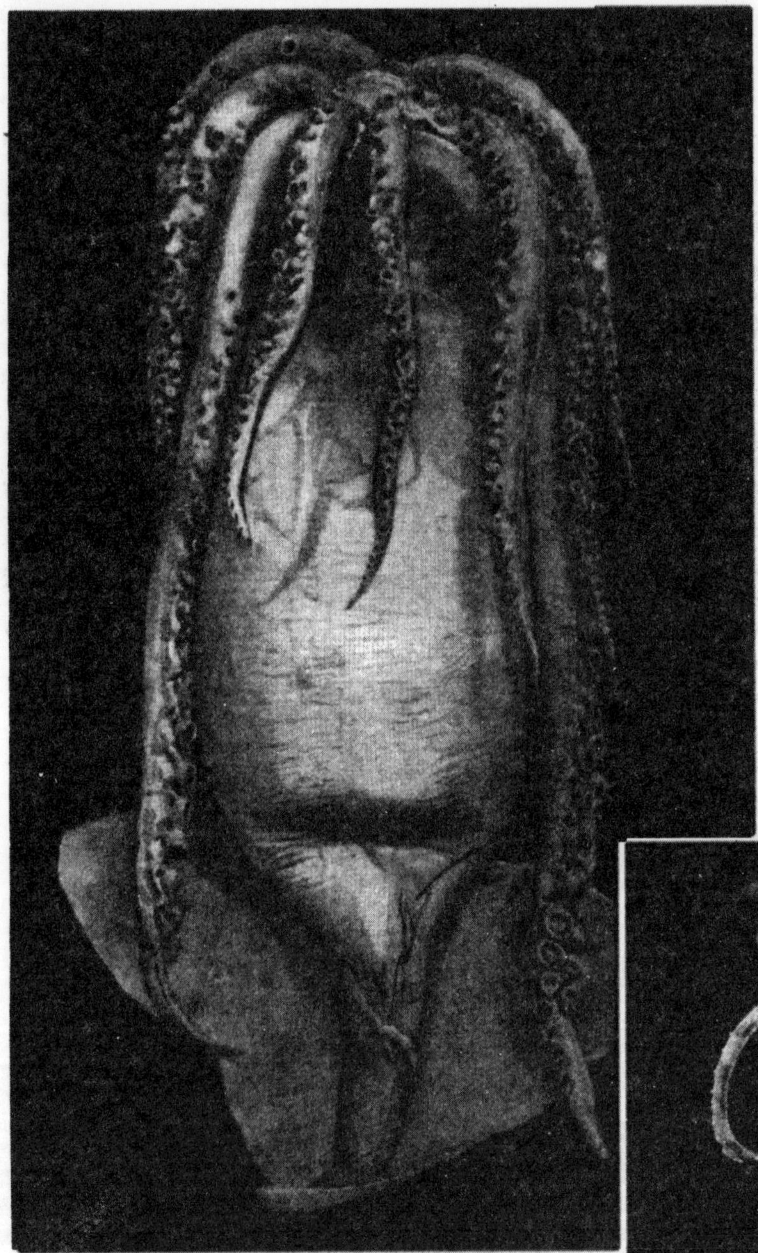

when it comes to "dirty work." Some years ago over two hundred lobsters were temporarily housed in a single large tank at a certain public aquarium. At the end of twelve hours' non-stop scrimmage only seventeen of the two hundred possessed a complete outfit of legs and claws. Even in a diplomatically managed collection such as that of the London Zoological Society, where the creatures are given shelters in the rockwork into which they can retire when attacked, a certain number of lobster understudies are always kept in reserve to replace casualties. Crustaceans are capable of replacing any appendage which may be lost in battle. A damaged limb is at once cast adrift at a basal joint and a new limb immediately commences to form. This appears at the next moult as a tiny caricature of the undamaged partner and very imperfectly calcified. Several moults may be required before the limb reaches full development, and should the animal be in bad health when damaged it may be unable to

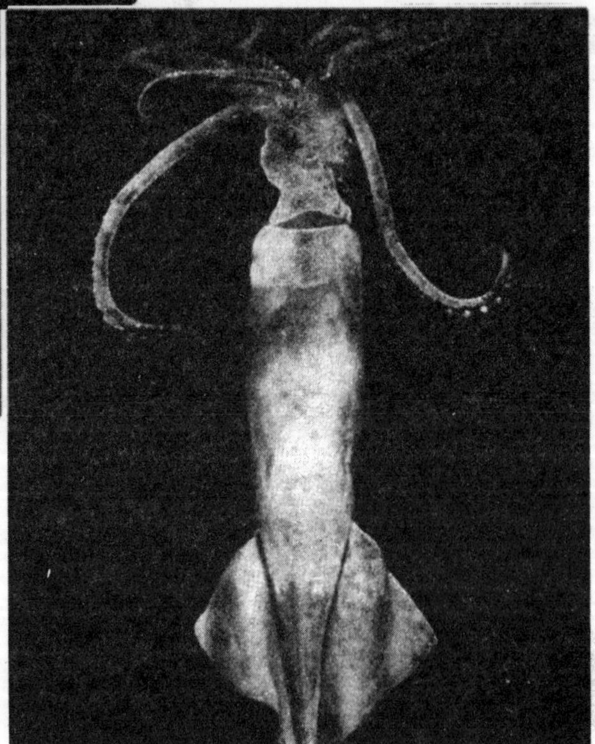

W. S. Berridge

SQUIDS OF THE ATLANTIC

Squids are surface swimming molluscs and the giant squids may measure fifty feet including the tentacles. Battles between these and the toothed whales are common, for these great mammals of the sea are very fond of a squid supper.

enlarged so that it sometimes far exceeds the rest of the animal. Such a weapon may be employed to close a burrow, or borrowed shell, as in the case of the hermit crab, and frequently plays an important part in the act of courtship. But its primary function is unquestionably that of a lethal weapon. Some foreign crabs have claws far exceeding those of any known lobster. The terrible *Pseudocarcinus* of Tasmania develops a claw two and a half feet in length and capable of crushing a man's ankle. The spider crab of Japan has its six-foot arms tipped with nips that shear their way through most non-metallic substances. The common English crab is in France termed "Le crabe enragé," a most apt title for a creature that spends its life looking for trouble.

The common lobster is probably without a peer

cast aside the damaged limb. A large crab or lobster when securely tucked in a rock cranny has been known to seize the incautious human hand attempting to draw it forth, and to hold the enemy in an iron grip until the rising tide has averted the tragedy.

Most molluscs are quite incapable of fighting. This does not apply, however, to the members of the higher group—the *Cephalopoda*, which embraces the octopus, squid, and cuttlefish. The octopus is a "first-class fighting man," for it not only habitually wages war upon crabs and lobsters, but is at constant feud with its own species. An octopus having exhausted his own supply of crabs stealthily insinuates a tip of one sucker-clad arm amongst a brother's coil and attempts to purloin one just as it is being carried to the parrot-like beak. At once the robbed one closes with the robber and a Homeric tug of war ensues. An octopus may carry three hundred suckers on each of its eight arms, and each sucker can exert a pull of anything up to twenty pounds, according to the size of the animal. Although the arms of an octopus emanating from European waters seldom exceed two feet in length, in Australia specimens of forty feet in diameter are not uncommon.

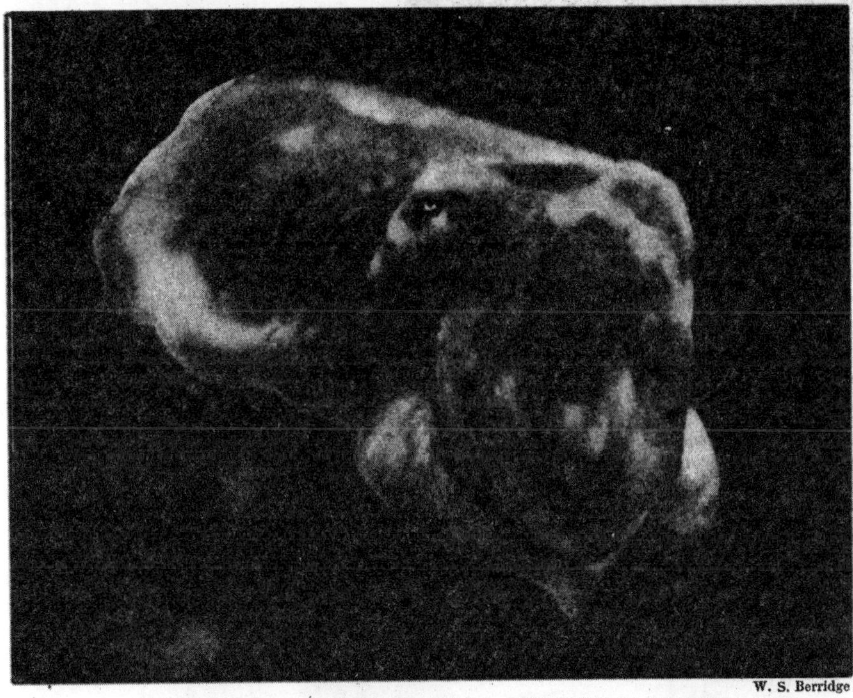

W. S. Berridge

CUTTLEFISH AND OCTOPUS: FIGHTERS BOTH

In the dimness of the sea the cuttlefish and octopus wage many a stern fight for food, not with each other but often with rivals each of his own kind. The octopus (top) is a particularly deadly fighter, especially of crabs and lobsters. In the Aquarium at the London Zoo fights between one octopus and another for the possession of a crab often take place.

Squid and cuttlefish, being surface swimmers and used to catching fish "on the fin," are even more active than the bottom-haunting octopus, and are liable to attack on sight. The body of a gigantic squid of the North Atlantic and Antarctic seas may measure twenty feet, while the long arms can reach twenty-five to thirty feet in advance of the eyes.

The toothed whales habitually feed on squid, and their skins are often latticed with long scars inflicted by the huge incisor-shaped suckers of the molluscs. Each sucker is ribbed with horny rings bearing enormous recurved hooks which assist materially in maintaining a firm hold. Our native octopus will fence with a lobster for hours, manoeuvring for a rearward position whence to secure the formidable claws. Octopods will also fight together for the greater part of the day, but it is doubtful if cuttlefish ever engage in conflicts with one another. The extraordinary breeding habits of the group do not necessitate the sexes coming into close contact with one another, so that it is very problematic whether the bride-to-be stands by whilst rival admirers strive for the honour of her restless hands—or rather tentacles.

MARVELS OF THE ZOO THAT NEVER WAS: LAMIA, MERMAID, UNICORN AND SATYR

The scientist is credited with having brought to light many marvellous things in the animal world but it is forgotten that, in doing this, he has deprived men of a number of strange but engaging beasts—wyverns, cockatrices, hippogryphs and so on. The land and the sea were credited by the old writers with a wonderful fauna to which there was no limit either in number or feature, save the writer's imagination and the credulity of his readers. Here we have some old friends, the lamia (bottom left) which sucked the blood of children, horribly, by night. Then comes a mermaid (bottom right) said to have been irresistible if only one had been at sea long enough, a unicorn (top left), and a sea satyr.

Chapter CLV

The Zoo That Never Was

By Lewis Bettany

THE earliest inhabitants of "The Zoo That Never Was" must surely have been the marvellous creatures invented by the old Greek and Latin poets and romancers. I mean, of course, the Sirens, the Harpies, the Centaurs, the Gorgons, the Phœnix, the Chimaera, the Sphinx and the Uranids. To these may be added the Unicorn, the Lamia and the Biblical Leviathan and Behemoth. The latter couple have often been recognized as the whale and the hippopotamus; but William Blake represents the one as a sort of sea serpent and the other as a monstrous elephant with truncated legs and proboscis.

Monstrous the mythical beasts of the classics certainly are; even the Sirens, the least offensive in form, are provided with wings by the post-Homeric poets. According to Homer, these beings live on an island situated between Aeaea and the rock of Scylla, near the south-western coast of Italy; and they have the power of singing with such magical effect as to charm to their doom all persons that hear them. Accordingly, in his wanderings through the Mediterranean Odysseus, forewarned by Circe, stopped the ears of his companions with wax and tied himself to the mast of his ship when he was passing the fatal island, and so escaped destruction. Of the number and names of the Sirens Homer says nothing. As Ligeia, Leucosia and Parthenope they figure in such later legends as the "Voyage of the Argonauts" and the "Rape of Persephone"; while their modern progeny, rendered more attractive and sympathetic by the course of years, includes the British mermaid and the Teutonic Lorelei.

THE Harpies are much "more fearful wild-fowls" than the Sirens. In Homer they are merely, as their name denotes, "the swift robbers," the personified storm winds who carry off persons who suddenly disappear from the earth. Homer mentions only one by name, Podaige, who was married to Zephyrus and gave birth to the two horses of Achilles, Xanthus and Balius. But as early as the time of Aeschylus they are depicted as ugly creatures with wings. Later, Latin poets, such as Virgil and Horace, represent them as obscene, bird-like creatures with the heads of maidens, with faces pale from hunger, and with long claws on their hands, who, whenever a meal has been prepared for enemies of the gods, dart down from the air upon it and either devour it or render it uneatable by dropping some stinking substance upon it.

Doubtless it was from this disgusting habit of the Harpies that Dean Swift borrowed a hint for some of the filthier tricks which he ascribes to his Yahoos. Nor, indeed, is this the sole debt which the author of "Gulliver's Travels" owes to classical mythology. He must, I fancy, have derived his Houyhnhnms, his wise horses, the culminating stroke of his satire on human nature, from the Centaurs, one of which half-human half-equine beings, Cheiron, the instructor of Achilles, was renowned for his skill in music, medicine, gymnastics and the art of prophecy. In the earliest accounts of them the Centaurs are a race of gigantic men, covered all over with hair, who inhabit the mountains and forests of Thessaly and lead a rude and savage life, occasionally carrying off the women of their neighbours and ranging the country like animals.

By later writers they are described as monsters (hippocentaurs) whose bodies are partly those of men, partly those of horses. The offspring of Ixion by his mares, they are chiefly celebrated for their fight with the Lapithae at the marriage-feast of Peirithous, which led to their expulsion from Thessaly and to their taking refuge on Mount Pindus, on the frontiers of Epirus. They appear in two forms, in one as men down to the legs and feet, the back part consisting in the body, tail and hind legs of a horse; in the other as men from the head to the loins, the remainder being the body of a horse with its tail and four legs.

IF the Centaurs may be reckoned the noblest specimens of the combination in one body of the human and the animal form, the Gorgons must certainly be regarded as the most horrible. Homer knows only one Gorgon, who (Odyssey XI) is one of the frightful phantoms to be found in the realm of Hades. Hesiod, however, mentions three, Stheino, Euxyale and Medusa. They are represented as girded with serpents and possessing golden wings, brazen hands and claws, large tusks like those of boars, and heads covered with scales like those of serpents.

Medusa, who alone of the sisters was mortal, was even more appalling in appearance. Originally she was a beautiful maiden; but unhappily she became the victim of Athena's wrath. Having contended with the goddess for the prize of beauty and having added to her offence by bearing children to Poseidon in one of her rival's temples, she was condemned to wear her hair changed into serpents; which gave her so terrifying an aspect that everyone who looked upon her was turned into stone. Finally the affronted goddess commissioned Perseus to destroy her. Furnished with a mirror given him by Athena and borrowing from the nymphs a bag, winged sandals and the helmet of Hades, which latter piece of armour served to render him invisible, Perseus came upon the Gorgons in their sleep and, looking at Medusa through the safeguarding medium of the mirror, cut off her head which, having hidden in the bag, he delivered over to Athena, who placed it in the centre of her shield or breast-plate.

QUAINT SEA-MONK

This engraving, derived from Gesner's "History," illustrates the sea-monk and one of the tallest fishing stories ever told. This monkish fish or fishy monk is said to have appeared off the coast of Norway in a storm. Fishermen may have seen it but they did not catch it.

Of the Phoenix, "the Arabian bird" resembling an eagle, with feathers partly red and partly golden, who lives for five hundred years, sole example of his species, and then builds himself a funeral-pile of spices on which he dies and from which he rises again ; of the Chimaera, a fire-breathing female monster slain by Bellerophon, the forepart of whose body was that of a lion, the middle that of a goat and the hind part that of a dragon ; of the Sphinx, the daughter of the Chimaera, a female monster, having the winged body of a lion and the breasts and upper parts of a woman, who propounded to the Thebans a riddle which was solved by Oedipus alone ; of Briareus and his brothers Gyges and Cottus, sons of Uranus born with fifty heads and a hundred arms, who assisted Zeus in his war with the Titans and gained the victory for him by hurling three hundred rocks at once against his enemies ; of these and of kindred figures of classical legend I lack space to give particulars. They are, after all, mere inventions and are devoid of the larger and symbolical significance which attaches to the Sirens, the Harpies, the Centaurs and the Gorgons. None of them is likely to be resuscitated by a modern author, as the Vampire has been revived by Mr. Bram Stoker, as the Centaur has been re-created by Mr. Algernon Blackwood, or as the Lamia or serpent-woman has been re-incarnated by Oliver Wendell Holmes.

Of candidates for "The Zoo that Never Was" who have been proposed, or, rather, invented, by modern authors, I can think of two only who possess a real animal physiognomy, De Maupassant's invisible Horla, and Mr. Blackwood's all too visible and odorous Wendigo. Indeed, when we leave classical times we have to travel right down to the fifteenth and sixteenth centuries before we come across a really new collection of strange beasts. Even of these many are included on the authority of Aristotle and Pliny, who, though they may be called the pioneers of natural history, were precluded by their carelessness and credulity and by their lack of access to comprehensive menageries from the opportunity of becoming trained and scientific inquirers.

ANOTHER FISHY TALE

Here is another of the strange fish invented in medieval times. Creatures of this sort, called "bishop fish" by old Gesner, were said to rise from the waves, suddenly and solemnly, as far as their waist, but whether to bless or curse the sailors we do not know.

Strange illustrations of mythical creatures are found in Conrad von Megenberg's "Das Buch der Natur," published at "Augspurg, October 30th, 1475," and become now so very rare that the copy of the first edition preserved in the library of the British Museum contains six only of the original twelve engravings and two hundred and eighty-five only of the original two hundred and ninety-two leaves. Among the strange creatures depicted in the illustrations are a dragon, a four-legged monk, a mermaid with two tails, a winged mermaid, a sphinx lacking breasts but provided with a supererogatory long tail, and another sphinx who atones for being supplied with this appendage by being deprived of front legs and wings.

The successor, however, to Aristotle and Pliny is not Conrad von Megenberg, but Conrad von Gesner, though we must not forget Olaus Magnus, Archbishop of Upsala and Metropolitan of Sweden, who, before his death in 1568, brought out a Latin work dealing *inter alia* with the fauna of Scandinavia, or the Rev. Edward Topsell, Chaplain in the Church of St. Botolph, Aldersgate, who, in 1607, published "A Historie of Four-Footed Beastes" which was half original and half compiled from Gesner's "History."

LAMB TREE THAT GREW IN TARTARY

As late as the end of the seventeenth century they were still talking about the lamb tree. The lamb either grew in a pod or sprouted from the top of the plant. The stalk being flexible the animal could graze on the grass within reach but when that was exhausted it died

FAMOUS BARNACLE TREE GOOSE

The Arctic goose visiting the British Isles in winter was supposed to develop from the shellfish, whence it was given its name, as explained in page 103. It was a common trick to connect—and so explain—one inexplicable natural phenomenon with another.

CONRAD VON GESNER, the Swiss naturalist, sometimes called "the German Pliny," was born at Zurich in 1516. His early studies in medicine, botany, classical literature, and natural history were prosecuted at Zurich, Strasburg, Bourges and Paris. In 1537 he was appointed Professor of Greek at Lausanne University, which chair he exchanged for that of physics and natural history at Zurich in 1541, where he taught and practised as a physician till his death (1565). He wrote in all ninety works, seventy-two of which were published and eighteen left uncompleted. One of his most important books is his "Historia Animalium" (1551-58), the work, indeed, on which his fame is founded.

This history ("Conradi Gesneri medici Tigurini Historia Animalium") was published in three large folio volumes between 1551 and 1587, and is rightly

described on the title-page—in Latin, which I translate—as "a work which will be most useful and at the same time most delightful to philosophers, doctors, grammarians, philologists, poets and all who are interested in various matters and languages." The first volume, which describes viviparous quadrupeds, contains 1,114 pages; the second, which is concerned with oviparous quadrupeds and birds, numbers 780 pages; the third, which deals with fishes, marine animals and serpents, runs to about 1,400 pages. It will be gathered, then, that the total work comprises some 3,300 pages, and that, as each page consists of 62 lines each containing on an average twelve words, this "History of Animals" is written in about two and a half million words.

MONSTERS OF MEDIEVAL SEAS: SEA-SERPENT AND WHALE

The "Great Sea-Serpent" has been explained variously as floating wreckage, a sail-fish, and a school of porpoises. However, none of these descriptions serve to explain away several well authenticated appearances at sea of unaccountable creatures. Below is an old picture of the sea-serpent, while above we have a bold adventurer camping on a so-called whale.

For a layman, totally inexpert in natural history, to express an opinion on the temporary or permanent value of such a book as Gesner's would, of course, be the sheerest impertinence. All he may say is that the "Historia Animalium," text and illustrations, seems to be a monument to the author's industry, and to succeed in its aim of assembling all that was known of animals in Europe in the first half of the sixteenth century.

It is interesting to see that the British Museum copy of the first edition of the work, which bears the bookplate of "Francis Hawes, Esquire, Receiver General of His Majesty's Customs, 1715," seems at one time to have been the property of Sir Joseph Banks, the eighteenth-century naturalist who accompanied Captain Cook on one of his voyages to the South Seas, and subsequently was for many years President of the Royal Society.

What such voyaging and exploring naturalists as Banks, Darwin and Hooker (the botanist) must have thought of the impossible necks of Gesner's camels, of the tube-like trunk of his elephant, and of the ludicrously unveracious picture of his hippopotamus, which "the German Pliny" quaintly describes as "equus fluviatalis, turpissima quadrupes" ("the river horse, a most wicked animal") it is not at all difficult to imagine. A little reading of the text of the "History" and a cursory examination of the plates will indeed soon lead the reader to the conclusion that, whatever sort of an anatomist he may have been, the author was an armchair student and no traveller. Gesner almost confesses as much by citing as authorities in his formidable bibliography no less then 251 books, the works of Hebrew, Greek, Latin, German, Italian and French authors. He is, it may fairly be presumed, a compiler and collector rather than an independent and original investigator.

His sea wolf, a ferocious looking creature bearing an erection of bristles all down its spine from head to tail, which he has the hardihood to declare is "sometimes found on the shore of the British Ocean," is as obviously fabulous as his beautiful and purely heraldic unicorn, which is carefully distinguished (Monoceros) from the accurately engraved rhinoceros, or as his egregious ape, which displays long and pendulous breasts, dangles a sort of crutch stick in her left hand, and sports a beard under her chin of which one of Mr. Jacobs' sailors would not be ashamed. His cynocephalus, a human creature with a dog's head, he is quite content to take on trust from Aelianus. But for the genuineness of his satyr he can vouch, at least at second hand. I translate his account, which runs as follows:

I think this monster ought to be included in the history of Satyrs. The picture of it which I append was sent to me by Georgius Fabricius of Misnia, Germany, a gentleman of eminent learning and culture, who sent me along with it a description in these words: "This quadruped was caught in the domain of the Bishop of Salzburg in what they call the Harzsberg forest. Its colour ranged from pale yellow to reddish. It had a strange ferocity and fled the sight of men. Wherever it could, it withdrew into the shade. Finally when it could neither be forced nor enticed to take food, after a few days it became extinct. Its back feet [legs] were different from and much longer than its front. What the rest of the body was like can easily be gathered from the drawing. It was captured in the year of our salvation 1531.

A "FEARFUL WILD-FOWL" OF THE OLD BOOKS
The Blue Boar and the Green Man are common on inn-signs, but their origin was purely heraldic. Even an inn-keeper never had the courage to trade under the sign of a four-legged duck, but courage was the one thing that old zoologists never lacked—on paper. This dreadful, quadrupedal fowl was actually postulated by some ancient wiseacres as being a real living creature.

Despite this testimony, the satyr is not in any sense a freak. It is a sheer fraud, invention, or imposition. Of the same class is the sea monk, illustrated in page 1772, of which we have this description:

> This sea monster was caught in our time in Norway in a tempestuous sea. As soon as they saw it, people gave it the name of monk. Sometime, as an evil omen and to the great fear of men, certain portents with human faces appear in the Firth of Forth wearing, it seems, the cowls of monks and standing up out of the water as high as the navel.

Own brother to the sea monk is the sea bishop, seen in Poland in episcopal habit, says the author, in 1531. Other creatures belonging to the same menagerie are a mermaid with animal ears; a merman or marine Pan with two horns; sea serpents thirty or forty feet long, which are harmless; and others, three or four times as big, with hideous heads, which are extremely ferocious and attack and devour ships and sailors. Whether Gesner was displaying his credulity or pulling his readers' legs in exhibiting such palpably pictorial monsters it is difficult to decide, for an element of rare *naiveté* enters into his story of the beneficent ray, which I quote next:

> Olaus Magnus in a map which sets before our eyes the northern coasts of Europe depicts a ray in the ocean which, when it saw a man swimming and even submerged, who was in danger of being dragged down into the deep by a multitude of dogs and whelps, stirred by a certain natural sympathy, for a long time defended and eventually preserved him. I am glad to find place here for a print of this incident taken from the map; though Magnus has been at no pains to represent either the dogs or the ray properly.

In his comment on the picture of the dogs and the ray, Gesner is inaccurate. The ray is a really splendid and fearsome creature. But the dogs are not depicted at all, for the swimmer is represented as being attacked by three fishes. An author who makes so gross a mistake in describing one of the drawings which he has selected to illustrate his own text can hardly be expected to inspire confidence.

His su (opossum) and his haüt (sloth) are not at all unlike the real animals, save in one respect. In representing them with human heads, he remains faithful once too often to his love of the marvellous.

Modern monsters, I need hardly add, can find few if any believers, save those who go down to the sea in ships. Sailor after sailor may bear witness to the appearance of mermaid and sea serpent; but such witness is invariably scouted alike by the man of science and by the man in the street. It may happen, of course, for all we laymen know, that some great animal, lurking in the depths of the ocean or in the bowels of the earth, has yet to be discovered. But until such discovery is made the megatherium may fairly be said to have become extinct. One would like, however, to know more about a certain mysterious beast which, according to a book published in 1928, "Oddities: a Book of Unexplained Facts," by R. T. Gould, might have been seen prowling about Devonshire on the evening of February 8th, 1855, and left what were called "Devil's hoofmarks." This is Mr. Gould's account of the strange footprints:

> The track appeared more like that of a biped than a quadruped, and the steps were generally eight inches in advance of one another. The impression of the feet closely resembled that of a donkey's shoe . . . Here and there it appeared as if cloven . . . The creature seems to have approached the door of several houses and then retreated. [Its steps] passed in some instances over the roofs of haystacks and houses.

Whom or what can this portent have been? Obviously neither one of Mr. Machen's "little people" nor one of Mr. Blackwood's "elementals," it seems to have resembled those noctambulants which Sir Arthur Conan Doyle's Mr. Sherlock Holmes more than once succeeded in running to earth.

General Index

This Index gives direct reference to the individual varieties of animal life described or illustrated in the body of WONDERS OF ANIMAL LIFE. It is not a classified index, and general headings, such as Birds, Insects, Fish, etc., include references to general information only, the individual creatures being found under their own names. In the case of individual classes which are distinguished by one name such as the Crab, Ant, or Beetle, the various types distinguished by a descriptive adjective are indexed alphabetically under the class heading, thus: the Leaf-eating Ant will be found under the heading **Ant,** leaf-eating. *A generous system of cross references covers all doubtful cases. The illustrations are indicated by figures in italics, thus:* **Comb,** of bees, *252, 253*

I

J

K

List of Errata

Corrections in Text

Page 185, col. 2, line 2—*for* Argos *read* Argus.
„ 672, col. 1, line 15—*for* Tennant *read* Tennent.
„ 1080, col. 2, line 3—*for* babirussa *read* babirusa.
„ 1171, col. 1, line 32—*for* tachnid flies *read* tachinid flies.

In Descriptions of Pictures

„ 162—*delete* in its actual size.
„ 197—*for* swallow-tail butterfly *read* elephant hawk-moth.
„ 225—*for* dragon-fly *read* dragon-fly nymph.
„ 249—*for* the sheath is barbed, etc., *read* the sting is barbed.
„ 261—*for* lion cub *read* tiger cub. *Delete from* notice that the lion cub, etc.
„ 268—*for* blackbuck *read* blesbok.
„ 281—*for* cast up by the tide *read* clustered on a post.
„ 344—*for* a herd of seals *read* sea-lions.
Page 410—*for* Kenworth *read* Kensworth.
„ 488—*for* dyticus *read* dytiscus.
„ 538—*for* bottom right *read* bottom left; *for the words* black-headed gull (bottom left) *to* numbers of grubs *read* the greater black-backed gull bred in years gone by on the flats of Kent and Essex. Essentially an oceanic species it will often come inland and even attack young lambs.
„ 597—*for* rhino *read* hippo.
„ 715—bottom right—*for* fiddle crab *read* fiddler crab.
„ 902—photos bottom left and bottom right to be reversed.
„ 928—delete final sentence.
„ 1070—upper block should be completely reversed.
„ 1407—*for* jaws *read* saws; *for* reflexed jaws etc., *read* reflexed saws of a sawfly used for egg-laying.
„ 1414—*right hand picture should be described as* a sheep medd, a wingless blood-sucking fly which lives on the skin of the sheep and brings forth a puparium.

Printed in Great Britain by the Amalgamated Press, Ltd., The Fleetway House, London, E.C.4.